Hymns for Praise and Service

COMPILED BY

HOMER RODEHEAVER
GEORGE W. SANVILLE

MUSIC EDITOR

B. D. ACKLEY

PUBLISHED BY

The Rodeheaver Hall-Mack Company

Sacred Music Publishers

WINONA LAKE :: INDIANA

PREFACE

We are happy to present to you HYMNS FOR PRAISE AND SERVICE, our new hymn book. We believe it is an aristocrat in the field of song-book publications, excelling all others, perpetuating the finest traditions of The Rodeheaver Company.

It represents for us a significant accomplishment. In the weeding out from thousands of the best songs available, the final choice has been those proven to be superior from every standpoint.

To this task we have been dedicated in the making of each of our publications. Now, in HYMNS FOR PRAISE AND SERVICE we feel the pinnacle has been reached. Justifiable pride is ours in this new book.

May God add His blessing to the work that has been done. May this volume be used in His service to inspire congregations everywhere to better singing.

THE PUBLISHERS

Hymns for Praise and Service

1   WHAT A FRIEND WE HAVE IN JESUS

Joseph Scriven   Charles C. Converse

1. What a Friend we have in Je - sus,   All our sins and griefs to bear!
2. Have we tri - als and temp - ta - tions?   Is there trou-ble an - y-where?
3. Are we weak and heav-y - la - den,   Cumbered with a load of care?—

What a priv - i - lege to car - ry   Ev - 'ry-thing to God in pray'r!
We should nev - er be dis - cour - aged, Take it to the Lord in pray'r.
Pre - cious Saviour, still our ref - uge,—Take it to the Lord in pray'r.

O what peace we oft - en for - feit,   O what needless pain we bear,
Can we find a friend so faith - ful Who will all our sor-rows share?
Do thy friends despise, for-sake thee? Take it to the Lord in pray'r;

All because we do not car - ry   Ev - 'ry-thing to God in pray'r!
Je - sus knows our ev - 'ry weak - ness, Take it to the Lord in pray'r.
In His arms He'll take and shield thee, Thou wilt find a sol - ace there.

2 IN THE GARDEN

C. A. M.

C. Austin Miles

1. I come to the gar-den a-lone, While the dew is still on the ros-es; And the voice I hear, Fall-ing on my ear; The Son of God dis-clos-es.

2. He speaks, and the sound of His voice Is so sweet the birds hush their sing-ing, And the mel-o-dy That He gave to me, With-in my heart is ring-ing.

3. I'd stay in the gar-den with Him Tho' the night a-round me be fall-ing, But He bids me go; Thru the voice of woe, His voice to me is call-ing.

CHORUS

And He walks with me, and He talks with me, And He tells me I am His own, And the joy we share as we tar-ry there, None oth-er has ev-er known.

3 THE OLD RUGGED CROSS

George Bennard

George Bennard

1. On a hill far a-way stood an old rug-ged cross, The em-blem of
2. Oh, the old rug-ged cross, so de-spised by the world, Has a won-drous at-
3. In the old rug-ged cross, stained with blood so di-vine, A won - drous
4. To the old rug-ged cross I will ev - er be true, Its shame and re-

suf-f'ring and shame; And I love that old cross where the dear-est and best
trac-tion for me; For the dear Lamb of God left His glo - ry a-bove
beau - ty I see; For 'twas on that old cross Je - sus suf-fered and died
proach gladly bear; Then He'll call me some day to my home far a - way,

CHORUS

For a world of lost sin-ners was slain. So I'll cher-ish the old rug-ged
To   bear it to dark Cal - va - ry.
To   par-don and sanc-ti - fy me.
Where His glo-ry for-ev-er I'll share.   cross,   the

cross, ... Till my tro-phies at last I lay down; I will cling to the
old rug-ged cross,

old rug-ged cross, ... And ex-change it some day for a   crown.
cross,   the old rug - ged cross,

4   ROCK OF AGES

AUGUSTUS M. TOPLADY   THOMAS HASTINGS

1. Rock of A - ges, cleft for me, Let me hide my - self in Thee;
2. Could my tears for - ev - er flow, Could my zeal no lan-guor know,
3. While I draw this fleet - ing breath, When my eyes shall close in death,

Let the wa - ter and the blood, From Thy wound - ed side which flowed,
These for sin could not a - tone; Thou must save, and Thou a - lone:
When I rise to worlds unknown, And be - hold Thee on Thy throne,

Be of sin the dou - ble cure, Save from wrath and make me pure.
In my hand no price I bring, Sim - ply to Thy cross I cling.
Rock of A - ges, cleft for me, Let me hide my - self in Thee.

5   NEARER, MY GOD, TO THEE

SARAH F. ADAMS   ARR. by LOWELL MASON

1. Near - er, my God, to Thee, Near - er to Thee! E'en though it
2. Though like the wan - der - er, The sun gone down, Dark - ness be
3. There let the way ap - pear, Steps un - to heav'n: All that Thou
4. Then, with my wak - ing tho'ts Bright with Thy praise, Out of my
5. Or if on joy - ful wing, Cleav - ing the sky, Sun, moon, and

NEARER, MY GOD, TO THEE

be 'a cross   That rais-eth me;   Still all my song shall be,
o-ver me,   My rest a stone;   Yet in   my dreams I'd be
send-est me, In mer-cy giv'n: An-gels to beck-on me,
sto-ny griefs Beth-el I'll raise;   So   by   my woes to be
stars for-got, Up-wards I'll fly,   Still all my song shall be,

Near-er, my God, to Thee, Near-er, my God, to Thee, Near-er to Thee!

6   JESUS, LOVER OF MY SOUL

Charles Wesley   S. B. Marsh
                                                  FINE

1. { Je-sus, Lov-er of my soul, Let me to Thy bos-om fly,
     While the near-er wa-ters roll, While the tem-pest still is high! }
2. { Oth-er ref-uge have I none; Hangs my help-less soul on Thee:
     Leave, ah, leave me not a-lone, Still sup-port and com-fort me! }
3. { Thou, O Christ, art all I want; More than all in Thee I find;
     Raise the fall-en, cheer the faint, Heal the sick, and lead the blind. }
4. { Plenteous grace with Thee is found, Grace to cov-er all my sin;
     Let the heal-ing streams a-bound, Make and keep me pure with-in. }

D.C.—Safe in-to the ha-ven guide, O re-ceive my soul at last!
D.C.—Cov-er my de-fense-less head With the shad-ow of Thy wing.
D.C.—False and full of sin I am, Thou art full of truth and grace.
D.C.—Spring Thou up with-in my heart, Rise to all e-ter-ni-ty.

                                                        D.C.

Hide me, O my Sav-iour, hide,   Till the storm of life is past;
All my trust on Thee is stayed, All my help from Thee I bring;
Just and ho-ly is Thy name, I am all un-right-eous-ness;
Thou of life the foun-tain art; Free-ly let me take of Thee;

ABIDE WITH ME

Henry F. Lyte, 1847

William Henry Monk, 1861

1. A - bide with me, fast falls the e - ven - tide;
2. Swift to its close ebbs out life's lit - tle day;
3. I need Thy pres - ence ev - ery pass - ing hour;
4. I fear no foe, with Thee at hand to bless;
5. Hold Thou Thy cross be - fore my clos - ing eyes;

The dark - ness deep - ens; Lord, with me a - bide:
Earth's joys grow dim, its glo - ries pass a - way;
What but Thy grace can foil the temp - ter's power?
Ills have no weight, and tears no bit - ter - ness.
Shine through the gloom, and point me to the skies.

When oth - er help - ers fail, and com - forts flee,
Change and de - cay in all a - round I see;
Who like Thy - self my guide and stay can be?
Where is death's sting? where, grave, thy vic - to - ry?
Heaven's morn - ing breaks, and earth's vain shad - ows flee:

Help of the help - less, O a - bide with me.
O Thou Who chang - est not a - bide with me.
Through cloud and sun - shine, O a - bide with me.
I tri - umph still, if Thou a - bide with me.
In life, in death, O Lord, a - bide with me. A - MEN.

HE LEADETH ME

Joseph H. Gilmore

William B. Bradbury

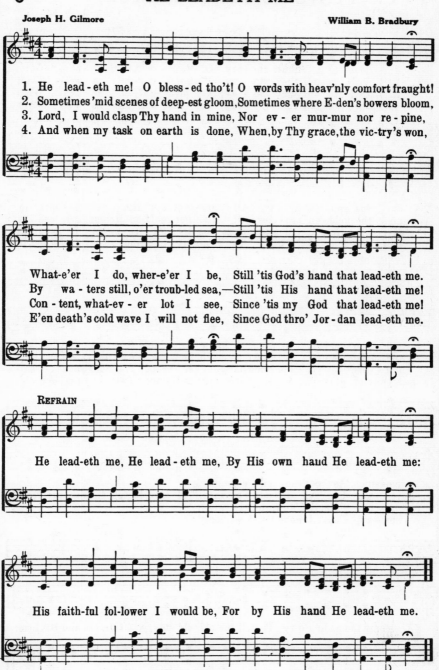

1. He lead-eth me! O bless-ed tho't! O words with heav'nly comfort fraught!
2. Sometimes 'mid scenes of deep-est gloom, Sometimes where E-den's bowers bloom,
3. Lord, I would clasp Thy hand in mine, Nor ev-er mur-mur nor re-pine,
4. And when my task on earth is done, When, by Thy grace, the vic-try's won,

What-e'er I do, wher-e'er I be, Still 'tis God's hand that lead-eth me.
By wa-ters still, o'er troub-led sea,—Still 'tis His hand that lead-eth me!
Con-tent, what-ev-er lot I see, Since 'tis my God that lead-eth me!
E'en death's cold wave I will not flee, Since God thro' Jor-dan lead-eth me.

REFRAIN

He lead-eth me, He lead-eth me, By His own hand He lead-eth me:

His faith-ful fol-lower I would be, For by His hand He lead-eth me.

9   I LOVE TO TELL THE STORY

Katherine Hankey   William G. Fischer

1. I love to tell the sto-ry Of un-seen things a-bove, Of
2. I love to tell the sto-ry; More won-der-ful it seems Than
3. I love to tell the sto-ry; 'Tis pleas-ant to re-peat What
4. I love to tell the sto-ry; For those who know it best Seem

Je-sus and His glo-ry, Of Je-sus and His love. I love to
all the gold-en fan-cies Of all our gold-en dreams. I love to
seems each time I tell it, More won-der-ful-ly sweet. I love to
hun-ger-ing and thirst-ing To hear it like the rest. And when, in

tell the sto-ry, Be-cause I know 'tis true, It sat-is-fies my
tell the sto-ry, It did so much for me; And that is just the
tell the sto-ry; For some have nev-er heard The mes-sage of sal-
scenes of glo-ry, I sing the new, new song, 'Twill be the old, old

CHORUS

long-ings, As noth-ing else can do.
rea-son I tell it now to thee.   I love to tell the sto-ry! 'Twill
va-tion From God's own ho-ly word.
sto-ry, That I have loved so long.

be my theme in glo-ry To tell the old, old sto-ry Of Je-sus and His love.

SWEET HOUR OF PRAYER

W. W. Walford   William B. Bradbury

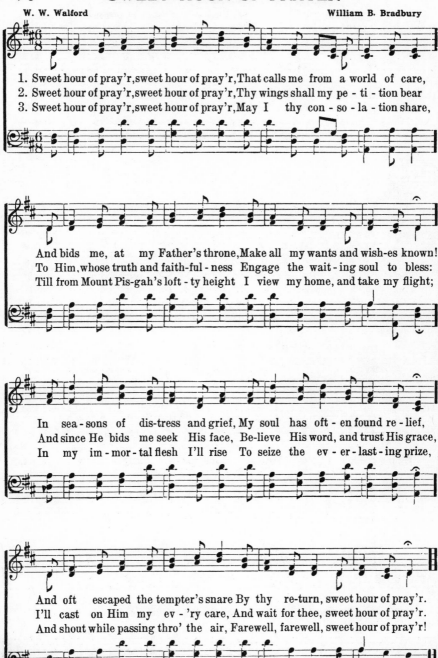

1. Sweet hour of pray'r, sweet hour of pray'r, That calls me from a world of care,
2. Sweet hour of pray'r, sweet hour of pray'r, Thy wings shall my pe-ti-tion bear
3. Sweet hour of pray'r, sweet hour of pray'r, May I thy con-so-la-tion share,

And bids me, at my Father's throne, Make all my wants and wish-es known!
To Him, whose truth and faith-ful-ness Engage the wait-ing soul to bless:
Till from Mount Pis-gah's loft-ty height I view my home, and take my flight;

In sea-sons of dis-tress and grief, My soul has oft-en found re-lief,
And since He bids me seek His face, Be-lieve His word, and trust His grace,
In my im-mor-tal flesh I'll rise To seize the ev-er-last-ing prize,

And oft escaped the tempter's snare By thy re-turn, sweet hour of pray'r.
I'll cast on Him my ev-'ry care, And wait for thee, sweet hour of pray'r.
And shout while passing thro' the air, Farewell, farewell, sweet hour of pray'r!

11 HELP SOMEBODY TODAY

MRS. FRANK M. BRECK

CHAS. H. GABRIEL

1. Look all around you, find some one in need, Help somebod-y to-day!
2. Man-y are wait-ing a kind, lov-ing word, Help somebod-y to-day!
3. Man-y have bur-dens too heav-y to bear, Help somebod-y to-day!
4. Some are dis-cour-aged and wea-ry in heart, Help somebod-y to-day!

Tho' it be lit-tle— a neigh-bor-ly deed— Help somebod-y to-day!
Thou hast a mes-sage, O let it be heard, Help somebod-y to-day!
Grief is the por-tion of some ev-'ry where, Help somebod-y to-day!
Some one the jour-ney to heav-en should start, Help somebod-y to-day!

CHORUS

Help somebod-y to-day,........ Some-bod-y a-long life's way;...... Let
to-day, homeward way;

sor-row be end-ed, The friendless befriended, Oh, help somebody to-day!

12   JESUS LIVES

W. C. Poole   B. D. Ackley

1. Send the mes-sage o'er the world, Je-sus lives!   Let your
2. Send the mes-sage ev-er new, Je-sus lives!   Might-y
3. Send the mes-sage ev-ery-where, Je-sus lives!   Lives to

Je-sus lives!

ban-ners be un-furled, Je-sus lives!   Lift your song in glad-dest praise,
works for all to do, Je-sus lives!   Lives to con-quer death and sin,
ban-ish grief and care, Je-sus lives!   Lives to help the souls who call,

Je-sus lives!

To the Lord your an-thems raise, For His glo-rious word and ways, Je-sus lives!
Lives to ush-er heav-en in, Lives to help us vict'ry win, Je-sus lives!
Lives to lift the souls who fall, And in Him we con-quer all, Je-sus lives!

CHORUS

He lives to give us vic-to-ry, From pow'r of sin and death to free,

He lives to reign e-ter-nal-ly, Je-sus lives! Je-sus lives!

13 SAVIOUR, LIKE A SHEPHERD LEAD US

DOROTHY ANN THRUPP   WILLIAM B. BRADBURY

1. Sav - iour, like a Shep-herd lead us, Much we need Thy ten-der care;
2. We are Thine, do Thou be - friend us, Be the Guardian of our way;
3. Thou hast promised to re - ceive us, Poor and sin-ful tho' we be;
4. Ear - ly let us seek Thy fa - vor; Ear - ly let us seek Thy will;

In Thy pleasant pas-tures feed us, For our use Thy folds pre-pare:
Keep Thy flock, from sin de - fend us, Seek us when we go a - stray:
Thou hast mer - cy to re - lieve us, Grace to cleanse, and pow'r to free:
Bless - ed Lord and on - ly Sav -iour, With Thy love our bos-oms fill:

Bless-ed Je - sus, Bless-ed Je - sus, Thou hast bought us, Thine we are;
Bless-ed Je - sus, Bless-ed Je - sus, Hear Thy chil - dren when they pray;
Bless-ed Je - sus, Bless-ed Je - sus, Ear-ly let us turn to Thee;
Bless-ed Je - sus, Bless-ed Je - sus, Thou hast loved us, love us still;

Bless-ed Je - sus, Bless-ed Je - sus, Thou hast bought us, Thine we are.
Bless-ed Je - sus, Bless-ed Je - sus, Hear Thy children when they pray.
Bless-ed Je - sus, Bless-ed Je - sus, Ear-ly let us turn to Thee.
Bless-ed Je - sus, Bless-ed Je - sus, Thou hast loved us, love us still.

14 WALKING IN THE KING'S HIGHWAY

A. H. Ackley

B. D. Ackley

1. Days are filled with glad-ness, nights are filled with song, Walk-ing in the
2. Mu - sic from the home-land fills me with de - light, Walk-ing in the
3. Crown'd with ten-der mer-cies, guard-ed by His love, Walk-ing in the

high-way......

King's high-way;......   And the world grows brighter, as we pass a-long,
King's high-way;......   Vis-ions of the glo-ry break up-on my sight,
King's high-way;......   Je - sus gives a fore-taste of the joys a-bove,

the King's highway I'm walking,

CHORUS

Walk-ing in the King's high-way. Walk-ing, walk-ing in the King's high-way,

yes, I'm

Walk-ing in the King's high-way   To the place of man - y mansions,
the King's highway,

I shall come at last, Walk-ing in the King's high-way.

15 LIVING FOR JESUS

COPYRIGHT 1917, RENEWAL 1945
THE RODEHEAVER CO., OWNER

T. O. Chisholm

C. Harold Lowden

1. Liv-ing for Je-sus a life that is true, Striving to please Him in all that I do,
2. Liv-ing for Je-sus who died in my place, Bearing on Calv'ry my sin and disgrace,
3. Liv-ing for Je-sus wher-ev-er I am, Do-ing each du-ty in His Ho-ly Name,
4. Liv-ing for Je-sus thru earth's little while, My dearest treasure, the light of His smile,

Yield-ing allegiance, glad-hearted and free, This is the pathway of blessing for me.
Such love constrains me to answer His call, Fol-low His leading and give Him my all.
Will-ing to suf-fer af-flic-tion or loss, Deeming each tri-al a part of my cross.
Seek-ing the lost ones He died to re-deem, Bringing the weary to find rest in Him.

CHORUS UNISON *A little slower*

O Je-sus, Lord and Sav-iour, I give my-self to Thee; For Thou, in Thy a-

tone-ment, Didst give Thy-self for me; I own no oth-er Mas-ter, My

rit.

heart shall be Thy throne, My life I give, henceforth to live, O Christ, for Thee alone.

16 WHILE IT IS DAY

T. O. Chisholm

B. D. Ackley

1. "While it is day" my hands must be bus-y, Work-ing the work God
2. Life is a trust, how sol-emn, how sa-cred! To each his work the

sent me to do; Soon comes the night when no man can la-bor,
Fa-ther as-signs; To each his place and por-tion of la-bor,

REFRAIN

When the last sands of life have run through... "While it is day!" It is the
Gath'ring the fruits or train-ing the vines.

Mas-ter's voice; "While it is day!" I must o-bey; Shad-ows are

length-en-ing, I must be work-ing, "While it is day!" "While it is day!"

17 BRIGHTEN THE CORNER WHERE YOU ARE

Ina Duley Ogdon

Charles H. Gabriel

1. Do not wait un-til some deed of great-ness you may do, Do not
2. Just a-bove are cloud-ed skies that you may help to clear, Let not
3. Here for all your tal-ent you may sure-ly find a need, Here re-

wait to shed your light a-far, To the man-y du-ties ev-er near you
nar-row self your way de-bar, Tho' in-to one heart a-lone may fall your
flect the Bright and Morning Star, E-ven from your humble hand the bread of

REFRAIN

now be true, Bright-en the cor-ner where you are.
song of cheer, Bright-en the cor-ner where you are. Bright-en the cor-ner
life may feed, Bright-en the cor-ner where you are.

where you are! Bright-en the cor-ner where you are! Some one far from
Shine for Je-sus where you are!

har-bor you may guide a-cross the bar, Bright-en the cor-ner where you are.

18 HIS DEAREST NAME

A. H. A.

A. H. Ackley

Effective as a solo

1. God has a Son with the dear - est name, His name is Je - sus,
2. He is a Sav - iour from sin, I know, His name is Je - sus,
3. His love a lone can transform the earth, His name is Je - sus,

His name is Je - sus, Who to the heart of the world lays claim,
His name is Je - sus, O why not trust Him and find it so,
His name is Je - sus, Give to all na - tions the heav - 'nly birth,

REFRAIN

His name is Je - sus the Lord.
His name is Je - sus the Lord. No oth - er name is so
His name is Je - sus the Lord.

pre - cious and sweet, No oth - er name, with God's love so re - plete,

To countless souls He has saved from de - feat, His dear - est name is Je - sus.

19 ARE YE ABLE, SAID THE MASTER

Earl Marlatt

Harry S. Mason

1. "Are ye a-ble," said the Mas-ter, "To be cru-ci-fied with me?"
2. "Are ye a-ble," to re-mem-ber, When a thief lifts up his eyes,
3. "Are ye a-ble," when the shad-ows Close a-round you with the sod,
4. "Are ye a-ble," still the Mas-ter Whis-pers down e-ter-ni-ty,

"Yea," the stur-dy dream-ers an-swered, "To the death we fol-low Thee."
That His par-doned soul is wor-thy Of a place in Par-a-dise?
To be-lieve that spir-it tri-umphs, To commend your soul to God?
And he-ro-ic spir-its an-swer, Now, as then in Gal-i-lee.

REFRAIN

"Lord, we are a-ble," Our spir-its are Thine, Re-mold them,

make us like Thee, di-vine. Thy guid-ing ra-diance a-bove

us shall be A bea-con to God, To love and loy-al-ty.

20 WHEN WE WALK WITH JESUS

A. H. Ackley

B. D. Ackley

1. When we walk with Je-sus ev-'ry-thing we need He sup-plies ac-cord-ing
2. When we walk with Je-sus we are un-a-fraid, And we face the world with
3. Ev-'ry hour is pre-cious on the jour-ney home, With the Great Companion

to His Word, And His gra-cious pres-ence all our dreams ex-ceed, When we
courage strong; Tho' the foes be might-y, we are un-dis-mayed, There is
by our side; His kind words of com-fort when the shad-ows come, Keep our

CHORUS

walk with Him in sweet ac-cord.
vic-t'ry all the way a-long. He's the One..... the One who
spir-its true and sat-is-fied. He's the One

saves the soul, Let us cling, to Him thro' joy and pain, Let us
O let us cling.

walk with Je-sus till we reach the goal, And with Him in glo-ry we shall reign.

21 I NEED JESUS

COPYRIGHT 1924, RENEWAL 1952
THE RODEHEAVER CO., OWNER
INTERNATIONAL COPYRIGHT SECURED

George O. Webster   Chas. H. Gabriel

1. I need Je-sus, my need I now con-fess; No friend like Him in times of deep dis-tress; I need Je-sus, the need I glad-ly own; Tho' some may bear their load a-lone, Yet I need Je-sus.

2. I need Je-sus, I need a friend like Him, A friend to guide when paths of life are dim; I need Je-sus when foes my soul as-sail; A-lone I know I can but fail,— So I need Je-sus.

3. I need Je-sus, I need Him to the end; No one like Him—He is the sin-ners' Friend; I need Je-sus, no oth-er friend will do; So con-stant, kind, so strong, and true,—Yes, I need Je-sus.

CHORUS

I need Je-sus, I need Je-sus, I need Je-sus with me, I need Je-sus al-ways, I need Je-sus ev-'ry day; ev-'ry day; Need Him in the sun-shine hour, Need Him when the storm-clouds low'r; Ev-'ry day a-long my way, Yes, I need Je-sus.

SALVATION IS FREE

A. H. A.   A. H. Ackley

1. Sal - va - tion is free, it can nev - er be bought, It's some-thing that's
2. Sal - va - tion is free, God de-clares it is so, By faith you may
3. Sal - va - tion is free, all that you need to do, Is o - pen your

giv - en a - way. The gift of God's grace for which long you have sought
have it with - in, This mo-ment, right now you can cer - tain - ly know,
heart and re - ceive The Sav - iour who died on the cross to save you,

CHORUS

Is yours for the tak - ing to - day.
That Je-sus has saved you from sin. Sal - va - tion is free, sal - va - tion is
And all who on Him will be - lieve.

free, For ev - 'ry - one in - clud - ing you, Just give up your
and you

sin and let Je - sus come in, That's all that He asks you to do.

23 FILL ME NOW

E. H. Stokes,

Jno. R. Sweney

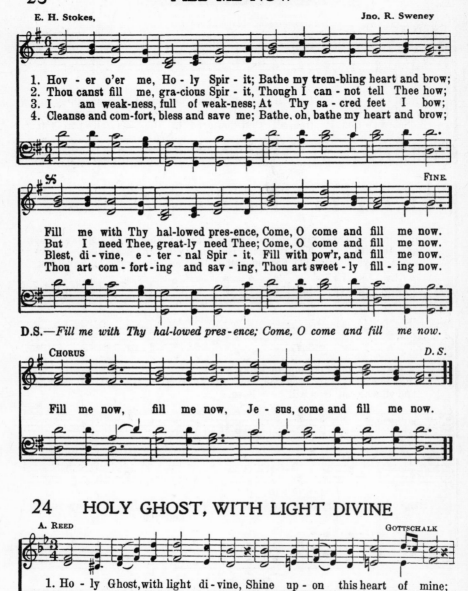

1. Hov - er o'er me, Ho - ly Spir - it; Bathe my trem-bling heart and brow;
2. Thou canst fill me, gra-cious Spir - it, Though I can - not tell Thee how;
3. I am weak-ness, full of weak-ness; At Thy sa - cred feet I bow;
4. Cleanse and com-fort, bless and save me; Bathe, oh, bathe my heart and brow;

FINE

Fill me with Thy hal-lowed pres-ence, Come, O come and fill me now.
But I need Thee, great-ly need Thee; Come, O come and fill me now.
Blest, di - vine, e - ter - nal Spir - it, Fill with pow'r, and fill me now.
Thou art com - fort-ing and sav - ing, Thou art sweet-ly fill - ing now.

D.S.—*Fill me with Thy hal-lowed pres-ence; Come, O come and fill me now.*

CHORUS

D.S.

Fill me now, fill me now, Je - sus, come and fill me now.

24 HOLY GHOST, WITH LIGHT DIVINE

A. REED

GOTTSCHALK

1. Ho - ly Ghost, with light di - vine, Shine up - on this heart of mine;
2. Ho - ly Ghost, with pow'r di - vine, Cleanse this guilt - y heart of mine;
3. Ho - ly Ghost, with joy di - vine, Cheer this saddened heart of mine;
4. Ho - ly Spir - it, all di - vine, Dwell with - in this heart of mine;

HOLY GHOST, WITH LIGHT DIVINE

Chase the shades of night a - way, Turn my dark-ness in - to day.
Long hath sin with-out con-trol, Held do - min - ion o'er my soul.
Bid my ma - ny woes de - part, Heal my wounded bleed-ing heart.
Cast down ev - 'ry i - dol throne, Reign supreme and—reign a - lone.

25 WITH THY SPIRIT FILL ME

Oswald J. Smith
Legato
B. D. Ackley

1. Lord, pos - sess me now, I pray, Make me whol - ly Thine to - day;
2. Lord, I yield my - self to Thee, All I am or hope to be
3. Lord, com - mis - sion me, I pray! Souls are dy - ing ev - 'ry day;

Glad - ly do I own Thy sway, With Thy spir - it fill me.
Now and thru e - ter - ni - ty, With Thy spir - it fill me.
Help me lead them in Thy way, With Thy spir - it fill me.

CHORUS

With Thy spir - it fill me, With Thy spir - it fill me:

Make me whol - ly Thine, I pray, With Thy spir - it fill me.

26 HELP ME SING ON

John R. Clements

B. D. Ackley

Unison

1. Help me sing on when my heart breaks in sad-ness; Help me sing
2. Help me sing on when my foes are a-round me; Help me sing
3. Help me sing on though the hours are dis-tress-ing; Help me sing

on when the tears dim my sight; Give me a morn,— a bright
on a-mid war-ring and strife; Grant me Thy grace when the
on to the end of the way; Make each dis-com-fort re-

morn-ing of glad-ness, Shine thru the dark-ness and ban-ish my night.
world would con-found me, Keep-ing me calm when the bat-tle is rife.
turn me a bless-ing; Keep me at work till the close of the day.

CHORUS

Help me sing on, Lord, help me sing on, ... In tune with Thy

Help me sing, help me sing on, help me sing, help me sing on,

will till life's jour-ney is done; Help me sing on, Lord, help me sing

Help me sing, help me sing on, Help me sing,

HELP ME SING ON

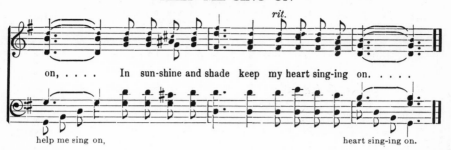

on, ... In sun-shine and shade keep my heart sing-ing on. ....

help me sing on, heart sing-ing on.

27 TODAY IS MINE

Virgil P. Brock Blanche Kerr Brock

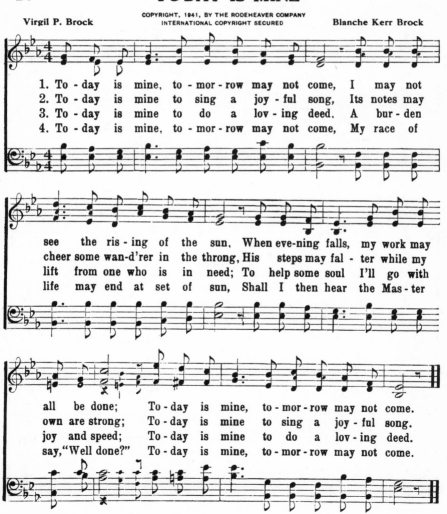

1. To-day is mine, to-mor-row may not come, I may not
2. To-day is mine to sing a joy-ful song, Its notes may
3. To-day is mine to do a lov-ing deed. A bur-den
4. To-day is mine, to-mor-row may not come, My race of

see the ris-ing of the sun, When eve-ning falls, my work may
cheer some wan-d'rer in the throng, His steps may fal-ter while my
lift from one who is in need; To help some soul I'll go with
life may end at set of sun, Shall I then hear the Mas-ter

all be done; To-day is mine, to-mor-row may not come.
own are strong; To-day is mine to sing a joy-ful song.
joy and speed; To-day is mine to do a lov-ing deed.
say, "Well done?" To-day is mine, to-mor-row may not come.

ONWARD, CHRISTIAN SOLDIERS

Sabine Baring-Gould   ST. GERTRUDE 6. 5. 6. 5. D. With Refrain   Arthur S. Sullivan

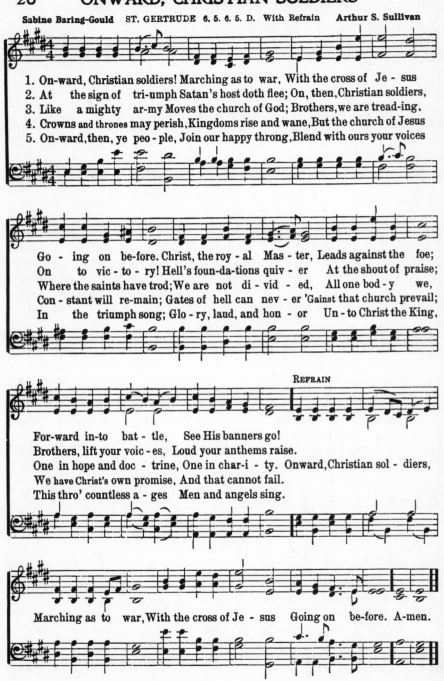

1. On-ward, Christian soldiers! Marching as to war, With the cross of Je - sus
2. At the sign of tri-umph Satan's host doth flee; On, then, Christian soldiers,
3. Like a mighty ar-my Moves the church of God; Brothers, we are tread-ing,
4. Crowns and thrones may perish, Kingdoms rise and wane, But the church of Jesus
5. On-ward, then, ye peo - ple, Join our happy throng, Blend with ours your voices

Go - ing on be-fore. Christ, the roy - al Mas - ter, Leads against the foe;
On to vic - to - ry! Hell's foun-da-tions quiv - er At the shout of praise;
Where the saints have trod; We are not di - vid - ed, All one bod - y we,
Con - stant will re-main; Gates of hell can nev - er 'Gainst that church prevail;
In the triumph song; Glo - ry, laud, and hon - or Un - to Christ the King,

REFRAIN

For-ward in-to bat - tle, See His banners go!
Brothers, lift your voic - es, Loud your anthems raise.
One in hope and doc - trine, One in char-i - ty. Onward, Christian sol - diers,
We have Christ's own promise, And that cannot fail.
This thro' countless a - ges Men and angels sing.

Marching as to war, With the cross of Je - sus Going on be-fore. A-men.

NO ONE INVITED HIM HOME

A. H. A.

A. H. Ackley

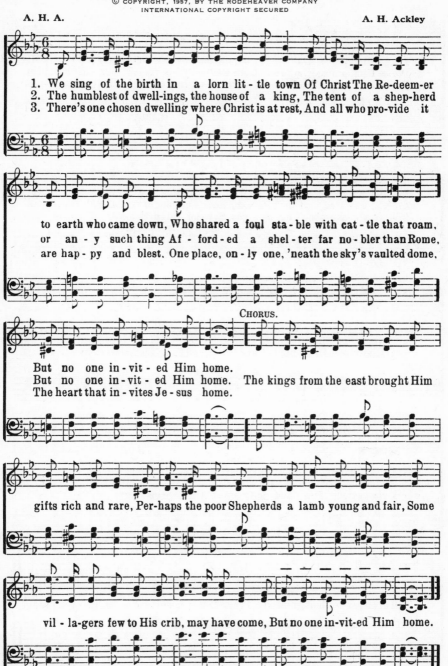

1. We sing of the birth in a lorn lit-tle town Of Christ The Re-deem-er
2. The humblest of dwell-ings, the house of a king, The tent of a shep-herd
3. There's one chosen dwelling where Christ is at rest, And all who pro-vide it

to earth who came down, Who shared a foul sta-ble with cat-tle that roam,
or an-y such thing Af-ford-ed a shel-ter far no-bler than Rome,
are hap-py and blest. One place, on-ly one, 'neath the sky's vaulted dome,

CHORUS.

But no one in-vit-ed Him home.
But no one in-vit-ed Him home. The kings from the east brought Him
The heart that in-vites Je-sus home.

gifts rich and rare, Per-haps the poor Shepherds a lamb young and fair, Some

vil-la-gers few to His crib, may have come, But no one in-vit-ed Him home.

PRAISE HIM! PRAISE HIM!

FANNY J. CROSBY

CHESTER G. ALLEN

1. Praise Him! praise Him! Je-sus, our bless-ed Re-deem-er! Sing, O Earth, His
2. Praise Him! praise Him! Je-sus, our bless-ed Re-deem-er! For our sins He
3. Praise Him! praise Him! Je-sus, our bless-ed Re-deem-er! Heav'nly por-tals

won-der-ful love pro-claim! Hail Him! hail Him! highest archangels in glo-ry;
suffered, and bled, and died; He our Rock, our hope of e-ter-nal sal-va-tion,
loud with ho-san-nas ring! Je - sus, Sav - ior, reigneth for-ev - er and ev - er;

Strength and hon - or give to His ho - ly name! Like a shep-herd, Je-sus will
Hail Him! hail Him! Je-sus the Cru - ci - fied. Sound His Praises! Je-sus who
Crown Him! crown Him! Prophet, and Priest, and King! Christ is com-ing! o-ver the

REFRAIN

guard His children, In His arms He carries them all day long:
bore our sorrows, Love unbounded, wonderful, deep and strong: Praise Him! praise Him!
world vic-to-rious, Pow'r and glo-ry un - to the Lord be-long:

tell of His ex-cel-lent greatness; Praise Him! praise Him! ev-er in joy-ful song!

31 OPEN MY HEART TO THY LOVE

A. H. Ackley
(Solo and Chorus)

B. D. Ackley

1. O - pen my heart to Thy love bless - ed Sav - iour, Hear me I
2. Pit - y my weak-ness and my wretch-ed blind-ness, Bend to Thine
3. I hear Thee call - ing, so pa - tient - ly call - ing, I would not
4. Let ev - 'ry vain and un - ho - ly am - bi - tion, Per - ish in

pray as I bow at Thine al - tar, Seek-ing Thy face and Thy
own will, my will so un - yield-ing, Rule Thou my soul, Lord, and
hin - der Thy King-dom from com - ing, Now is the time for Thy
me ere the thought give it breath-ing, Cre - ate with - in me love's

CHORUS

dear lov-ing fa - vor, O - pen my heart to Thy love.
fill it with kind-ness, O - pen my heart to Thy love.
Spir - it is fall - ing, O - pen my heart to Thy love.   O - pen my heart,
ho - ly con - di - tion, O - pen my heart to Thy love.

o - pen my heart, o - pen my heart to Thy Spir - it, Lord. O - pen my

heart to Thy bless - ed Word, O - pen my heart to Thy love. (to Thy love.)

32 IN THE SERVICE OF THE KING

A. H. Ackley

B. D. Ackley

1. I am hap-py in the serv-ice of the King, I am hap-py
2. I am hap-py in the serv-ice of the King, I am hap-py
3. I am hap-py in the serv-ice of the King, I am hap-py
4. I am hap-py in the serv-ice of the King, I am hap-py

Oh, so hap-py; I have peace and joy that noth-ing else can bring,
Oh, so hap-py; Thro' the sun-shine and the shad-ow I can sing,
Oh, so hap-py; To His guid-ing hand for-ev-er I will cling,
Oh, so hap-py; All that I pos-sess to Him I glad-ly bring,

REFRAIN.

In the serv-ice of the King. In the serv-ice

of the King Ev-'ry tal-ent I will bring; I have

peace and joy and bless-ing In the serv-ice of the King.

33 TELL THE WORLD WHAT YOU KNOW

A. H. A.   A. H. Ackley

1. Tell the world what you know a-bout Je-sus, Tell to all what He
2. Tell the world what you know a-bout Je-sus, Tell the peace and the
3. Tell the world what you know a-bout Je-sus, Tell a friend of this

means to you, If you know Him from your own ex-per-ience, Tell to
joy you know, If sal-va-tion from sin He has brought you, Tell the
Friend Who cares, If your life has been changed by the Sav-iour, Tell of

oth-ers what He can do.
news ev-ery-where you go.   **CHORUS** Tell the world what you know a-bout
Him and the love He bears.

Je-sus, What you know and can tell with-out doubt
                                                 with-out doubt   If you

have sav-ing know-ledge of Je-sus, Tell the world what you know, tell it out.

34 JESUS SET THE MUSIC RINGING

Rev. George O. Webster   C. Austin Miles

1. You ask what makes me hap-py The whole day long, Why I am al-ways
2. I can-not keep from sing-ing Since that glad day, When Je-sus took, in
3. His love each day is grow-ing More sweet to me, Each day new grace and

sing-ing A glad-some song; Ah, well do I re-mem-ber When
mer-cy, My sins a-way; He o-pened up a foun-tain Whence
beau-ty In Him I see; For all this world can of-fer From

song be-gan to start, 'Twas Je-sus set the mu-sic Ring-ing in my heart.
streams of gladness start, 'Twas Je-sus set the mu-sic Ring-ing in my heart.
Him I would not part, Since He has set the mu-sic Ring-ing in my heart.

CHORUS

In my heart . . . He set the mu-sic ringing, In my life . . . . a heav'n-ly

In my heart   In my life

glad-ness bringing; Ah, well do I re-mem-ber When song be-gan to start,

JESUS SET THE MUSIC RINGING

'Twas Je-sus set the mu-sic Ring-ing in my heart.
Ring-ing, ring-ing in my heart.

35   BEYOND THE SUNSET

Virgil P. Brock   Blanche Kerr Brock

1. Be - yond the sun - set, O bliss - ful morn - ing, When with our
2. Be - yond the sun - set no clouds will ga - ther, No storms will
3. Be - yond the sun - set a hand will guide me To God, the
4. Be - yond the sun - set, O glad re - un - ion, With our dear

Sav - iour heav'n is be - gun. Earth's toil-ing end - ed, O glo - rious
threat - en, no fears an - noy; O day of glad - ness, O day un-
Fa - ther, whom I a - dore; His glo - rious pres - ence, His words of
loved ones who've gone be - fore; In that fair home - land we'll know no

dawn - ing; Be - yond the sun - set, when day is done.
end - ing, Be - yond the sun - set, e - ter - nal joy!
wel - come, Will be my por - tion on that fair shore.
part - ing, Be - yond the sun - set for ev - er more!

36 THEN JESUS CAME

Oswald J. Smith   Homer Rodeheaver

1. One sat a-lone be-side the high-way beg-ging, His eyes were blind, the
2. From home and friends the e-vil spir-its drove him, A-mong the tombs he
3. Un-clean! un-clean! the lep-er cried in tor-ment, The deaf, the dumb, in
4. Their hearts were sad as in the tomb they laid him, For death had come and
5. So men to-day have found the Sav-iour a-ble, They could not con-quer

light He could not see; He clutched his rags and shiv-ered in the shad-ows,
dwelt in mis-er-y; He cut him-self as de-mon pow'rs pos-sessed him,
help-less-ness stood near; The fe-ver raged, dis-ease had gripped its vic-tim,
tak-en him a-way; Their night was dark and bit-ter tears were fall-ing,
pas-sion, lust and sin; Their bro-ken hearts had left them sad and lone-ly,

REFRAIN

Then Je-sus came and bade his dark-ness flee.
Then Je-sus came and set the cap-tive free.
Then Je-sus came and cast out ev-'ry fear.   When Je-sus comes the
Then Je-sus came and night was turned to day.
Then Je-sus came and dwelt, Him-self, with-in.

temp-ter's pow'r is bro-ken; When Je-sus comes the tears are wiped a-way. He takes the

gloom and fills the life with glo-ry, For all is changed when Je-sus comes to stay.

37 GOOD NIGHT AND GOOD MORNING

Lizzie DeArmond   Homer A. Rodeheaver

1. When comes to the wea-ry a bless-ed re-lease, When upward we
2. When fad-eth the day and dark shadows draw nigh, With Christ close at
3. When home-lights we see shin-ing bright-ly a-bove, Where we shall be

pass to His kingdom of peace, When free from the woes that on earth we must bear,
hand, it is not death to die; He'll wipe ev-'ry tear, roll a-way ev-'ry care;
soon, thro' His wonderful love, We'll praise Him who called us His heaven to share,

CHORUS.

We'll say "good-night," here, but "good-morning" up there.
We'll say "good-night," here, but "good-morning" up there. Good morning up there where
We'll say "good-night," here. but "good-morning" up there.

Christ is the Light, Good-morning up there where cometh no night; When we step from this

earth to God's heaven so fair, We'll say "good-night" here, but "good-morning" up there.

38 IF JESUS GOES WITH ME

C. A. M.   **C. Austin Miles**

1. It may be in the val-ley, where countless dangers hide; It may be in the
2. It may be I must car-ry the bless-ed word of life A-cross the burn-ing
3. But if it be my por-tion to bear my cross at home, While others bear their
4. It is not mine to ques-tion the judgments of my Lord, It is but mine to

sun-shine that I in peace a-bide; But this one thing I know— if
des-erts to those in sin-ful strife; And tho' it be my lot to
bur-dens be-yond the bil-lows' foam, I'll prove my faith in Him— con-
fol-low the lead-ings of His Word; But if to go or stay, or

it be dark or fair, If Je-sus is with me, I'll go an-y-where!
bear my col-ors there, If Je-sus goes with me, I'll go an-y-where!
fess His judgments fair, And, if He stays with me, I'll stay an-y-where!
wheth-er here or there, I'll be, with my Sav-iour, con-tent an-y-where!

CHORUS

If Je-sus goes with me, I'll go . . . an-y-where! 'Tis heav-en to me, Wher-
(I'll go)

e'er I may be, If He is there! I count it a priv-i-lege here His
(His cross, His)

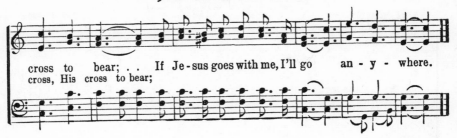

cross   to   bear; .. If Je-sus goes with me, I'll go   an-y-where.
cross, His cross to bear;

39   O LOVE THAT WILT NOT LET ME GO

George Matheson   MARGARET 8. 8. 8. 8. 6.   Albert L. Peace

1. O Love   that wilt not let   me go,..... I
2. O Light that fol-l'west all my way,.... I
3. O Joy   that seek-est me through pain,.... I
4. O Cross that lift-est up my head,.... I

rest   my wea-ry soul in Thee;   I give Thee back the life I   owe,
yield my flick'ring torch to Thee;   My heart restores its borrowed ray,
can-not close my heart to Thee;   I trace the rainbow thro' the rain,
dare not ask to fly from Thee;   I lay in dust life's glo-ry dead,

That   in Thine ocean depths its flow May richer, full-er be.
That in Thy sunshine's blaze its day May brighter, fair-er, be.
And   feel the promise is not vain That morn shall tearless be.
And from the ground there blossoms red Life that shall endless be.   A-men.

HE LIVES

A. H. A.

A. H. Ackley

1. I serve a ris-en Sav-iour, He's in the world to-day; I know that He is
2. In all the world a-round me I see His lov-ing care, And tho' my heart grows
3. Re-joice, re-joice, O Christian, lift up your voice and sing E-ter-nal hal-le-

liv-ing, what-ev-er men may say; I see His hand of mer-cy, I
wea-ry I nev-er will de-spair; I know that He is lead-ing, thru
lu-jahs to Je-sus Christ the King! The Hope of all who seek Him, the

hear His voice of cheer, And just the time I need Him He's al-ways near.
all the storm-y blast, The day of His ap-pear-ing will come at last.
Help of all who find, None oth-er is so lov-ing, so good and kind.

REFRAIN *Spirited*

He lives, He lives, Christ Je-sus lives to-day! He walks with me and
He lives, He lives,

talks with me a-long life's nar-row way. He lives, He lives, sal-
He lives, He lives,

rit. **ff**

va-tion to im-part! You ask me how I know He lives? He lives within my heart.

41 I WOULD BE TRUE

Howard Arnold Walter
Author of 3d stanza unknown

Joseph Yates Peek

1. I would be true, for there are those who trust me; I would be
2. I would be friend of all—the foe, the friend-less; I would be
3. I would be prayer-ful thru each bus-y mo-ment; I would be

pure, for there are those who care; I would be strong, for
giv-ing, and for-get the gift; I would be hum-ble,
con-stant-ly in touch with God; I would be tuned to

there is much to suf-fer; I would be brave, for there is
for I know my weak-ness; I would look up, and laugh, and
hear His slight-est whis-per; I would have faith to keep the

much to dare; I would be brave, for there is much to dare.
love, and lift; I would look up, and laugh, and love, and lift.
path Christ trod; I would have faith to keep the path Christ trod.

42 BLEST BE THE TIE

John Fawcett

Hans G. Naegeli

1. Blest be the tie that binds Our hearts in Chris-tian love; The
2. Be - fore our Fa - ther's throne We pour our ar - dent prayers; Our
3. We share our mu - tual woes, Our mu - tual bur - dens bear; And
4. When we a - sun - der part, It gives us in - ward pain; But

fel - low - ship of kin - dred minds Is like to that a - bove.
fears, our hopes, our aims are one, Our com - forts and our cares.
oft - en for each oth - er flows The sym - pa - thiz - ing tear.
we shall still be joined in heart, And hope to meet a - gain.

43 WALK IN THE LIGHT

MANOAH. C. M.

Bernard Barton

From Francis J. Haydn

1. Walk in the light! so shalt thou know That fel - low - ship of love
2. Walk in the light! and thou shalt find Thy heart made tru - ly His
3. Walk in the light! and thou shalt own Thy dark - ness passed a - way,
4. Walk in the light! and e'en the tomb No fear - ful shade shall wear;

His Spir - it on - ly can be - stow Who reigns in light a - bove.
Who dwells in cloud - less light en - shrined, In whom no dark - ness is.
Be - cause that light hath on thee shone In which is per - fect day.
Glo - ry shall chase a - way its gloom, For Christ hath conquered there.

MEN OF GOD, AWAKE, ARISE!

Virgil P. Brock

Blanche Kerr Brock

1. Men of God, a-wake, a-rise, (a-rise) Lift your ban-ners to the breeze; Men of God, a-wake, a-rise, (a-rise) For-ward march and nev-er cease. Shout a-loud the bat-tle song, (bat-tle song) Right must tri-umph o-ver wrong. Men of God, a-wake, Men of God, a-rise;

2. Men of God, a-wake, a-rise, (a-rise) Take the hel-met, sword and shield; Men of God, a-wake, a-rise, (a-rise) Nev-er fal-ter, nev-er yield. As cru-sad-ers true and bold. (true and bold) High your flam-ing torch to hold. Men of God, a-wake, Men of God, a-rise;

3. Men of God, a-wake, a-rise, (a-rise) Christ is call-ing you to-day; Men of God, a-wake, a-rise, (a-rise) Go ye forth, His will o-bey. May your an-swer ev-er be, (ev-er be) "Here am I, O Lord, send me," Men of God, a-wake, Men of God, a-rise;

After last verse

molto rit.

Men of God, a-wake, a-rise! Men of God, a-wake, a-rise!

O WORD OF GOD INCARNATE

Chenies.

William Walsham How, 1867.　　　　Timothy R. Matthews, 1855.

1. O Word of God in - car - nate, O Wis - dom from on high,
2. The Church from her dear Mas - ter Re-ceived the gift di - vine,
3. It float - eth like a ban - ner Be - fore God's host un - furled;
4. O make Thy Church, dear Sav - ior, A lamp of pur - est gold,

O Truth un-changed, un-chang - ing, O Light of our dark sky,
And still that light she lift - eth O'er all the earth to shine.
It shin - eth like a bea - con A - bove the dark-ling world:
To bear be - fore the na - tions Thy true light as of old!

We praise thee for the ra - diance That from the hal-lowed page,
It is the gold - en cas - ket Where gems of truth are stored;
It is the chart and com - pass That o'er life's surg - ing sea,
O teach Thy wan-d'ring pil - grims By this their path to trace,

A lan - tern to our foot-steps, Shines on from age to age.
It is the heav'n-drawn pic-ture Of Christ the liv - ing Word.
'Mid mists and rocks and dark - ness, Still guides, O Christ, to Thee.
Till, clouds and dark-ness end - ed, They see Thee face to face! A-MEN.

HOLY QUIETNESS

M. P. FERGUSON   Arr. from W. S. MARSHALL

1. Joys are flow-ing like a riv - er, Since the Com-fort - er has come;
2. Spring-ing in - to life and gladness, All a-round this glorious Guest,
3. Like a rain that falls from heav-en, Like the sun-light from the sky,
4. What a won-der - ful sal - va - tion, Where we al - ways see His face!

He a - bides with us for - ev - er, Makes the trust-ing heart His home.
Ban-ished un - be - lief and sad-ness, And we just o - bey and trust.
So the Ho - ly Ghost is giv - en, Com-ing on us from on high.
What a peaceful hab - i - ta - tion, What a qui - et rest-ing place.

CHORUS

Blessed qui - et-ness, ho - ly qui-et-ness, What as - sur - ance in my soul;

On the storm-y sea, Speaking peace to me, How the bil-lows cease to roll.

47 O WONDERFUL DAY

Virgil P. Brock

Blanche Kerr Brock

1. The Sav - iour has said He is com - ing a - gain
2. The trum - pet shall sound and the dead shall a - rise
3. When all the re - deemed meet their heav - en - ly King,

O won - der - ful day; He's com - ing in glo - ry for - ev - er to reign,
O won - der - ful day; To - geth - er we'll meet our dear Lord in the skies,
O won - der - ful day; Our eyes shall be - hold Him, a new song we'll sing,

CHORUS

O won - der - ful, day. O won - der - ful
won - der - ful day

day. *O won - der - ful day, O glo - ri - ous day; O glo - ri - ous day;

When the Sav-iour comes to reign We will sing a glad re-frain, O won-der-ful

*For antiphonal use by congregation and choir; Soloist or quartet and choir; or, by choir divided into two groups. Verses effective when sung by soloist or small group, with all voices on: "O wonderful day."

O WONDERFUL DAY

day. *O won-der-ful day O glo-ri-ous day; O glo-ri-ous day;

Final Ending
Adagio
rall.

When the Sav-iour comes to reign. Won-der-ful day!

48 SING AND SMILE AND PRAY

COPYRIGHT, 1934. THE RODEHEAVER CO., OWNER
INTERNATIONAL COPYRIGHT SECURED

Virgil P. Brock

Blanche Kerr Brock

1. Sing the clouds a-way, night will turn to day; If you sing and
2. Smile the clouds a-way, night will turn to day; If you smile and
4. Sing and smile and pray, that's the on-ly way; If you sing and

FINE

sing and sing, You'll sing the clouds a-way.
smile and smile, You'll smile the clouds a-way.   3. Pray the clouds a-way,
smile and pray, You'll drive the clouds a-way.

D. C. 4th Verse

Pray and pray and pray; Night will turn to day, No mat-ter what they say.

49 WIN THEM ONE BY ONE

C. A. M.

C. Austin Miles

In march time

1. If to Christ our on-ly King Men re-deemed we strive to bring,
2. Side by side we stand each day Saved are we, but lost are they;
3. On-ly cow-ards dare re-fuse, Dare this gift of God mis-use;

Just one way may this be done—We must win them one by one.
They will come if we but dare Speak a word backed up by prayer.
Ere some friend goes to his grave, Speak a word his soul to save.

CHORUS

So, you bring the one next to you, And I'll bring the one next to me; In
If you'll bring the one next to you, And I bring the one next to me; In

1

all kinds of weather we'll all work to-geth-er, And see what can be done,

2

no time at all we'll have them all, So win them, win them one by one.

50 AS A VOLUNTEER

W. S. Brown   Chas. H. Gabriel

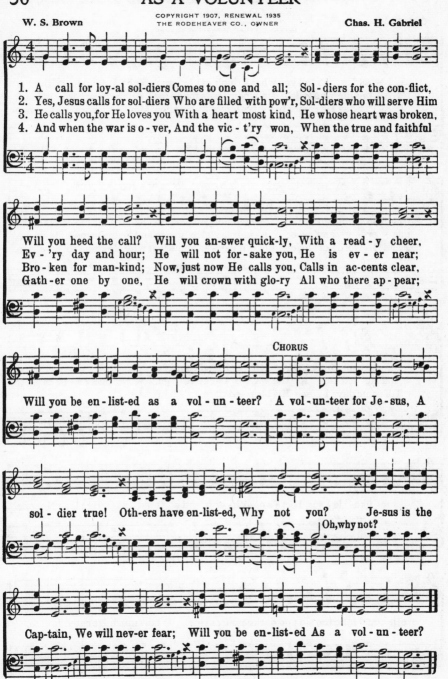

1. A call for loy-al sol-diers Comes to one and all; Sol-diers for the con-flict,
2. Yes, Jesus calls for sol-diers Who are filled with pow'r, Sol-diers who will serve Him
3. He calls you, for He loves you With a heart most kind, He whose heart was broken,
4. And when the war is o-ver, And the vic-t'ry won, When the true and faithful

Will you heed the call? Will you an-swer quick-ly, With a read-y cheer,
Ev-'ry day and hour; He will not for-sake you, He is ev-er near;
Bro-ken for man-kind; Now, just now He calls you, Calls in ac-cents clear,
Gath-er one by one, He will crown with glo-ry All who there ap-pear;

Chorus

Will you be en-list-ed as a vol-un-teer? A vol-un-teer for Je-sus, A

sol-dier true! Oth-ers have en-list-ed, Why not you? Je-sus is the
Oh, why not?

Cap-tain, We will nev-er fear; Will you be en-list-ed As a vol-un-teer?

51 NO ONE EVER CARED FOR ME LIKE JESUS

C. F. W.   C. F. WEIGLE

1. I would love to tell you what I think of Je - sus Since I found in Him a
2. All my life was full of sin when Jesus found me, Al! my heart was full of
3. Ev - 'ry day He comes to me with new as-surance, More and more I un - der-

friend so strong and true; I would tell you how He changed my life completely,
mis - er - y and woe; Je - sus plac'd His strong and loving arms a - bout me,
stand His words of love; But I'll nev - er know just why He came to save me,

He did something that no oth - er friend could do.
And He led me in the way I ought to go.
Till some day I see His bless-ed face a - bove,

CHORUS

No one ev - er cared for me like Je - sus, There's no oth - er friend so kind as He; No one else could take the sin and darkness from me, O how much He cared for me.

52 PUT THINE ARMS AROUND ME

A. H. A.

A. H. Ackley

1. Put Thine arms a-round me; All my fears de-part When Thine arms of
2. Put Thine arms a-round me, Then shall I find rest, Com-fort to sus-
3. Put Thine arms a-round me, Keep me by Thy grace: Death can nev-er

REFRAIN

mer - cy Fold me to Thy heart...
tain me, Help to do my best.... Put Thine arms a-round me,
take me, From Thy strong em-brace....

O my bless-ed Sav - iour, Put Thine arms a-round me, Hear my hum-ble,

con-trite pray'r; I am poor and need - y, Thou art strong and might-y,

Put Thine arms a - round me, I need Thy ten-der care.

53 THE SON OF GOD GOES FORTH TO WAR

Reginald Heber ALL SAINTS C. M. D. **Henry S. Cutler**

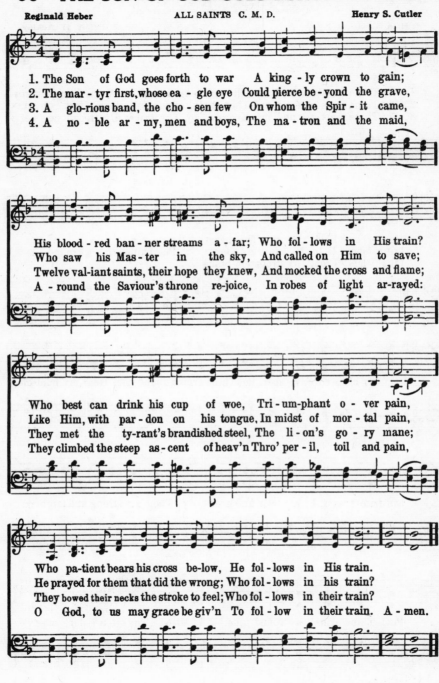

1. The Son of God goes forth to war A king-ly crown to gain;
2. The mar-tyr first, whose ea-gle eye Could pierce be-yond the grave,
3. A glo-rious band, the cho-sen few On whom the Spir-it came,
4. A no-ble ar-my, men and boys, The ma-tron and the maid,

His blood-red ban-ner streams a-far; Who fol-lows in His train?
Who saw his Mas-ter in the sky, And called on Him to save;
Twelve val-iant saints, their hope they knew, And mocked the cross and flame;
A-round the Saviour's throne re-joice, In robes of light ar-rayed:

Who best can drink his cup of woe, Tri-um-phant o-ver pain,
Like Him, with par-don on his tongue, In midst of mor-tal pain,
They met the ty-rant's brandished steel, The li-on's go-ry mane;
They climbed the steep as-cent of heav'n Thro' per-il, toil and pain,

Who pa-tient bears his cross be-low, He fol-lows in His train.
He prayed for them that did the wrong; Who fol-lows in his train?
They bowed their necks the stroke to feel; Who fol-lows in their train?
O God, to us may grace be giv'n To fol-low in their train. A-men.

HIGHER GROUND

Johnson Oatman, Jr.   Chas. H. Gabriel

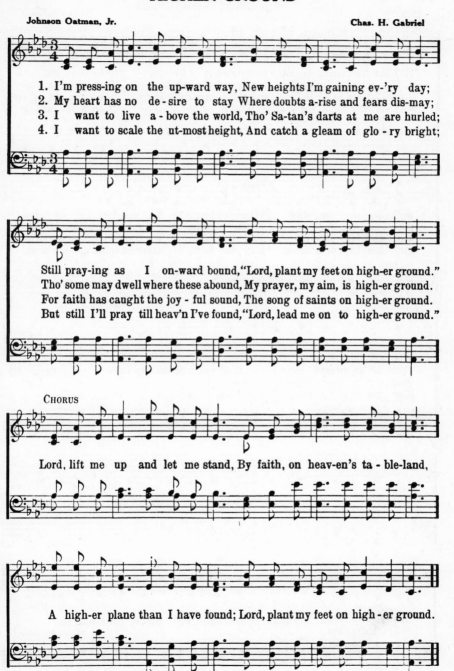

1. I'm press-ing on the up-ward way, New heights I'm gaining ev-'ry day;
2. My heart has no de - sire to stay Where doubts a-rise and fears dis-may;
3. I   want to live a - bove the world, Tho' Sa-tan's darts at me are hurled;
4. I   want to scale the ut-most height, And catch a gleam of glo - ry bright;

Still pray-ing as   I on-ward bound, "Lord, plant my feet on high-er ground."
Tho' some may dwell where these abound, My prayer, my aim, is high-er ground.
For faith has caught the joy - ful sound, The song of saints on high-er ground.
But still I'll pray till heav'n I've found, "Lord, lead me on to high-er ground."

CHORUS

Lord, lift me up and let me stand, By faith, on heav-en's ta - ble-land,

A high-er plane than I have found; Lord, plant my feet on high - er ground.

55 SPEAK, MY LORD

G. B.

George Bennard

1. Hear the Lord of har-vest sweet-ly call-ing, "Who will go and work for Me to-day? Who will bring to Me the lost and dy-ing? Who will point them to the nar-row way?"

2. When the coal of fire . . touched the proph-et, Mak-ing him as pure, as pure can be, When the voice of God said, "Who'll go for us?" Then he an-swered, "Here I am, send me."

3. Mil-lions now in sin and shame are dy-ing, Lis-ten to their sad and bit-ter cry; Has-ten, broth-er, has-ten to the res-cue; Quick-ly an-swer, "Mas-ter, here am I."

4. Soon the time for reap-ing will be o-ver; Soon we'll gath-er for the har-vest-home; May the Lord of har-vest smile up-on us, May we hear His bless-ed, "Child, well done."

CHORUS

Speak, my Lord, speak, my Lord, Speak, and I'll be quick to an-swer Thee; Speak, my Lord, speak, my Lord, Speak, and I will answer, "Lord, send me."

Speak, my Lord, Speak, my Lord, to answer Thee; Speak, my Lord, "Lord, send me."

WONDERFUL LOVE, JOY AND PEACE

Virgil P. Brock

Blanche Kerr Brock

1. Won-der-ful LOVE God freely be-stows, Won-der-ful JOY, my heart o-ver-flows!
2. Meas-ure-less is God's wonderful love, Pour-ing in streams from heaven a-bove;
3. Un-end-ing is this wonderful joy, Full and complete which naught can destroy;
4. Mar-vel-ous is this won-der-ful peace, Peace like a riv-er nev-er to cease:

Won-der-ful peace, so pre-cious, di-vine, Gifts of His Spir-it, now they are mine.
Foun-tain e-ter-nal, flow-ing for me, Plen-te-ous mer-cy, full and so free.
Fill-ing my heart and flood-ing my soul, Ev-er a-bid-ing tho' sor-rows roll.
With its rich treasure naught can compare, In all its full-ness I have a share.

CHORUS

O won-der-ful love, meas-ure-less love sent from a-bove, O won-der-ful

Joy, un-end-ing joy naught can de-stroy: O won-der-ful peace, marvelous

peace nev-er to cease; O won-der-ful love, wonderful joy, won-der-ful peace!

57 MORE LIKE THE MASTER

C. H. G.
COPYRIGHT 1906, RENEWAL 1934
THE RODEHEAVER CO., OWNER
Chas. H. Gabriel

1. More like the Mas-ter I would ev - er be, More of His meek-ness,
2. More like the Mas-ter is my dai - ly prayer; More strength to car-ry
3. More like the Mas-ter I would live and grow; More of His love to

more hu-mil - i - ty; More zeal to la - bor, more cour-age to be true,
cross - es I must bear; More ear-nest ef - fort to bring His kingdom in;
oth - ers I would show; More self-de - ni - al, like His in Gal-i - lee,

rit.

CHORUS

More con - se - cra - tion for work He bids me do. . . . Take Thou my
More of His Spir - it, the wan-der - er to win. . . .
More like the Mas-ter I long to ev - er be. . . . Take my heart, O

heart, . . I would be Thine a-lone; . . Take Thou my heart . . and
take my heart, I would be Thine a-lone; Take my heart, O take my heart and

make it all Thine own; . . Purge me from sin, . . . O Lord, I now im-
make it all Thine own; Purge Thou me from ev-'ry sin, O Lord, I

plore, ... Wash me and keep ... me Thine for-ev-er-more.
now im-plore, Wash and keep, O wash and keep me Thine for-ev-er-more.

58 THE LIGHT OF THE WORLD IS JESUS

P. P. B.

P. P. Bliss

1. The whole world was lost in the darkness of sin; The Light of the world is Je-sus;
2. No darkness have we who in Je-sus a-bide; The Light of the world is Je-sus;
3. Ye dwellers in darkness with sin-blinded eyes; The Light of the world is Je-sus;
4. No need of the sunlight in heaven we're told; The Light of the world is Je-sus;

Like sunshine at noonday His glo-ry shone in, The Light of the world is Je-sus.
We walk in the Light when we follow our Guide, The Light of the world is Je-sus.
Go, wash at His bidding, and light will a-rise, The Light of the world is Je-sus.
The Lamb is the Light in the cit-y of gold, The Light of the world is Je-sus.

CHORUS.

Come to the Light, 'tis shining for thee; Sweetly the Light has dawned upon me,

Once I was blind, but now I can see: The Light of the world is Je-sus.

59 DWELLING IN BEULAH LAND

C. A. M.   C. Austin Miles

1. Far a-way the noise of strife up-on my ear is fall-ing, Then I know the
2. Far be-low the storm of doubt up-on the world is beat-ing, Sons of men in
3. Let the storm-y breez-es blow, their cry can-not a-larm me, I am safe-ly
4. Viewing here the works of God, I sink in con-tem-pla-tion, Hear-ing now His

sins of earth be-set on ev-'ry hand; Doubt and fear and things of earth in
bat-tle long the en-e-my with-stand; Safe am I with-in the cas-tle
shelter'd here, pro-tect-ed by God's hand; Here the sun is al-ways shin-ing,
bless-ed voice, I see the way He plann'd; Dwell-ing in the Spir-it, here I

vain to me are call-ing, None of these shall move me from Beu-lah Land.
of God's word re-treat-ing, Nothing there can reach me—'tis Beu-lah Land.
here there's naught can harm me, I am safe for-ev-er in Beu-lah Land.
learn of full sal-va-tion, Glad-ly will I tar-ry in Beu-lah Land.

CHORUS

I'm liv-ing on the moun-tain, un-der-neath a cloud-less sky, I'm
Praise God!

drink-ing at the fountain that nev-er shall run dry, O yes! I'm feast-ing on the

DWELLING IN BEULAH LAND

man-na from a boun-ti-ful sup-ply For I am dwell-ing in Beu-lah Land.

60   AT CALVARY

Wm. R. Newell   D. B. Towner

1. Years I spent in van-i-ty and pride, Car-ing not my Lord was
2. By God's Word at last my sin I learned; Then I trem-bled at the
3. Now I've giv'n to Je-sus ev-'ry-thing, Now I glad-ly own Him
4. Oh, the love that drew sal-va-tion's plan! Oh, the grace that bro't it

cru-ci-fied, Know-ing not it was for me He died On Cal-va-ry.
law I'd spurned, Till my guilt-y soul im-plor-ing turned To Cal-va-ry.
as my King, Now my rap-tured soul can on-ly sing Of Cal-va-ry.
down to man! Oh, the might-y gulf that God did span At Cal-va-ry!

CHORUS

Mer-cy there was great, and grace was free; Par-don there was mul-ti-

plied to me; There my burdened soul found lib-er-ty, At Cal-va-ry.

61 MY REDEEMER

P. P. Bliss

James McGranahan

1. I will sing of my Re-deem-er, And His won-drous love to me;
2. I will tell the won-drous sto-ry, How my lost es-tate to save,
3. I will praise my dear Re-deem-er, His tri-um-phant pow'r I'll tell,
4. I will sing of my Re-deem-er, And His heav'n-ly love to me;

On the cru-el cross He suf-fered, From the curse to set me free.
In His bound-less love and mer-cy, He the ran-som free-ly gave.
How the vic-to-ry He giv-eth O-ver sin, and death, and hell.
He from death to life hath bro't me, Son of God with Him to be.

CHORUS

Sing, oh, sing ...... of my Re-deem-er,
of my Re-deem-er, Sing, oh, sing of my Re-deem-er,

With His blood .... He pur-chased me, ...
He pur-chased me, With His blood He pur-chased me,

On the cross .... He sealed my par-don,
He sealed my par-don, On the cross He sealed my par-don,

Paid the debt, ... and made me free. . . . .
and made me free,   and made me free.

62 NEAR TO THE HEART OF GOD

COPYRIGHT 1903, RENEWAL 1931
THE LORENZ PUB. CO., OWNER

C. B. McAfee

1. There is a place of qui - et rest, Near to the heart of God,
2. There is a place of com - fort sweet, Near to the heart of God,
3. There is a place of full re - lease, Near to the heart of God,

A place where sin can - not mo - lest, Near to the heart of God.
A place where we our Sav - ior meet, Near to the heart of God.
A place where all is joy and peace, Near to the heart of God.

REFRAIN

O Je - sus, blest Re - deem - er, Sent from the heart of God,

Hold us, who wait be - fore Thee, Near to the heart of God.

63 SINCE JESUS CAME INTO MY HEART

R. H. McDaniel   Chas. H. Gabriel

1. What a won-der-ful change in my life has been wrought Since Je-sus came
2. I have ceased from my wand'ring and go-ing a-stray, Since Je-sus came
3. I'm pos-sessed of a hope that is stead-fast and sure, Since Je-sus came
4. There's a light in the val-ley of death now for me, Since Je-sus came
5. I shall go there to dwell in that cit-y I know, Since Je-sus came

in-to my heart; I have light in my soul for which long I had sought,
in-to my heart; And my sins which were man-y are all washed a-way,
in-to my heart; And no dark clouds of doubt now my path-way ob-scure,
in-to my heart; And the gates of the cit-y be-yond I can see,
in-to my heart; And I'm hap-py, so hap-py, as on-ward I go,

Chorus

Since Je-sus came in-to my heart. Since Je-sus came in-to my
Since Je-sus came in, came

heart, Since Je-sus came in-to my heart; Floods of joy o'er my
in-to my heart, Since Je-sus came in, came in-to my heart;

soul like the sea-bil-lows roll, Since Je-sus came in-to my heart.

64 'TIS THE BLESSED HOUR OF PRAYER

Fanny J. Crosby

W. H. Doane

1. 'Tis the bless-ed hour of prayer, when our hearts low-ly bend, And we
2. 'Tis the bless-ed hour of prayer, when the Sav-iour draws near, With a
3. 'Tis the bless-ed hour of prayer, when the tempt-ed and tried To the
4. 'Tis the bless-ed hour of prayer; trust-ing Him, we be-lieve That the

gath-er to Je-sus, our Sav-iour and Friend; If we come to Him in
ten-der com-pas-sion His chil-dren to hear; When He tells us we may
Sav-iour who loves them their sor-rows con-fide; With a sym-pa-thiz-ing
blessing we're need-ing we'll sure-ly re-ceive; In the full-ness of this

faith His pro-tect-ion to share, What a balm for the wea-ry! O how
cast at His feet ev-'ry care, What a balm for the wea-ry! O how
heart He re-moves ev-'ry care; What a balm for the wea-ry! O how
trust we shall lose ev-'ry care; What a balm for the wea-ry! O how

REFRAIN

sweet to be there! Bless-ed hour of prayer, bless-ed hour of prayer;

What a balm for the wea-ry! O how sweet to be there!

65 MY SAVIOUR'S LOVE

C. H. G.

Charles H. Gabriel

1. I stand a-mazed in the pres-ence Of Je-sus the Naz-a-rene,
2. For me it was in the gar-den He pray'd; "Not My will, but Thine,"
3. In pit-y an-gels be-held Him, And came from the world of light
4. He took my sins and my sor-rows, He made them His ver-y own;
5. When with the ran-som'd in glo-ry His face I at last shall see,

And won-der how He could love me, A sin-ner condem'd, un-clean.
He had no tears for His own griefs, But sweat-drops of blood for mine.
To com-fort Him in the sor-rows He bore for my soul that night.
He bore the bur-den to Cal-v'ry, And suf-fer'd, and died a-lone.
'Twill be my joy thro' the a-ges To sing of His love for me.

CHORUS

How mar-vel-ous! how won-der-ful! And my song shall ev-er be:
Oh, how' mar-vel-ous! oh, how won-der-ful!

How mar-vel-ous! how won-der-ful Is my Sav-ior's love for me!
Oh, how mar-vel-ous! oh, how won-der-ful

66 HIS LOVE SET ME FREE

Lizzie DeArmond

Jas. C. Moore

1. No lon-ger I'm un-der the law's con-dem-na-tion, His
2. O won-der-ful grace that my sins were for-giv-en, His
3. My sight He re-stored when I wan-dered in blind-ness, His
4. Now joy to my heart is this dear Sav-ior bring-ing, His

love set me free! Thru Je-sus I'm claim-ing a
love set me free! He's gone to pre-pare me a
love set me free! He cleansed me from guilt thru His
love set me free! "All glo-ry to God" in my

CHORUS

per-fect sal-va-tion, His love set me free!
man-sion in heav-en, His love set me free! His love set me
great lov-ing-kind-ness His love set me free!
glad-ness I'm sing-ing, His love set me free!

free! His love set me free! "All glo-ry to

Je-sus" for-ev-er I'll sing, His love set me free!

67 BLESSED ASSURANCE

Fanny J. Crosby

Mrs. Jos. F. Knapp

1. Bless-ed as-sur-ance, Je-sus is mine! O what a fore-taste of
2. Per-fect sub-mis-sion, per-fect de-light, Vi-sions of rap-ture now
3. Per-fect sub-mis-sion, all is at rest, I in my Sav-iour am

glo - ry di - vine! Heir of sal - va - tion, pur-chase of God,
burst on my sight! An - gels de-scend-ing, bring from a - bove
hap - py and blest; Watch-ing and wait - ing, look-ing a - bove,

CHORUS

Born of His Spir - it, washed in His blood.
Ech - oes of mer - cy, whis-pers of love. This is my sto - ry,
Filled with His good - ness, lost in His love.

this is my song, Prais-ing my Sav-iour all the day long; This is my

sto - ry, this is my song, Prais-ing my Sav-iour all the day long.

68 I KNOW GOD'S PROMISE IS TRUE

Mrs. C. H. M.

Mrs. C. H. Morris

1. For God so loved this sin-ful world, His Son he free-ly gave,
2. I was a way-ward, wand-'ring child, A slave to sin and fear,
3. The "who-so-ev-er" of the Lord, I trust-ed was for me;
4. E-ter-nal life be-gun be-low Now fills my heart and soul;

That who-so-ev-er would be-lieve, E-ter-nal life shall have.
Un-til this bless-ed prom-ise fell Like mu-sic on my ear.
I took Him at His gra-cious word, From sin He set me free.
I'll sing His praise for-ev-er-more, Whose blood has made me whole.

CHORUS

'Tis true, O yes, 'tis true.......... God's won-der-ful
'Tis true, O yes, the prom-ise is true,

prom-ise is true, ...   For I've trust-ed, and test-ed, and
'tis true,

tried it, And I know God's prom-ise is true.....
'tis true.

69 SOMEBODY CARES

Fannie Edna Stafford   Homer A. Rodeheaver

1. Some-bod-y knows when your heart aches, And ev'ry-thing seems to go wrong;
2. Some-bod-y cares when you're tempted, And your mind grows diz-zy and dim;
3. Some-bod-y loves you when wea - ry;   Some-bod-y loves you when strong;

Some-bod-y knows when the shad-ows Need chas-ing a - way with a song;
Some-bod-y cares when you're weakest, And far-thest a - way from Him;
Al - ways is wait-ing to help you, He watch-es you—one of the throng

Some-bod - y knows when you're lone - ly,   Tir - ed, dis-cour-aged and blue;
Some-bod - y grieves when you're fall - en,   You are not lost from His sight;
Need-ing His friend-ship so ho - ly,   Needing His watch-care so true;

Some-bod-y wants you to know Him, And know that He dear - ly loves you.
Some-bod-y waits for your com - ing, And He'll drive the gloom from your night.
His name? We call His name Je - sus; He loves ev - 'ry one, He loves you.

A MIGHTY FORTRESS IS OUR GOD

MARTIN LUTHER
Tr. by FREDERICK H. HEDGE

EIN' FESTE BURG P. M.

MARTIN LUTHER

1. A might-y fortress is our God, A bul-wark nev-er fail-ing:
2. Did we in our own strength confide, Our striving would be los-ing;
3. And tho' this world with dev-ils filled Should threaten to un-do us;
4. That word a-bove all earthly pow'rs, No thanks to them, a-bid-eth;

Our help-er He, a-mid the flood Of mor-tal ills pre-vail-ing.
Were not the right Man on our side, The man of God's own choos-ing.
We will not fear, for God hath willed His truth to tri-umph thro' us.
The Spir-it and the gifts are ours, Thro' Him who with us sid-eth.

For still our ancient foe Doth seek to work us woe; His craft and pow'r are great,
Dost ask who that may be? Christ Jesus, it is He; Lord Sa-ba-oth His name,
The prince of darkness grim, We tremble not for him; His rage we can en-dure,
Let goods and kindred go, This mortal life al-so: The bod-y they may kill:

And, armed with cru-el hate, On earth is not his e-qual.
From age to age the same, And He must win the bat-tle.
For lo! his doom is sure, One lit-tle word shall fell him.
God's truth a-bid-eth still, His kingdom is for-ev-er. A-men.

71 DAY IS DYING IN THE WEST

Mary A. Lathbury   EVENING PRAISE 7. 7. 7. 7. 4. With Refrain   William F. Sherwin

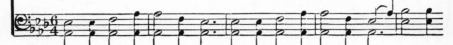

1. Day   is   dy - ing in   the west, Heav'n is touching earth with rest; Wait and
2. Lord   of   life, beneath the dome Of   the u - ni-verse, Thy home, Gath-er
3. While the deep'ning shadows fall, Heart of Love, en - fold-ing all, Thro' the
4. When for - ev - er from our sight Pass the stars, the day, the night, Lord of

worship while the night Sets her ev-'ning lamps alight Thro' all the   sky.
us, who seek Thy face, To the fold of Thy embrace, For Thou art   nigh.
glo - ry and the grace Of the stars that veil Thy face, Our hearts as-cend.
an - gels, on our eyes Let   e - ter-nal morning rise, And shadows end!

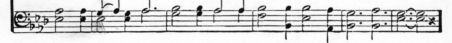

REFRAIN

Ho - ly, ho - ly, ho - ly, Lord God of   Hosts! Heav'n and earth are full of

Thee! Heav'n and earth are praising Thee, O Lord most   High!   A - men.

72 TO GOD BE THE GLORY

Fanny J. Crosby

William H. Doane

1. To God be the glo-ry,—great things He hath done, So loved He the world that He
2. O per - fect re-demp-tion, the purchase of blood, To ev - 'ry be-liev-er the
3. Great things He hath taught us, great things He hath done, And great our rejoicing thro

gave us His Son, Who yield-ed His life an a-tone-ment for sin, And o-pened the
prom-ise of God; The vil - est of-fend-er who tru-ly be-lieves, That moment from
Je - sus the Son; But pu - rer, and higher, and greater will be Our won-der, our

CHORUS

Life-gate that all may go in.
Je - sus a par-don receives. Praise the Lord, praise the Lord, Let the earth hear His
transport, when Jesus we see.

voice! Praise the Lord, praise the Lord, Let the peo-ple re - joice! O come to the

Fa-ther, thro' Je-sus the Son, And give Him the glo-ry,—great things He hath done.

73 SAFELY THROUGH ANOTHER WEEK

John Newton   SABBATH MORN 7.7.7.7.7.7   Lowell Mason

1. Safe - ly through an - oth - er week, God has brought us on our way;
2. While we pray for pard'ning grace, Thro' the dear Re - deem - er's name,
3. Here we come Thy name to praise; May we feel Thy pres-ence near:
4. May Thy gos - pel's joy - ful sound Con - quer sin - ners, com-fort saints;

Let us now a bless - ing seek, Wait-ing in His courts to - day.
Show Thy rec - on - cil - ed face, Take a - way our sin and shame;
May Thy glo - ry meet our eyes, While we in Thy house ap - pear:
Make the fruits of grace a - bound, Bring re - lief for all com-plaints:

Day of all the week the best, Em-blem of e - ter - nal rest.
From our world - ly cares set free, May we rest this day in Thee.
Here af - ford us, Lord, a taste Of our ev - er - last - ing feast.
Thus may all our Sab-baths prove, Till we join the church a - bove.

Day of all the week the best, Emblem of e - ter - nal rest.
From our world - ly cares set free, May we rest this day in Thee.
Here af - ford us, Lord, a taste Of our ev - er - last-ing feast.
Thus may all our Sabbaths prove, Till we join the church a-bove. A - men.

74 O GOD, OUR HELP IN AGES PAST

Isaac Watts   ST. ANNE C. M.   William Croft

1. O God, our help in a-ges past, Our hope for years to come,
2. Be-fore the hills in or-der stood, Or earth re-ceived her frame,
3. A thous-and a-ges, in Thy sight, Are like an ev-'ning gone;
4. Time, like an ev-er-roll-ing stream, Bears all its sons a-way;
5. O God, our help in a-ges past, Our hope for years to come;

Our shel-ter from the storm-y blast, And our e-ter-nal home!
From ev-er-last-ing Thou art God, To end-less years the same.
Short as the watch that ends the night, Be-fore the ris-ing sun.
They fly, for-got-ten, as a dream Dies at the ope-ning day.
Be Thou our guide while life shall last, And our e-ter-nal home! A-men.

75 DEAR LORD AND FATHER OF MANKIND

John G. Whittier   ELTON 8. 6. 8. 8. 6.   Frederick C. Maker

1. Dear Lord and Father of mankind, Forgive our fev'rish ways! Reclothe us in our
2. In simple trust, like theirs who heard, Beside the Syrian sea, The gracious calling
3. O Sabbath rest by Gal-i-lee! O calm of hills a-bove, Where Jesus knelt to
4. Drop Thy still dews of qui-et-ness, Till all our strivings cease; Take from our souls the
5. Breathe thro' the heats of our desire Thy coolness and Thy balm; Let sense be dumb, let

rightful mind; In pur-er lives Thy serv-ice find, In deeper rev'rence, praise.
of the Lord, Let us, like them, without a word, Rise up and fol-low Thee.
share with Thee The silence of e-ter-ni-ty, In-ter-pret-ed by love!
strain and stress, And let our ordered lives confess The beauty of Thy peace.
flesh retire: Speak thro' the earthquake, wind and fire, O still small voice of calm! A-men.

I GAVE MY LIFE FOR THEE

Frances R. Havergal

P. P. Bliss

1. "I gave My life for thee, My pre-cious blood I shed,
2. "My Fa-ther's house of light, My glo-ry-cir-cled throne,
3. "And I have bro't to thee, Down from My home a-bove,
4. Oh! let thy life be giv'n, Thy years for Him be spent;

That thou might'st ransomed be, And quick-ened from the dead;
I left for earth-ly night, For wand'rings sad and lone;
Sal-va-tion full and free, My par-don and My love;
World-fet-ters all be riv'n, And joy with suf-f'ring blent!

I gave, I gave My life for thee, What hast thou giv'n for Me?
I left, I left it all for thee, Hast thou left aught for Me?
I've borne, I've borne it all for thee, What hast thou borne for Me?
I bring, I bring rich gifts to thee, What hast thou brought to Me?

77

JESUS, SAVIOUR PILOT ME

Edward Hopper

J. E. Gould
FINE.

1. Je-sus, Sav-iour, pi-lot me O-ver life's tem-pes-tuous sea;
D.C.—Chart and com-pass come from Thee, Je-sus, Sav-iour, pi-lot me.
2. As a moth-er stills her child, Thou canst hush the o-cean wild.
D.C.—Wondrous Sov-'reign of the sea; Je-sus, Sav-iour, pi-lot me.
3. When at last I near the shore, And the fear-ful breakers roar,
D.C.—May I hear Thee say to me; "Fear not, I will pi-lot thee."

JESUS SAVIOUR PILOT ME

D. C.

Un-known waves a-round me roll, Hid - ing rocks and treach'rous shoal;
Boist'rous waves o - bey Thy will When Thou say'st to them be still!"
'Twixt me and the peaceful rest, Then, while lean - ing on Thy breast,

78   O DAY OF REST AND GLADNESS

Christopher Wordsworth   MENDEBRAS 7. 6. 7. 6. D.   Arr. by Lowell Mason

1. O   day of rest and gladness, O day of joy and light, O balm of care and
2. On thee, at the cre - a - tion, The light first had its birth; On thee, for our sal -
3. To - day on wea - ry na-tions The heav'nly manna falls; To ho - ly con - vo -
4. New grac-es ev - er gaining From this our day of rest, We reach the rest re -

sad-ness,   Most beau-ti-ful, most bright: On thee, the high and low-ly, [Thro'
va - tion,   Christ rose from depths of earth; On thee, our Lord, vic-to-rious, The
ca - tions   The sil-ver trump-et calls, Where gospel light is glow - ing With
main-ing   To spir-its of the blest; To Ho - ly Ghost be prais-es,   To

a - ges joined in tune, Sing "Holy, holy, holy," To the great God Tri-une.
Spirit sent from heav'n; And thus on thee, most glorious, A tri-ple light was giv'n.
pure and radiant beams, And living water flowing With soul-refreshing streams.
Father, and to Son; The church her voice upraises To Thee, blest Three in One. A-men.

79 JESUS NEVER FAILS

A. A. Luther   A. A. Luther

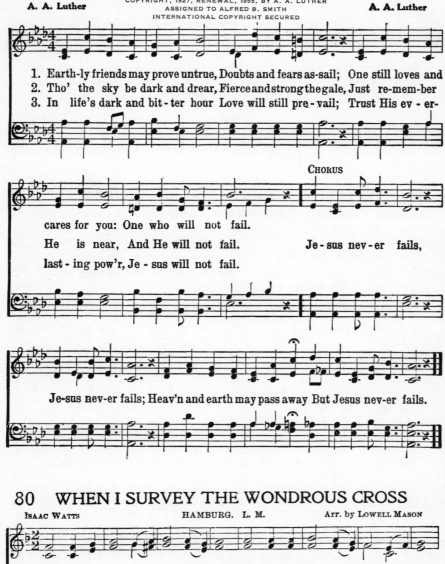

1. Earth-ly friends may prove untrue, Doubts and fears as-sail; One still loves and
2. Tho' the sky be dark and drear, Fierce and strong the gale, Just re-mem-ber
3. In life's dark and bit-ter hour Love will still pre-vail; Trust His ev-er-

Chorus

cares for you: One who will not fail.

He is near, And He will not fail.   Je-sus nev-er fails,

last-ing pow'r, Je-sus will not fail.

Je-sus nev-er fails; Heav'n and earth may pass away But Jesus nev-er fails.

80 WHEN I SURVEY THE WONDROUS CROSS

Isaac Watts   HAMBURG. L. M.   Arr. by Lowell Mason

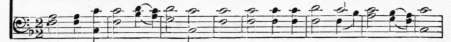

1. When I sur-vey the won-drous cross On which the Prince of glo-ry died,
2. For-bid it, Lord, that I should boast Save in the death of Christ, my Lord;
3. See, from His head, His hands, His feet, Sor-row and love flow min-gled down;
4. Were the whole realm of na-ture mine, That were a pres-ent far too small:

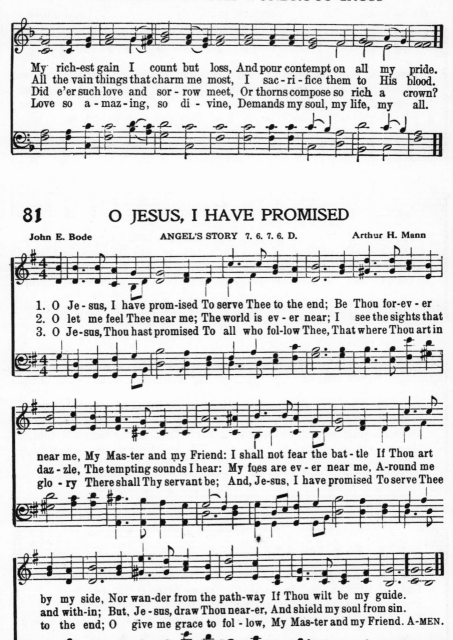

My rich-est gain I count but loss, And pour contempt on all my pride.
All the vain things that charm me most, I sac-ri-fice them to His blood.
Did e'er such love and sor-row meet, Or thorns compose so rich a crown?
Love so a-maz-ing, so di-vine, Demands my soul, my life, my all.

81   O JESUS, I HAVE PROMISED

John E. Bode   ANGEL'S STORY 7. 6. 7. 6. D.   Arthur H. Mann

1. O Je-sus, I have prom-ised To serve Thee to the end; Be Thou for-ev-er
2. O let me feel Thee near me; The world is ev-er near; I see the sights that
3. O Je-sus, Thou hast promised To all who fol-low Thee, That where Thou art in

near me, My Mas-ter and my Friend: I shall not fear the bat-tle If Thou art
daz-zle, The tempting sounds I hear: My foes are ev-er near me, A-round me
glo-ry There shall Thy servant be; And, Je-sus, I have promised To serve Thee

by my side, Nor wan-der from the path-way If Thou wilt be my guide.
and with-in; But, Je-sus, draw Thou near-er, And shield my soul from sin.
to the end; O give me grace to fol-low, My Mas-ter and my Friend. A-MEN.

LOVE DIVINE, ALL LOVES EXCELLING

Charles Wesley · BEECHER 8. 7. 8. 7. D. · John Zundel

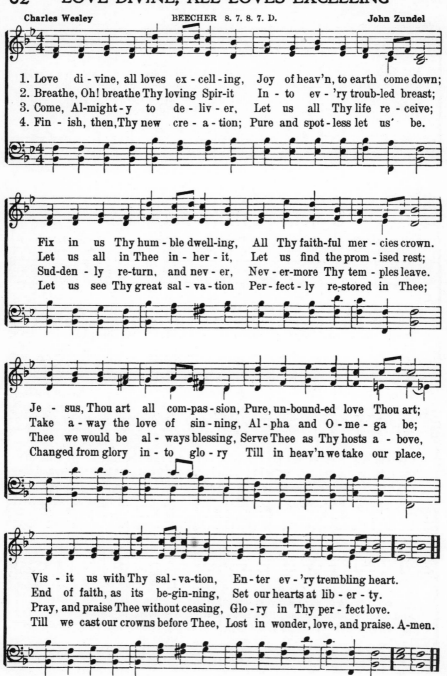

1. Love di - vine, all loves ex - cell - ing, Joy of heav'n, to earth come down;
2. Breathe, Oh! breathe Thy loving Spir-it In - to ev - 'ry troub-led breast;
3. Come, Al-might - y to de - liv - er, Let us all Thy life re - ceive;
4. Fin - ish, then, Thy new cre - a - tion; Pure and spot-less let us' be.

Fix in us Thy hum - ble dwell-ing, All Thy faith-ful mer - cies crown.
Let us all in Thee in - her - it, Let us find the prom - ised rest;
Sud-den - ly re-turn, and nev - er, Nev - er-more Thy tem - ples leave.
Let us see Thy great sal - va - tion Per - fect - ly re-stored in Thee;

Je - sus, Thou art all com-pas-sion, Pure, un-bound-ed love Thou art;
Take a - way the love of sin - ning, Al - pha and O - me - ga be;
Thee we would be al - ways blessing, Serve Thee as Thy hosts a - bove,
Changed from glory in - to glo - ry Till in heav'n we take our place,

Vis - it us with Thy sal - va-tion, En - ter ev - 'ry trembling heart.
End of faith, as its be-gin-ning, Set our hearts at lib - er - ty.
Pray, and praise Thee without ceasing, Glo - ry in Thy per - fect love.
Till we cast our crowns before Thee, Lost in wonder, love, and praise. A - men.

83 I LOVE THY KINGDOM, LORD

Timothy Dwight   ST. THOMAS S. M.   Aaron Williams, Collection

1. I love Thy king-dom, Lord, The house of Thine a-bode,
2. I love Thy Church, O God! Her walls be-fore Thee stand,
3. For her my tears shall fall; For her my pray'rs as-cend;
4. Be-yond my high-est joy I prize her heav'nly ways,
5. Sure as Thy truth shall last, To Zi-on shall be giv'n

The Church our blest Redeemer saved With His own pre-cious blood.
Dear as the ap-ple of Thine eye, And grav-en on Thy hand.
To her my cares and toils be giv'n; Till toils and cares shall end.
Her sweet com-mun-ion, solemn vows, Her hymns of love and praise.
The brightest glories earth can yield, And brighter bliss of heav'n. A-men.

84 A CHARGE TO KEEP I HAVE

Charles Wesley   BOYLSTON S. M.   Lowell Mason

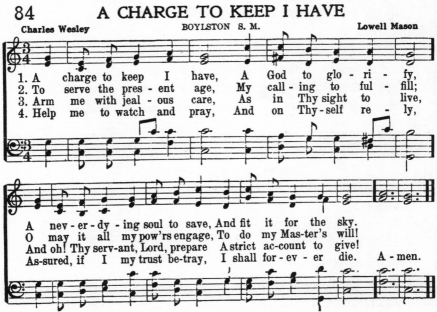

1. A charge to keep I have, A God to glo-ri-fy,
2. To serve the pres-ent age, My call-ing to ful-fill;
3. Arm me with jeal-ous care, As in Thy sight to live,
4. Help me to watch and pray, And on Thy-self re-ly,

A nev-er-dy-ing soul to save, And fit it for the sky.
O may it all my pow'rs engage, To do my Mas-ter's will!
And oh! Thy serv-ant, Lord, prepare A strict ac-count to give!
As-sured, if I my trust be-tray, I shall for-ev-er die. A-men.

85
SURRENDER

Oswald J. Smith

B. D. Ackley

DUET

1. All   I have I yield to Je - sus, His for - ev - er-more I'll be;
2. Full sur-ren-der! Oh, how eas - y When I come, con-fess-ing all;
3. Peace and rest in Him I'm find - ing, For His bur-den is so light;

To   His will I now sur-ren - der, He is ev-'ry-thing to me. . . .
Cast-ing ev-'ry care on Je - sus, Ev - er lis-t'ning for His call. . . .
He has bro-ken ev-'ry fet - ter, Made me vic-tor in the fight. . . .

REFRAIN

Oh, the joy of full sur-ren - der! How   it thrills me thro' and thro'!

Ev - 'ry tal-ent for my Sav-iour, While I seek His will to do.

86
OLD-TIME POWER

P. R.

Paul Rader

CHORUS

Spir - it, now melt and move All of our hearts with love,

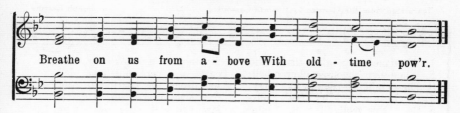

Breathe on us from a - bove With old - time pow'r.

87   GOD OF OUR FATHERS

NATIONAL HYMN. 10, 10, 10, 10

Daniel C. Roberts, 1876

George W. Warren, 1892

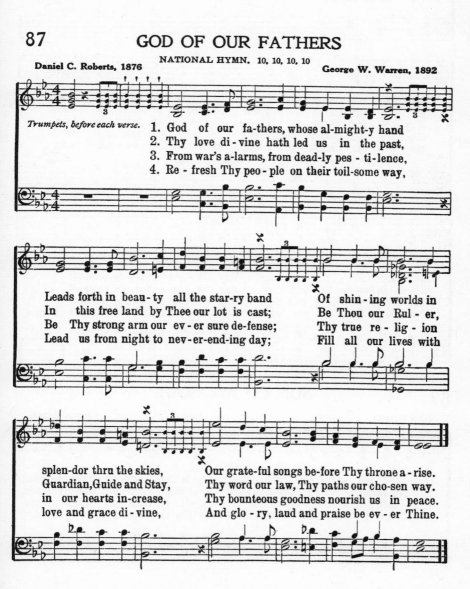

Trumpets, before each verse.

1. God of our fa-thers, whose al-might-y hand
2. Thy love di - vine hath led us in the past,
3. From war's a-larms, from dead-ly pes - ti-lence,
4. Re - fresh Thy peo - ple on their toil-some way,

Leads forth in beau-ty all the star-ry band Of shin-ing worlds in
In   this free land by Thee our lot is cast; Be Thou our Rul - er,
Be Thy strong arm our ev - er sure de-fense; Thy true re - lig - ion
Lead us from night to nev-er-end-ing day; Fill all our lives with

splen-dor thru the skies, Our grate-ful songs be-fore Thy throne a - rise.
Guardian, Guide and Stay, Thy word our law, Thy paths our cho-sen way.
in our hearts in-crease, Thy bounteous goodness nourish us in peace.
love and grace di - vine, And glo - ry, laud and praise be ev - er Thine.

88 WHEN MORNING GILDS THE SKIES

Translated from the German by Edward Caswall

Joseph Barnby

1. When morn-ing gilds the skies, My heart a-wak-ing cries,
2. When-e'er the sweet church bell Peals o-ver hill and dell
3. The night be-comes as day, When from the heart we say,
4. In heav'n's e-ter-nal bliss The love-liest strain is this,
5. Be this, while life is mine, My can-ti-cle di-vine,

May Je-sus Christ be praised! A-like at work and pray'r,
May Je-sus Christ be praised! Oh! hark to what it sings,
May Je-sus Christ be praised! The pow'rs of dark-ness fear,
May Je-sus Christ be praised! Let earth, and sea, and sky,
May Je-sus Christ be praised! Be this th'e-ter-nal song

To Je-sus I re-pair; May Je-sus Christ be praised!
As joy-ous-ly it rings, May Je-sus Christ be praised!
When this sweet chant they hear, May Je-sus Christ be praised!
From depth to height re-ply, May Je-sus Christ be praised!
Through all the a-ges long, May Je-sus Christ be praised! A-men.

89 SUN OF MY SOUL

JOHN KEBLE

PETER RITTER

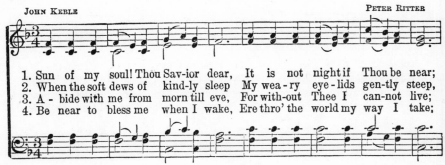

1. Sun of my soul! Thou Sav-ior dear, It is not night if Thou be near;
2. When the soft dews of kind-ly sleep My wea-ry eye-lids gen-tly steep,
3. A-bide with me from morn till eve, For with-out Thee I can-not live;
4. Be near to bless me when I wake, Ere thro' the world my way I take;

SUN OF MY SOUL

Oh, may no earth-born cloud a - rise To hide Thee from Thy servant's eyes!
Be my last tho't—how sweet to rest For-ev - er on my Sav-iour's breast!
A - bide with me when night is nigh, For without Thee I dare not die.
A - bide with me till in Thy love I lose my - self in heav'n a-bove.

90 NEAR THE CROSS

Fanny J. Crosby

W. H. Doane

1. Je - sus, keep me near the Cross, There a pre - cious Foun - tain,
2. Near the Cross, a trem-bling soul, Love and mer - cy found me;
3. Near the Cross! oh, Lamb of God, Bring its scenes be - fore me;
4. Near the Cross I'll watch and wait, Hop - ing, trust - ing, ev - er,

Free to all a heal - ing stream, Flows from Cal - v'ry's moun - tain.
There the Bright and Morn-ing Star Shed its beams a - round me.
Help me walk from day to day With its shad - ow o'er me.
Till I reach the gold - en strand, Just be - yond the riv - er.

CHORUS

In the Cross, in the Cross, Be my glo - ry ev - er;

Till my rap - tured soul shall find Rest be - yond the riv - er.

91 'TIS MIDNIGHT; AND ON OLIVES' BROW

William B. Tappan   OLIVES' BROW L. M.   William B. Bradbury

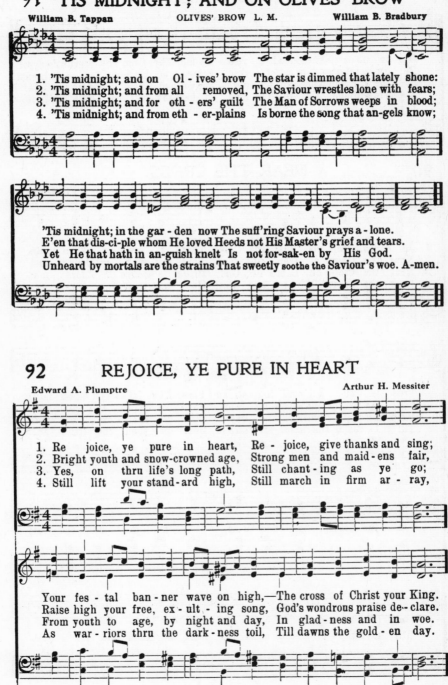

1. 'Tis midnight; and on Ol - ives' brow The star is dimmed that lately shone:
2. 'Tis midnight; and from all removed, The Saviour wrestles lone with fears;
3. 'Tis midnight; and for oth - ers' guilt The Man of Sorrows weeps in blood;
4. 'Tis midnight; and from eth - er-plains Is borne the song that an-gels know;

'Tis midnight; in the gar - den now The suff'ring Saviour prays a - lone.
E'en that dis-ci-ple whom He loved Heeds not His Master's grief and tears.
Yet He that hath in an-guish knelt Is not for-sak-en by His God.
Unheard by mortals are the strains That sweetly soothe the Saviour's woe. A-men.

92 REJOICE, YE PURE IN HEART

Edward A. Plumptre   Arthur H. Messiter

1. Re joice, ye pure in heart, Re - joice, give thanks and sing;
2. Bright youth and snow-crowned age, Strong men and maid-ens fair,
3. Yes, on thru life's long path, Still chant - ing as ye go;
4. Still lift your stand-ard high, Still march in firm ar - ray,

Your fes - tal ban - ner wave on high,—The cross of Christ your King.
Raise high your free, ex - ult - ing song, God's wondrous praise de-clare.
From youth to age, by night and day, In glad-ness and in woe.
As war - riors thru the dark-ness toil, Till dawns the gold - en day.

REJOICE, YE PURE IN HEART

REFRAIN

Re - joice, re - joice, Re - joice, give thanks and sing! A - MEN.
Re - joice, re - joice,

93   HE LIFTED ME

COPYRIGHT, 1935, RENEWAL. HOMER A. RODEHEAVER, OWNER

Charlotte G. Homer   Chas. H. Gabriel

1. In loving kind-ness Je - sus came, My soul in mer - cy to re-claim,
2. He called me long be - fore I heard, Be-fore my sin - ful heart was stirred,
3. His brow was pierced with man-y a thorn, His hands by cru - el nails were torn,
4. Now on a high - er plane I dwell, And with my soul I know 'tis well;

And from the depths of sin and shame Thro' grace He lift - ed me.......
But when I took Him at His word, For-giv'n He lift - ed me.......
When from my guilt and grief, for-lorn, In love He lift - ed me.......
Yet how or why, I can - not tell, He should have lift - ed me.......

He lift-ed me.

CHORUS

From sink-ing sand He lift - ed me, With ten-der hand He lift - ed me,

From shades of night to planes of light, O praise His name, He lift-ed me!

94 FAITH OF OUR FATHERS

FREDERICK W. FABER

HENRI F. HEMY

1. Faith of our fa-thers! liv-ing still In spite of dungeon, fire and sword,
2. Our fathers, chained in pris-ons dark, Were still in heart and conscience free:
3. Faith of our fa-thers! we will love Both friend and foe in all our strife:

O how our hearts beat high with joy Whene'er we hear that glo-rious word!
How sweet would be their children's fate, If they, like them, could die for thee!
And preach thee, too, as love knows how, By kind-ly words and vir-tuous life:

Faith of our fa-thers! ho-ly faith! We will be true to thee till death!
Faith of our fa-thers! ho-ly faith! We will be true to thee till death!
Faith of our fa-thers! ho-ly faith! We will be true to thee till death!

95 MORE ABOUT JESUS

E. E. Hewitt

John R. Sweney

1. More a-bout Je-sus would I know, More of His grace to oth-ers show;
2. More a-bout Je-sus let me learn, More of His ho-ly will dis-cern;
3. More a-bout Je-sus on His throne, Rich-es in glo-ry all His own;

MORE ABOUT JESUS

FINE.

More of His sav - ing full-ness see, More of His love who died for me.
Spir - it of God, my teach-er be, Show-ing the things of Christ to me.
More of His kingdom's sure in-crease; More of His com-ing, Prince of Peace.

D. S.—*More of His sav - ing full - ness see, More of His love who died for me.*

REFRAIN

D.S.

More, more a - bout Je - sus; More, more a - bout Je - sus;

96   BE THOU NEAR

Oswald J. Smith

B. D. Ackley

1. When my heart is filled with sor-row, Be Thou near; When I fear to face the
2. When the trials of life op-press me, Be Thou near; When temptations fierce dis-
3. When the friends I love for-sake me, Be Thou near; When my en - e-mies o'er-

CHORUS

mor - row, Be Thou near.
tress me, Be Thou near.   Be Thou near me, O my Sav-iour, When my heart is
take me, Be Thou near.

filled with fear; When I feel my faith is fail-ing, Bless-ed Sav-iour, Be Thou near.

97 MORE LOVE TO THEE

Elizabeth Prentiss

W. H. Doane

1. More love to Thee, O Christ, More love to Thee! Hear Thou the
2. Once earth-ly joy I craved, Sought peace and rest; Now Thee a-
3. Then shall my lat-est breath Whis-per Thy praise; This be the

prayer I make On bend-ed knee; This is my ear-nest plea:
lone I seek, Give what is best; This all my prayer shall be:
part-ing cry My heart shall raise; This still its prayer shall be:

More love, O Christ, to Thee, More love to Thee, More love to Thee!

98 THERE'S A WIDENESS IN GOD'S MERCY

Rev. F. W. Faber

Lizzie S. Tourjee

1. There's a wide-ness in God's mer-cy Like the wide-ness of the sea;
2. There is wel-come for the sin-ner, And more grac-es for the good;
3. For the love of God is broad-er Than the meas-ure of man's mind,
4. If our love were but more sim-ple, We should take Him at His word;

There's a kind-ness in His jus-tice, Which is more than lib-er-ty.
There is mer-cy with the Sav-iour; There is heal-ing in His blood.
And the heart of the E-ter-nal Is most won-der-ful-ly kind.
And our lives would be all sunshine In the sweetness of our Lord.

99 MAJESTIC SWEETNESS SITS ENTHRONED

Samuel Stennett   ORTONVILLE C. M.   Thomas Hastings

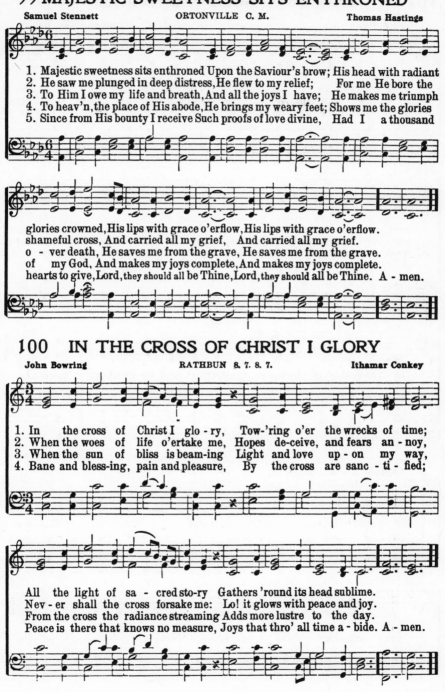

1. Majestic sweetness sits enthroned Upon the Saviour's brow; His head with radiant
2. He saw me plunged in deep distress, He flew to my relief;   For me He bore the
3. To Him I owe my life and breath, And all the joys I have;   He makes me triumph
4. To heav'n, the place of His abode, He brings my weary feet; Shows me the glories
5. Since from His bounty I receive Such proofs of love divine,   Had I   a thousand

glories crowned, His lips with grace o'erflow, His lips with grace o'erflow.
shameful cross, And carried all my grief,   And carried all my grief.
o - ver death, He saves me from the grave, He saves me from the grave.
of   my God, And makes my joys complete, And makes my joys complete.
hearts to give, Lord, they should all be Thine, Lord, they should all be Thine. A - men.

100   IN THE CROSS OF CHRIST I GLORY

John Bowring   RATHBUN 8. 7. 8. 7.   Ithamar Conkey

1. In   the cross of   Christ I glo - ry,   Tow-'ring o'er   the wrecks of time;
2. When the woes of   life o'ertake me, Hopes de-ceive, and fears an - noy,
3. When the sun of   bliss is beam-ing Light and love   up - on   my way,
4. Bane and bless-ing, pain and pleasure,   By   the cross are sanc - ti - fied;

All the light of sa - cred sto-ry Gathers 'round its head sublime.
Nev - er shall the cross forsake me: Lo! it glows with peace and joy.
From the cross the radiance streaming Adds more lustre to the day.
Peace is there that knows no measure, Joys that thro' all time a - bide. A - men.

101 PRECIOUS, HOLY KEEPSAKES

Virgil P. Brock

Blanche Kerr Brock

1. We have man - y precious keep-sakes which we cher-ish, And the
2. If we love Him we will cher - ish these dear keep - sakes, Which He
3. Je - sus gave to us these pre-cious, ho - ly keep - sakes, When He

mem - o - ries they bring we oft re - call; But the keep-sakes left to us
pur-chased by His death on Cal - va - ry; There He gave His life a ran-
went to be with God in heav'n to reign; And He said "this is my blood,

by our dear Sav - iour, Are the dear-est and the sweet-est of them all.
som for trans-gres - sors, Hang-ing on the cross of shame for you and me.
my brok-en bod - y, This do ye in mem-'ry till I come a - gain."

D. S. bless-ing as we share the cup and bread.

CHORUS

Pre - cious keep-sakes, ho - ly keep-sakes; His own day and His own

D. S.

ta - ble which we spread, In re-mem-b'ring our dear Sav-iour, There is

102 STAND UP, STAND UP FOR JESUS

George Duffield

Adam Geibel

SOLO OR UNISON

1. Stand up, stand up for Je - sus, Ye sol-diers of the cross; Lift high His roy-al
2. Stand up, stand up for Je - sus, The trump-et call o - bey, Forth to the mighty
3. Stand up, stand up for Je - sus, Stand in His strength alone; The arm of flesh will
4. Stand up, stand up for Je - sus, The strife will not be long; This day the noise of

ban - ner, It must not suf-fer loss; From vic-t'ry un-to vic-t'ry His ar-my
con - flict, In this His glo-rious day; "Ye that are men now serve Him" Against un-
fail you, Ye dare not trust your own; Put on the gos-pel ar - mor, Each piece put
bat - tle, The next, the victor's song: To him that o - ver-com-eth, A crown of

rit.

shall He lead, Till ev-'ry foe is vanquished And Christ is Lord in - deed.
numbered foes; Let cour-age rise with dan - ger, And strength to strength oppose.
on with prayer; Where du-ty calls or dan - ger, Be nev - er want-ing there.
life shall be; He with the King of glo - ry Shall reign e - ter - nal - ly.

CHORUS *Harmony*

Stand up   for Je - sus, Ye sol-diers of the cross; .. Lift
    stand up

high His roy - al ban - ner, It must not, it must not suf - fer loss.

WONDERFUL

A. H. A.   A. H. ACKLEY

1. Won-der-ful birth, to a man-ger He came, Made in the like-ness of man, to pro-claim God's boundless love for a world sick with sin, Pleading with sin-ners to let Him come in.

2. Won-der-ful life, full of serv-ice so free, Friend to the poor and the need-y was He; Un-fail-ing goodness on all He bestowed, Un-dy-ing faith in the vil-est He showed.

3. Won-der-ful death, for it meant not de-feat, Cal-va-ry made His great mis-sion com-plete, Wrought our redemption, and when He a-rose, Ban-ished for-ev-er the last of our foes.

4. Won-der-ful hope, He is com-ing a-gain, Com-ing as King o'er the na-tions to reign; Glo-ri-ous prom-ise, His word can-not fail, His righteous kingdom at last must pre-vail!

CHORUS

Wonder-ful name He bears, Wonder-ful crown He wears, Wonder-ful blessings His triumphs af-ford; Won-der-ful Cal-va-ry, Wonder-ful grace for me, Wonder-ful love of my Wonder-ful Lord!

104 HALLELUJAH! WHAT A SAVIOUR

P. P. Bliss

P. P. Bliss

Moderato **p**

1. "Man of Sor-rows," what a name For the Son of God who came
2. Bear-ing shame and scoff-ing rude, In my place con-demned He stood;
3. Guilt-y, vile and help-less, we: Spot-less Lamb of God was He:
4. "Lift-ed up" was He to die, "It is fin-ished," was His cry;
5. When He comes, our glo-rious King, All His ran-somed home to bring,

Ru-ined sin-ners to re-claim! Hal-le-lu-jah! what a Sav-iour!
Sealed my par-don with His blood: Hal-le-lu-jah! what a Sav-iour!
"Full a-tone-ment!" can it be? Hal-le-lu-jah! what a Sav-iour!
Now in heav'n ex-alt-ed high: Hal-le-lu-jah! what a Sav-iour!
Then a-new this song we'll sing: Hal-le-lu-jah! what a Sav-iour!

105 WE MAY NOT CLIMB THE HEAVENLY STEEPS

John G. Whittier

SERENITY C. M.

William V. Wallace

1. We may not climb the heav'n-ly steeps To bring the Lord Christ down;
2. But warm, sweet, ten-der e-ven yet A pres-ent help is He;
3. The heal-ing of His seam-less dress Is by our beds of pain;
4. Thro' Him the first fond pray'rs are said Our lips of child-hood frame;
5. O Lord and Mas-ter of us all, What-e'er our name or sign,

In vain we search the low-est deeps, For Him no depths can drown.
And faith has still its Ol-i-vet, And love its Gal-i-lee.
We touch Him in life's throng and press, And we are whole a-gain.
The last low whispers of our dead Are burdened with His name.
We own Thy sway, we hear Thy call, We test our lives by Thine! A-men.

106 BREATHE UPON US, HOLY SPIRIT

A. H. Ackley

Legato

B. D. Ackley

1. Breathe up-on us, Ho-ly Spir-it, Fill us with Thy love di-vine,
2. Breathe up-on us, Ho-ly Spir-it, Fill us with Thy bless-ed peace,
3. Breathe up-on us, Ho-ly Spir-it, Fill us with Thy bound-less joy,

Fit us for the high-est ser-vice, Make and keep us whol-ly Thine.
Till the tu-mult and con-fu-sion Of our rest-less lives shall cease.
With the glad-ness of sal-va-tion, Which the world can not de-stroy.

CHORUS

Breathe up-on us, Ho-ly Spir-it, E-ven now Thy power dis-play,

rall

Hum-bly we in-voke Thy bless-ing, Breathe up-on us while we pray.

107 I NEED THEE EVERY HOUR

Annie S. Hawks

Robert Lowry

1. I need Thee ev-'ry hour, Most gra-cious Lord, No ten-der voice like
2. I need Thee ev-'ry hour, Stay Thou near by; Temp-ta-tions lose their
3. I need Thee ev-'ry hour, In joy or pain; Come quick-ly and a-
4. I need Thee ev-'ry hour, Most Ho-ly One; Oh! make me Thine in-

Thine Can peace af-ford.
pow'r When Thou art nigh.   I need Thee, O I need Thee; Ev-'ry hour I
bide, Or life is vain.
deed, Thou bless-ed Son!

need Thee; O bless me now, my Sav-iour, I come to Thee!

108   BREAK THOU THE BREAD OF LIFE

MARY ANN LATHBURY   WILLIAM F. SHERWIN

1. Break Thou the bread of life, Dear Lord, to me, As Thou didst
2. Bless Thou the Truth, dear Lord, To me— to me— As Thou didst
3. O send Thy Spir-it, Lord, Now un-to me, That He may
4. Thou art the bread of life, O Lord, to me, Thy ho-ly

break the loaves Be-side the sea; Be-yond the sa-cred page
bless the bread By Gal-i-lee; Then shall all bond-age cease,
touch my eyes, And make me see: Show me the truth con-cealed
Word the truth That sav-eth me; Give me to eat and live

I seek Thee, Lord; My spir-it pants for Thee, O Liv-ing Word.
All fet-ters fall; And I shall find my peace, My All in all.
With-in Thy Word, And in Thy book revealed I see the Lord.
With Theee a-bove; Teach me to love Thy truth, For Thou art love.

109 HOLY SPIRIT, FAITHFUL GUIDE

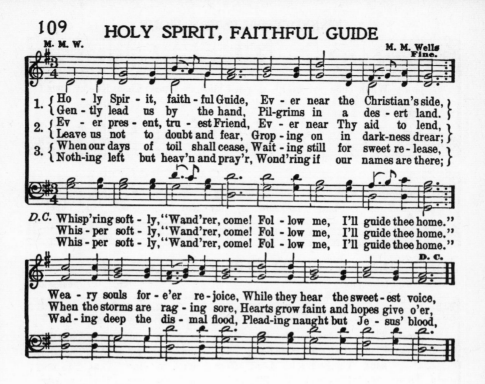

M. M. W.   M. M. Wells
Fine.

1. { Ho - ly Spir - it, faith - ful Guide, Ev - er near the Christian's side,)
   { Gen - tly lead us by the hand, Pil - grims in a des - ert land.)

2. { Ev - er pres - ent, tru - est Friend, Ev - er near Thy aid to lend,)
   { Leave us not to doubt and fear, Grop - ing on in dark - ness drear;)

3. { When our days of toil shall cease, Wait - ing still for sweet re - lease,)
   { Noth - ing left but heav'n and pray'r, Wond'ring if our names are there;)

D.C. Whisp'ring soft - ly, "Wand'rer, come! Fol - low me, I'll guide thee home."
     Whis - per soft - ly, "Wand'rer, come! Fol - low me, I'll guide thee home."
     Whis - per soft - ly, "Wand'rer, come! Fol - low me, I'll guide thee home."

Wea - ry souls for - e'er re - joice, While they hear the sweet - est voice,
When the storms are rag - ing sore, Hearts grow faint and hopes give o'er,
Wad - ing deep the dis - mal flood, Plead - ing naught but Je - sus' blood,

110 TAKE TIME TO BE HOLY

W. D. Longstaff   Geo. C. Stebbins

1. Take time to be ho - ly, Speak oft with thy Lord; A - bide in Him
2. Take time to be ho - ly, The world rush - es on; Spend much time in
3. Take time to be ho - ly, Let Him be thy Guide; And run not be-

al - ways, And feed on His Word. Make friends of God's chil - dren,
se - cret With Je - sus a - lone— By look - ing to Je - sus,
fore Him, What - ev - er be - tide. In joy or in sor - row,

TAKE TIME TO BE HOLY

Help those who are weak; For-get-ting in noth-ing His bless-ing to seek.
Like Him thou shalt be; Thy friends, in thy conduct His like-ness shall see.
Still fol-low thy Lord, And, look-ing to Je-sus, Still trust in His Word.

111   I WOULD BE LIKE JESUS

James Rowe.

B. D. Ackley.

1. Earth-ly pleas-ures vain-ly call me; I would be like Je - sus;
2. He has bro-ken ev-'ry fet-ter, I would be like Je - sus;
3. All the way from earth to Glo-ry, I would be like Je - sus;
4. That in heav-en He may meet me, I would be like Je - sus;

would be like Je-sus;

Noth-ing world-ly shall en-thrall me; I would be like Je - sus.
That my soul may serve Him bet-ter, I would be like Je - sus.
Tell-ing o'er and o'er the sto-ry, I would be like Je - sus.
That His words "Well done" may greet me, I would be like Je - sus.

would be like Je-sus.

CHORUS

Be like Je-sus, this my song, In the home and in the throng;

Be like Je-sus, all day long! I would be like Je - sus.

112 TAKE THE NAME OF JESUS WITH YOU

Mrs. Lydia Baxter

W. H. Doane

1. Take the name of Je-sus with you, Child of sor-row and of woe;
2. Take the name of Je-sus ev-er, As a shield from ev-'ry snare;
3. O the precious name of Je-sus! How it thrills our souls with joy,
4. At the name of Je-sus bow-ing, Fall-ing pros-trate at His feet,

It will joy and com-fort give you, Take it, then, wher-e'er you go.
If temp-ta-tions round you gath-er, Breathe that ho-ly name in prayer.
When His lov-ing arms re-ceive us, And His songs our tongues em-ploy!
King of kings in Heav'n we'll crown Him, When our jour-ney is com-plete.

CHORUS

Pre-cious name, O how sweet! Hope of earth and joy of Heav'n;
Precious name, O how sweet!

Pre-cious name, O how sweet!... Hope of earth and joy of Heav'n.
Precious name, O how sweet, how sweet!

113 WHERE CROSS THE CROWDED WAYS

Frank Mason North

GERMANY L. M.

Ludwig van Beethoven

1. Where cross the crowded ways of life, Where sound the cries of race and clan,
2. In haunts of wretch-ed-ness and need, On shadowed thresholds dark with fears,
3. From ten-der childhood's helplessness, From woman's grief, man's burdened toil,
4. The cup of wa-ter giv'n for Thee Still holds the freshness of Thy grace;
5. O Mas-ter from the mountain side, Make haste to heal these hearts of pain,
6. Till sons of men shall learn Thy love And fol-low where Thy feet have trod:

WHERE CROSS THE CROWDED WAYS

114 SAVIOUR, THY DYING LOVE

S. D. Phelps — SOMETHING FOR JESUS — Robert Lowry

115 FAIREST LORD JESUS

Crusaders' Hymn

Arr. by Richard S. Willis

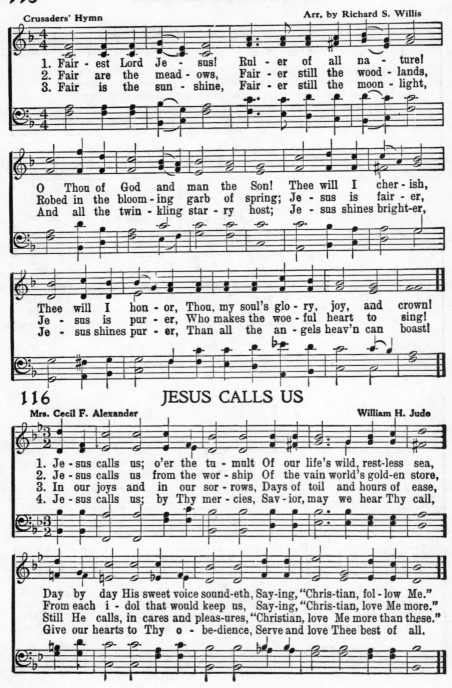

1. Fair - est Lord Je - sus! Rul - er of all na - ture!
2. Fair are the mead - ows, Fair - er still the wood - lands,
3. Fair is the sun - shine, Fair - er still the moon - light,

O Thou of God and man the Son! Thee will I cher - ish,
Robed in the bloom - ing garb of spring; Je - sus is fair - er,
And all the twin - kling star - ry host; Je - sus shines bright - er,

Thee will I hon - or, Thou, my soul's glo - ry, joy, and crown!
Je - sus is pur - er, Who makes the woe - ful heart to sing!
Je - sus shines pur - er, Than all the an - gels heav'n can boast!

116 JESUS CALLS US

Mrs. Cecil F. Alexander

William H. Jude

1. Je - sus calls us; o'er the tu - mult Of our life's wild, rest - less sea,
2. Je - sus calls us from the wor - ship Of the vain world's gold - en store,
3. In our joys and in our sor - rows, Days of toil and hours of ease,
4. Je - sus calls us; by Thy mer - cies, Sav - ior, may we hear Thy call,

Day by day His sweet voice sound - eth, Say - ing, "Chris - tian, fol - low Me."
From each i - dol that would keep us, Say - ing, "Chris - tian, love Me more."
Still He calls, in cares and pleas - ures, "Christian, love Me more than these."
Give our hearts to Thy o - be - dience, Serve and love Thee best of all.

ANYWHERE WITH JESUS

Jessie H. Brown

D. B. Towner

1. An - y-where with Je - sus I can safe - ly go; An - y-where He
2. An - y-where with Je - sus I need fear no ill, Tho' temp-ta - tions
3. An - y-where with Je - sus I am not a - lone; Oth - er friends may
4. An - y-where with Je - sus o - ver land or sea; Tell - ing souls in
5. An - y-where with Je - sus I can go to sleep, When the dark-'ning

leads me in this world be - low; An - y-where with-out Him dear - est
gath - er 'round my path-way still; He Him-self was temp-ted that He
fail me, He is still my own; Tho' His hand may lead me o - ver
dark - ness of sal - va - tion free; Read - y as He sum-mons me to
shad - ows 'round a - bout me creep; Know - ing I shall wak - en, nev - er

joys would fade; An - y-where with Je - sus I am not a - fraid.
might help me; An - y-where with Je - sus I may vic - tor be.
drear - y ways, An - y-where with Je - sus is a house of praise.
go or stay, An - y-where with Je - sus when He points the way.
more to roam, An - y-where with Je - sus will be home, sweet home.

CHORUS

An - y - where! an - y - where! Fear I can not know;

An - y - where with Je - sus I can safe - ly go.

118 NOW THE DAY IS OVER

Sabine Baring-Gould   MERRIAL 6. 5. 6. 5.   Joseph Barnby

1. Now the day is o - ver, Night is draw - ing nigh,
2. Je - sus, give the wea - ry Calm and sweet re - pose;
3. Grant to lit - tle chil - dren Vi - sions bright of Thee;
4. Thru the long night-watch - es, May Thine an - gels spread
5. When the morn - ing wak - ens, Then may I a - rise,

Shad - ows of the eve - ning Steal a - cross the sky.
With Thy ten - d'rest bless - ing May our eye - lids close.
Guard the sail - ors toss - ing On the deep blue sea.
Their white wings a - bove me, Watch-ing 'round my bed.
Pure and fresh and sin - less In Thy ho - ly eyes. A - MEN.

eve-ning Steal a - cross the sky.

119 SOFTLY NOW THE LIGHT OF DAY

George W. Doane   SEYMOUR 7. 7. 7. 7.   Carl M. von Weber

1. Soft - ly now the light of day Fades up - on my sight a - way;
2. Thou, whose all-per - vad - ing eye Naught es-capes, with-out, with - in,
3. Soon for me the light of day Shall for - ev - er pass a - way;
4. Thou who, sin - less, yet hast known All of man's in - firm - i - ty;

Free from care, from la - bor free, Lord, I would commune with Thee.
Par - don each in - firm - i - ty, O - pen fault, and se - cret sin.
Then, from sin and sor - row free, Take me, Lord, to dwell with Thee.
Then, from Thine e - ter - nal throne, Je - sus, look with pity-ing eye. A - MEN.

120 PASS ME NOT

Fanny J. Crosby

William H. Doane

1. Pass me not, O gen-tle Sav-iour, Hear my hum-ble cry,
2. Let me at a throne of mer-cy Find a sweet re-lief;
3. Trust-ing on-ly in Thy mer-it, Would I seek Thy face;
4. Thou the Spring of all my com-fort, More than life to me,

While on others Thou art call-ing, Do not pass me by.
Kneeling there in deep con-tri-tion, Help my un-be-lief. Sav-iour, Sav-iour,
Heal my wounded, broken spir-it, Save me by Thy grace.
Whom have I on earth beside Thee? Whom in heav'n but Thee?

Hear my humble cry; While on oth-ers Thou art call-ing, Do not pass me by.

121 AM I A SOLDIER OF THE CROSS

Isaac Watts

Thomas A. Arne

1. Am I a sol-dier of the cross, A fol-low'r of the Lamb?
2. Must I be car-ried to the skies On flow-'ry beds of ease,
3. Are there no foes for me to face? Must I not stem the flood?
4. Sure I must fight, if I would reign; In-crease my cour-age, Lord;

And shall I fear to own His cause, Or blush to speak His name?
While oth-ers fought to win the prize, And sailed thro' blood-y seas?
Is this vile world a friend to grace, To help me on to God?
I'll bear the toil, en-dure the pain, Sup-port-ed by Thy word.

122 KEEP ON BELIEVING

F. C. H.

Frank C. Huston

Not too fast

1. Some-times, the shadows gath-er, And mists obscure the way; Sometimes, the
2. Some-times, the way is drear-y, We seem to walk a-lone, For-get-ting
3. Some-times, our lov-ing serv-ice Seems destined but to fail; And e-vils
4. O soul, weighed down with sorrow, Be-neath a heav-y load, Re-mem-ber

clouds grow heavy, And dark-en all the day. How precious to re-mem-ber
that the Fa-ther Keeps watch above His own. How man-y needless sor-rows
that op-pose us, Seem cer-tain to pre-vail, How sweet the con-so-la-tion
God will help you, How-ev-er rough the road. His grace is still suf-fi-cient

FINE

Our Father's loving care,—That He still loves His children, And He answers prayer.
The faithless have to bear, For, God still loves His children, And He answers prayer.
That God is ev'rywhere,—That He still loves His children, And He answers prayer.
For ev-'ry load of care,—God ev-er loves His children, And He answers prayer.

D.S.—*Re-mem-ber God still loves you, And He an-swers prayer.*

CHORUS

Keep on be-liev-ing, God will an-swer prayer; Keep on be-liev-ing,

D. S.

nev-er de-spair; Tho' you be heav-y-lad-en, And burdened down with care,

123 THE HOPE OF THE WORLD IS JESUS

C. Austin Miles

B. D. Ackley

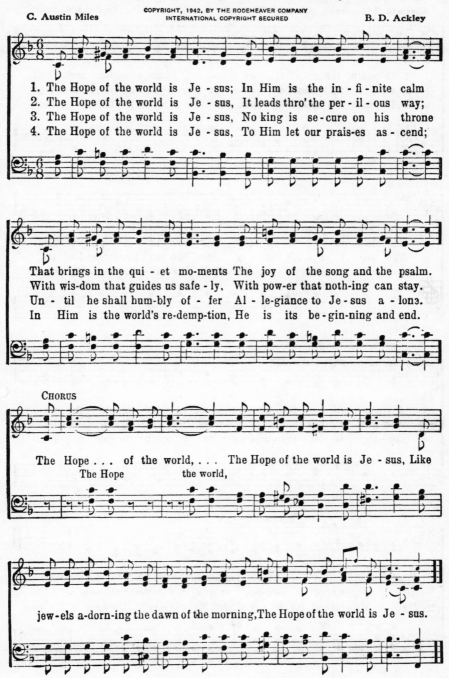

1. The Hope of the world is Je - sus; In Him is the in - fi - nite calm
2. The Hope of the world is Je - sus, It leads thro' the per - il - ous way;
3. The Hope of the world is Je - sus, No king is se - cure on his throne
4. The Hope of the world is Je - sus, To Him let our prais-es as - cend;

That brings in the qui - et mo-ments The joy of the song and the psalm.
With wis-dom that guides us safe - ly, With pow-er that noth-ing can stay.
Un - til he shall hum-bly of - fer Al - le-giance to Je - sus a - lone.
In Him is the world's re-demp-tion, He is its be - gin-ning and end.

CHORUS

The Hope . . . of the world, . . . The Hope of the world is Je - sus, Like
The Hope   the world,

jew-els a-dorn-ing the dawn of the morning, The Hope of the world is Je - sus.

124 BENEATH THE CROSS OF JESUS

Elizabeth C. Clephane   ST. CHRISTOPHER   7. 6. 8. 6. 8. 6. 8. 6.   Frederick C. Maker

1. Be-neath the cross of Je - sus I fain would take my stand,
2. Up - on that cross of Je - sus Mine eye at times can see
3. I take, O cross, thy shad - ow For my a - bid-ing place;

The shad - ow of a might-y rock With - in a wea - ry land;
The ver - y dy - ing form of One Who suf - fered there for me;
I ask no oth - er sun-shine than The sun - shine of His face;

A home with - in the wil - der - ness, A rest up - on the way,
And from my smit - ten heart with tears Two won - ders I con - fess,—
Con - tent to let the world go by, To know no gain or loss,

From the burn-ing of the noon-tide heat, And the burden of the day.
The won-ders of re-deem-ing love And my un-wor-thi-ness.
My sin - ful self my on - ly shame, My glo - ry all the cross. A - men.

LEAD ON, O KING ETERNAL

ERNEST W. SHURTLEFF   LANCASHIRE   HENRY SMART

1. Lead on, O King E - ter - nal, The day of march has come;
2. Lead on, O King E - ter - nal, Till sin's fierce war shall cease,
3. Lead on, O King E - ter - nal, We fol - low, not with fears;

Henceforth in fields of con - quest Thy tents shall be our home.
And ho - li - ness shall whis - per The sweet A - men of peace;
For glad-ness breaks like morn - ing Wher-e'er Thy face ap - pears;

Thro' days of prep - a - ra - tion Thy grace has made us strong,
For not with swords loud clash-ing, Nor roll of stir - ring drums;
Thy cross is lift - ed o'er us; We jour - ney in its light:

And now, O King e - ter - nal, We lift our bat - tle song.
With deeds of love and mer - cy, The heav'n-ly king - dom comes.
The crown a - waits the con - quest; Lead on, O God of might.

126 IT IS WONDERFUL

Frank E. Roush

Haldor Lillenas

1. I am liv-ing in the sun-shine of my great Re-deem-er's love It is
2. I am hap-py as I jour-ney in the straight and nar-row way, It is
3. Soon I'll see the throne in heav-en, where King Jesus reigns supreme, It is

won-der-ful, so ver-y won-der-ful! I am fa-vored with His bless-ings
won-der-ful, so ver-y won-der-ful! And the glo-ry song is ring-ing
won-der-ful, so ver-y won-der-ful! As I view the gold-en cit-y

D. S. *He is more than all the world and*

from the throne of grace a-bove, It is won-der-ful, So ver-y won-der-ful!
in my heart from day to day, It is won-der-ful, So ver-y won-der-ful!
this will be my endless theme: "It is won-der-ful, So ver-y won-der-ful!"

all its splen-dor here could be, It is won-der-ful, so ver-y won-der-ful!

CHORUS

O, I love my prec-ious Sav-iour, Christ the Lord of Gal-i-lee,

D. S.

For He pur-chased my sal-va-tion full and free.(full and free)

P. P. B.   P. P. Bliss

1. "Who-so-ev-er hear-eth," shout, shout the sound! Spread the bless-ed ti-dings
2. Who-so-ev-er com-eth, need not de-lay, Now the door is o-pen,
3. "Who-so-ev-er will!" the prom-ise is se-cure; "Who-so-ev-er will," for-

all the world a-round; Tell the joy-ful news wher-ev-er man is found,
en-ter while you may; Je-sus is the true, the on-ly Liv-ing Way:
ev-er must en-dure; "Who-so-ev-er will!" 'tis life for-ev-er-more;

CHORUS

"Who-so-ev-er will may come." "Who-so-ev-er will, who-so-ev-er will!"

Send the proc-la-ma-tion o-ver vale and hill; 'Tis a lov-ing

Fa-ther calls the wan-d'rer home: "Who-so-ev-er will may come."

128 IF YOUR HEART KEEPS RIGHT

Lizzie DeArmond

B. D. Ackley

1. If the dark shad-ows gath-er As you go a-long, Do not grieve for their
2. Is your life just a tan-gle Full of toil and care? Smile a bit as you
3. There are blos-soms of glad-ness 'Neath the win-ter's snow, From the gloom and the

com-ing, Sing a cheer-y song; There is joy for the tak-ing, It will soon be light—
jour-ney, Oth-ers' bur-dens share; You'll for-get all your troubles, Mak-ing their lives bright,
darkness Comes the morning's glow; Nev-er give up the bat-tle, You will win the fight,

CHORUS

Ev-'ry cloud wears a rain-bow If your heart keeps right.
Skies will grow blue and sun-ny If your heart keeps right. If your heart keeps right, If your
Gain the rest of the Vic-tor, If your heart keeps right.

heart keeps right, There's a song of glad-ness in the dark-est night; If your heart keeps right,

If your heart keeps right, Ev-'ry cloud will wear a rain-bow, If your heart keeps right.

BE STILL MY SOUL

KATHARINA VON SCHLEGEL
Tr. by JANE L. BORTHWICK

FINLANDIA

JEAN SIBELIUS

1. Be still, my soul: the Lord is on thy side; Bear pa-tient-ly the
2. Be still, my soul: thy God doth un-der-take To guide the fu-ture
3. Be still, my soul: the hour is has-tening on When we shall be for-

cross of grief or pain; Leave to thy God to or-der and pro-vide;
as He has the past. Thy hope, thy con-fi-dence let noth-ing shake;
ev-er with the Lord, When dis-ap-point-ment, grief, and fear are gone,

In ev-ery change He faith-ful will re-main. Be still, my soul: thy
All now mys-te-rious shall be bright at last. Be still, my soul: the
Sor-row for-got, love's pur-est joys re-stored. Be still, my soul: when

best, thy heaven-ly Friend Thro' thorny ways leads to a joy-ful end.
waves and winds still know His voice who ruled them while He dwelt below.
change and tears are past, All safe and bless-ed we shall meet at last. A-MEN.

130 A SONG IN MY SOUL

Oswald J. Smith

A. H. Ackley

1. There's an ache in my heart that the world cannot heal, There are tears that no
2. There's an ache in my heart but a song in my soul, There are tears but there's

an-gel can dry, If it were not for God I would faint neath the rod.
mu-sic as well; Tho' I faint neath the rod yet I'll still trust in God,

But I know that my Sav-iour is nigh.
For His good-ness I nev-er can tell.

CHORUS

There's a song in my soul that the

world can-not give, There is mu-sic no mor-tal can play; God has banished my

fears, and has dried all my tears, He has tak-en my heartache a-way.

131 OPEN MY EYES THAT I MAY SEE

C. H. S.

Clara H. Scott

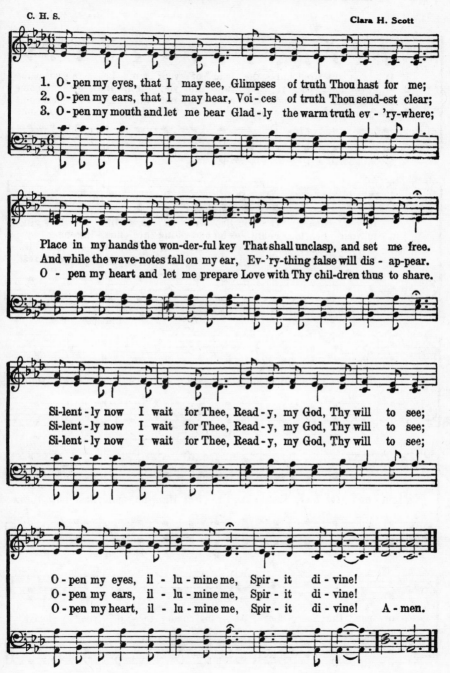

1. O-pen my eyes, that I may see, Glimpses of truth Thou hast for me;
2. O-pen my ears, that I may hear, Voi-ces of truth Thou send-est clear;
3. O-pen my mouth and let me bear Glad-ly the warm truth ev-'ry-where;

Place in my hands the won-der-ful key That shall unclasp, and set me free.
And while the wave-notes fall on my ear, Ev-'ry-thing false will dis-ap-pear.
O-pen my heart and let me prepare Love with Thy chil-dren thus to share.

Si-lent-ly now I wait for Thee, Read-y, my God, Thy will to see;
Si-lent-ly now I wait for Thee, Read-y, my God, Thy will to see;
Si-lent-ly now I wait for Thee, Read-y, my God, Thy will to see;

O-pen my eyes, il-lu-mine me, Spir-it di-vine!
O-pen my ears, il-lu-mine me, Spir-it di-vine!
O-pen my heart, il-lu-mine me, Spir-it di-vine! A-men.

132 LET JESUS COME INTO YOUR HEART

C. H. M.

Mrs. C. H. Morris

1. If you are tired of the load of your sin, Let Je-sus come
2. If 'tis for pu-ri-ty now that you sigh, Let Je-sus come
3. If there's a tem-pest your voice can-not still, Let Je-sus come
4. If you would join the glad songs of the blest, Let Je-sus come

in-to your heart; If you de-sire a new life to be-gin.
in-to your heart; Fountains for cleans-ing are flow-ing near by,
in-to your heart; If there's a void this world nev-er can fill,
in-to your heart; If you would en-ter the man-sions of rest,

CHORUS

Let Je-sus come in-to your heart. Just now, your

doubt-ings give o'er; Just now, re-ject Him no more: Just now, throw

o-pen the door; Let Je-sus come in-to your heart.

133 IN MY HEART THERE RINGS A MELODY

E. M. R.

ELTON M. ROTH

1. I have a song that Je - sus gave me, It was sent from
2. I love the Christ who died on Cal - v'ry, For He washed my
3. 'Twill be my end - less theme in glo - ry, With the an - gels

heav'n a - bove; There nev-er was a sweet-er mel - o - dy, 'Tis a
sins a - way; He put with - in my heart a mel - o - dy, And I
I will sing; 'Twill be a song with glo - rious har - mo - ny, When the

CHORUS

mel - o - dy of love.
know it's there to stay.   In   my heart there rings a mel - o - dy, There
courts of heav - en ring.

rings a mel - o - dy with heav-en's har - mo - ny;   In   my heart there

rings a mel - o - dy; There rings a mel - o - dy of love.

134 MY FAITH LOOKS UP TO THEE

Ray Palmer

Lowell Mason

1. My faith looks up to Thee, Thou lamb of Cal - va - ry, Saviour divine; Now hear me
2. May Thy rich grace impart Strength to my fainting heart, My zeal inspire; As Thou hast
3. While life's dark maze I tread And griefs around me spread, Be Thou my Guide; Bid darkness

when I pray, Take all my sin a - way, O let me from this day Be wholly Thine!
died for me, O may my love to Thee, Pure, warm and changeless be, A living fire!
turn to day, Wipe sorrow's tears away, Nor let me ev-er stray From Thee a-side.

135 MY JESUS, I LOVE THEE

Anonymous

A. J. Gordon

1. My Je - sus, I love Thee, I know Thou art mine, For Thee all the
2. I'll love Thee in life, I will love Thee in death, And praise Thee as
3. In mansions of glo - ry and end - less de - light, I'll ev - er a -

pleas - ures of sin I re - sign; My gra - cious Re - deem - er, my
long as Thou lend - est me breath; And say when the death-dew lies
dore Thee in heav - en so bright; I'll sing with the glit - ter - ing

Sav - ior art Thou; If ev - er I loved Thee, my Je - sus, 'tis now.
cold on my brow, If ev - er I loved Thee, my Je - sus, 'tis now.
crown on my brow, If ev - er I loved Thee, my Je - sus, 'tis now.

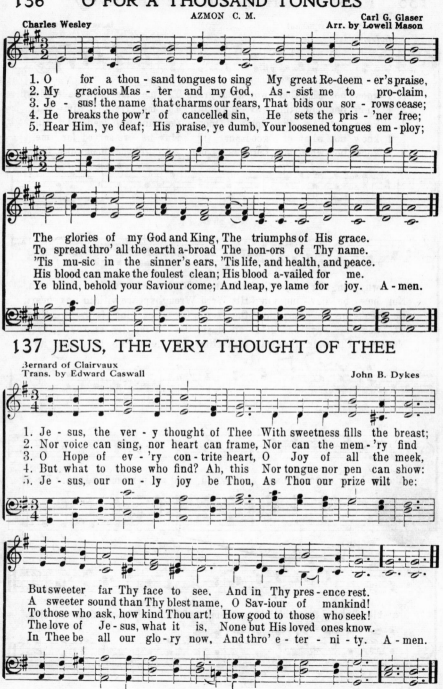

136 O FOR A THOUSAND TONGUES

AZMON C. M.

Charles Wesley

Carl G. Glaser
Arr. by Lowell Mason

1. O for a thou - sand tongues to sing My great Re-deem - er's praise,
2. My gracious Mas - ter and my God, As - sist me to pro-claim,
3. Je - sus! the name that charms our fears, That bids our sor - rows cease;
4. He breaks the pow'r of cancelled sin, He sets the pris - 'ner free;
5. Hear Him, ye deaf; His praise, ye dumb, Your loosened tongues em - ploy;

The glories of my God and King, The triumphs of His grace.
To spread thro' all the earth a-broad The hon-ors of Thy name.
'Tis mu-sic in the sinner's ears, 'Tis life, and health, and peace.
His blood can make the foulest clean; His blood a-vailed for me.
Ye blind, behold your Saviour come; And leap, ye lame for joy. A - men.

137 JESUS, THE VERY THOUGHT OF THEE

Bernard of Clairvaux
Trans. by Edward Caswall

John B. Dykes

1. Je - sus, the ver - y thought of Thee With sweetness fills the breast;
2. Nor voice can sing, nor heart can frame, Nor can the mem - 'ry find
3. O Hope of ev - 'ry con - trite heart, O Joy of all the meek,
4. But what to those who find? Ah, this Nor tongue nor pen can show:
5. Je - sus, our on - ly joy be Thou, As Thou our prize wilt be:

But sweeter far Thy face to see, And in Thy pres - ence rest.
A sweeter sound than Thy blest name, O Sav-iour of mankind!
To those who ask, how kind Thou art! How good to those who seek!
The love of Je - sus, what it is, None but His loved ones know.
In Thee be all our glo - ry now, And thro' e - ter - ni - ty. A - men.

138 I KNOW WHOM I HAVE BELIEVED

Maj. D. W. Whittle (El Nathan)

James McGranahan

Moderato

1. I know not why God's won-drous grace To me He hath made known,
2. I know not how this sav-ing faith To me He did im-part,
3. I know not how the Spir-it moves, Con-vinc-ing men of sin,
4. I know not what of good or ill May be re-served for me,
5. I know not when my Lord may come, At night or noon-day fair,

Nor why un-wor-thy—Christ in love Re-deemed me for His own.
Nor how be-liev-ing in His Word Wrought peace with-in my heart.
Re-veal-ing Je-sus thro' the Word, Cre-at-ing faith in Him.
Of wea-ry ways or gold-en days, Be-fore His face I see.
Nor if I'll walk the vale with Him, Or "meet Him in the air."

CHORUS

But "I know whom I have be-liev-ed, and am per-suad-ed that He is

a-ble To keep that which I've com-mit-ted Un-to Him a-gainst that day."

139   IT IS WELL WITH MY SOUL

H. G. SPAFFORD

P. P. BLISS

1. When peace, like a riv-er, at-tend-eth my way, When sor-rows like
2. Though Sa-tan should buf-fet, tho' tri-als should come, Let this blest as-
3. My sin— oh, the bliss of this glo-ri-ous tho't— My sin— not in
4. And, Lord, haste the day when the faith shall be sight, The clouds be rolled

sea-bil-lows roll; What-ev-er my lot, Thou hast taught me to say,
sur-ance con-trol, That Christ has re-gard-ed my help-less es-tate,
part, but the whole, Is nailed to the cross and I bear it no more,
back as a scroll, The trump shall re-sound and the Lord shall de-scend,

CHORUS

It is well, it is well with my soul.
And hath shed His own blood for my soul. It is well..... with my
Praise the Lord, praise the Lord, O my soul!
"E-ven so"—it is well with my soul. It is well

soul,...... It is well, it is well with my soul.
with my soul,

140 O THAT WILL BE GLORY

C. H. G.

Chas. H. Gabriel

141 MOTHER'S PRAYERS HAVE FOLLOWED ME

Lizzie DeArmond.   B. D. Ackley

1. I grieved my Lord from day to day, I scorned His love so full and
2. O'er des-ert wild, o'er mountain high A wan-der-er I chose to
3. He turned my dark-ness in-to light, This bless-ed Christ of Cal-va-

free, And though I wan-dered far a-way, My moth-er's
be, A wretch-ed soul con-demned to die, Still moth-er's
ry, I'll praise His name both day and night, That moth-er's

REFRAIN.

pray'rs have fol-lowed me. I'm com-ing home, I'm com-ing

home, To live my wast-ed life a-new, For moth-er's

pray'rs have fol-lowed me, Have fol-lowed me the whole world thro'.

142 SUNRISE

W. C. Poole

B. D. Ackley

1. When I shall come to the end of my way, When I shall rest at the
2. When in His beau-ty I see the great King, Join with the ran-somed His
3. When life is o - ver and day-light is passed, In heav-en's har - bor my

close of life's day, When "Wel-come home" I shall hear Je - sus say, O
prais - es to sing, When I shall join them my trib - utes to bring, O
an - chor is cast, When I see Je - sus my Sav - ior at last, O

CHORUS

that will be sun-rise for me. . . . . Sun-rise to-mor-row, sun-rise to-

mor - row, Sun-rise in glo-ry is wait-ing for me; Sun-rise to-mor-row,

sun-rise to - mor - row, Sun-rise with Je - sus for e - ter - ni - ty.

143 STANDING ON THE PROMISES

R. K. C.

R. KELSO CARTER

1. Stand-ing on the prom-is-es of Christ my King, Thro' e-ter-nal
2. Stand-ing on the prom-is-es that can-not fail, When the howl-ing
3. Stand-ing on the prom-is-es I now can see Per-fect, pres-ent
4. Stand-ing on the prom-is-es of Christ the Lord, Bound to Him e-
5. Stand-ing on the prom-is-es I can-not fall, Lis-t'ning ev-'ry

a-ges let His prais-es ring; Glo-ry in the highest I will shout and sing,
storms of doubt and fear as-sail, By the liv-ing Word of God I shall pre-vail,
cleansing in the blood for me; Standing in the lib-erty where Christ makes free,
ter-nal-ly by love's strong cord, O-ver-com-ing dai-ly with the Spir-it's sword,
mo-ment to the Spir-it's call, Rest-ing in my Sav-ior, as my all in all,

CHORUS

Standing on the promis-es of God. Stand-ing, stand-ing,
Standing on the promises, Standing on the promises,

Stand-ing on the promis-es of God my Sav-ior; Stand-ing,
Standing on the prom-is-es,

stand-ing, I'm stand-ing on the prom-is-es of God.
Stand-ing on the prom-is-es,

144 I WILL SING THE WONDROUS STORY

F. H. ROWLEY   PETER P. BILHORN

1. I will sing the won-drous sto - ry Of the Christ who died for me,
2. I was lost, but Je - sus found me, Found the sheep that went a - stray,
3. I was bruised, but Je - sus healed me; Faint was I from man-y a fall;
4. Days of dark-ness still come o'er me, Sor-row's paths I oft - en tread,
5. He will keep me till the riv - er Rolls its wa - ters at my feet;

How He left His home in glo - ry For the cross of Cal - va - ry.
Threw His lov - ing arms a - round me, Drew me back in - to His way.
Sight was gone, and fears pos-sessed me, But He freed me from them all.
But the Sav - iour still is with me; By His hand I'm safe - ly led.
Then He'll bear me safe - ly o - ver, Where the loved ones I shall meet.

CHORUS

Yes, I'll sing .... the won-drous sto - ry Of the
Yes, I'll sing   the won-drous sto - ry

Christ .... who died for me, ... Sing it with .... the saints in
Of the Christ   who died for me,   Sing it with

glo - ry, Gath-ered by ...... the crys-tal sea ......
the saints in glo - ry,   Gath-ered by   the crystal sea.

145 A MIGHTY REVIVAL

G. B.

George Bennard

1. Show-ers of bless-ing sent from a - bove, Sea-sons re-fresh-ing,
2. "Win-dows of heav-en He'll o-pen wide, Pour out a bless-ing,"
3. Long we have wait-ed for such a tide, For a re-viv-al

gift of God's love, This is the prom-ise, if we o-bey, A might-y re-
this is His word; E-ven a bless-ing we can't con-tain, A might-y re-
deep and world-wide, Now it is com-ing, e'en while we pray, A might-y re-

CHORUS

viv-al is com-ing this way.
viv-al He'll send us a-gain.   A might-y re-viv-al is com-ing this
viv-al is com-ing this way.

way, The ver-y re-viv-al we're need-ing to-day; It's com-ing from

heav-en, believe while you pray, A might-y re-viv-al is coming this way.

146 I AM THINE, O LORD

Fanny J. Crosby

W. H. Doane

1. I am Thine, O Lord, I have heard Thy voice, And it
2. Con - se - crate me now to Thy serv - ice, Lord, By the
3. O the pure de - light of a sin - gle hour That be -
4. There are depths of love that I can - not know Till I

told Thy love to me; But I long to rise in the arms of faith,
pow'r of grace di - vine; Let my soul look up with a stead-fast hope,
fore Thy throne I spend, When I kneel in prayer, and with Thee, my God,
cross the nar - row sea; There are heights of joy that I may not reach

And be clos - er drawn to Thee.
And my will be lost in Thine.
I com-mune as friend with friend!
Till I rest in peace with Thee.

REFRAIN

Draw me near - er, near - er, near - er,

near - er, bless-ed Lord, To the cross where Thou hast died; Draw me

near-er, near - er, near - er, bless-ed Lord, To Thy precious, bleed-ing side.

147   IS IT THE CROWNING DAY?

George Walker Whitcomb

Charles H. Marsh

1. Je - sus may come to - day, Glad day, Glad day! And I would see my
2. I may go home to - day, Glad day, Glad day! Seemeth I hear their
3. Why should I anxious be? Glad day, Glad day! Lights appear on the
4. Faith-ful I'll be to - day, Glad day, Glad day! And I will free-ly

Friend; Dangers and troubles would end   If Je - sus should come to -
song; Hail to the ra - di - ant throng! If I should go home to -
shore, Storms will affright nev-er - more, For He is "at hand" to -
tell   Why I should love Him so well, For He is my all to -

REFRAIN.

day.   Glad day, Glad day! Is it the crown - ing day? I'll

live for to - day, nor anx - ious be; Je - sus, my Lord I

ril.

soon shall see. Glad day, Glad day! Is it the crown-ing day?

148 HE ROSE TRIUMPHANTLY

Oswald J. Smith

B. D. Ackley

1. Our bless-ed Lord was slain, The Christ who came to reign, ...
   was slain, to reign,
2. They sorrowed when He died, Nor sought their tears to hide; ...
   He died, to hide;
3. The stone was rolled a - way, For Christ was raised that day; ....
   a - way. that day;

And in a grave He lay, To wait the com - ing day.
But soon their bit - ter pain Was turned to joy a - gain.
And now He lives a - bove To man - i - fest His love.

CHORUS Animato

He rose tri - um - phant - ly, In pow'r and maj - es - ty, The Sav - iour

rose no more to die; ..... O let us now pro - claim

The glo - ry of His name, And tell to all, He lives to - day.

149 SHALL WE GATHER AT THE RIVER

Robert Lowry   Robert Lowry

1. Shall we gath-er at the riv - er, Where bright an-gel feet have trod;
2. On the bo - som of the riv - er, Where the Sav-iour-King we own;
3. Ere we reach the shining riv - er, Lay we ev - 'ry bur - den down;
4. Soon we'll reach the shining riv - er, Soon our pil-grim-age will cease;

With its crys-tal tide, for - ev - er Flow-ing by the throne of God.
We shall meet, and sorrow nev - er 'Neath the glo - ry of the throne.
Grace our spir - its will de - liv - er, And pro-vide a robe and crown.
Soon our hap - py hearts will quiv - er With the mel - o - dy of peace.

REFRAIN

Yes, we'll gath-er at the riv - er, The beau-ti-ful, the beau-ti - ful riv - er,

Gath-er with the saints at the riv - er That flows by the throne of God.

150 GRACE GREATER THAN OUR SIN

Julia H. Johnston.

D. B. Towner.

1. Mar - vel - ous grace of our lov - ing Lord, Grace that ex - ceeds our
2. Sin and de-spair like the sea waves cold, Threat-en the soul with
3. Dark is the stain that we can - not hide, What can a - vail to
4. Mar - vel - ous, in - fi - nite, match-less grace, Free - ly bestowed on

sin and our guilt, Yon - der on Cal - va - ry's mount out - poured,
in - fi - nite- loss; Grace that is great - er, yes, grace un - told,
wash it a - way? Look, there is flow - ing a crim - son tide;
all who be - lieve; You that are long - ing to see His face,

CHORUS.

There where the blood of the Lamb was spilt. Grace, grace,
Points to the Ref - uge, the Might - y Cross.
Whit - er than snow you may be to - day.
Will you this mo - ment His grace re - ceive? Mar - vel - ous grace,

God's grace, Grace that will par-don and cleanse with-in; Grace
In - fi - nite grace, Mar - vel - ous

grace, God's grace, Grace that is great-er than all our sin.
grace, In - fi - nite grace,

151 CALVARY COVERS IT ALL

Mrs. W. G. T.   Mrs. Walter G. Taylor

1. Far dear-er than all that the world can im-part Was the mes-sage tha
2. The stripes that He bore and the thorns that He wore Told His mer-cy and
3. How matchless the grace, when I looked in the face Of this Je-sus, my
4. How bless-ed the tho't, that my soul by Him bought, Shall be His in the

came to my heart (to my heart); How that Je-sus a-lone for my
love ev-er-more (ev-er-more); And my heart bowed in shame as I
cru-ci-fied Lord (of my Lord); My re-demp-tion com-plete I then
glo-ry on high (His on high), Where with gladness and song I'll be

sin did a-tone, And Cal-va-ry cov-ers it all. . . . .
called on His name, And Cal-va-ry cov-ers it all. . . . .
found at His feet, And Cal-va-ry cov-ers it all. . . . .
one of the throng, And Cal-va-ry cov-ers it all. . . . .
cov-ers it all.

CHORUS

Cal-va-ry cov-ers it all, . . My past with its sin and stain; My

guilt and de-spair Je-sus took on Him there, And Cal-va-ry cov-ers it all.

152 O MASTER, LET ME WALK WITH THEE

Washington Gladden CANONBURY L. M. Robert Schumann

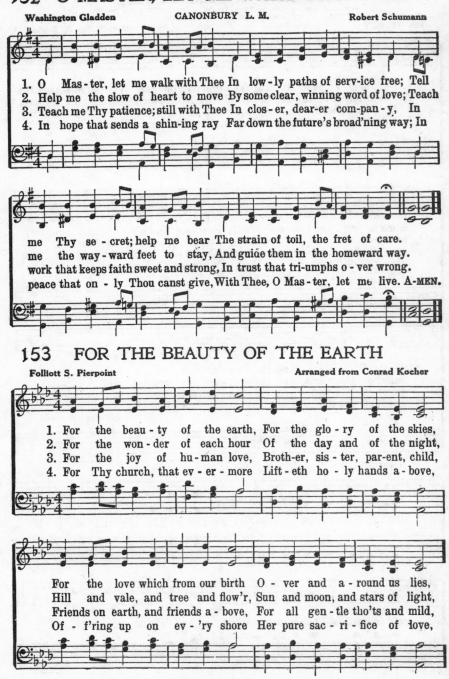

1. O Mas-ter, let me walk with Thee In low-ly paths of serv-ice free; Tell
2. Help me the slow of heart to move By some clear, winning word of love; Teach
3. Teach me Thy patience; still with Thee In clos-er, dear-er com-pan-y, In
4. In hope that sends a shin-ing ray Far down the future's broad'ning way; In

me Thy se-cret; help me bear The strain of toil, the fret of care.
me the way-ward feet to stay, And guide them in the homeward way.
work that keeps faith sweet and strong, In trust that tri-umphs o-ver wrong.
peace that on-ly Thou canst give, With Thee, O Mas-ter, let me live. A-MEN.

153 FOR THE BEAUTY OF THE EARTH

Folliott S. Pierpoint Arranged from Conrad Kocher

1. For the beau-ty of the earth, For the glo-ry of the skies,
2. For the won-der of each hour Of the day and of the night,
3. For the joy of hu-man love, Broth-er, sis-ter, par-ent, child,
4. For Thy church, that ev-er-more Lift-eth ho-ly hands a-bove,

For the love which from our birth O-ver and a-round us lies,
Hill and vale, and tree and flow'r, Sun and moon, and stars of light,
Friends on earth, and friends a-bove, For all gen-tle tho'ts and mild,
Of-f'ring up on ev-'ry shore Her pure sac-ri-fice of love,

FOR THE BEAUTY OF THE EARTH

REFRAIN

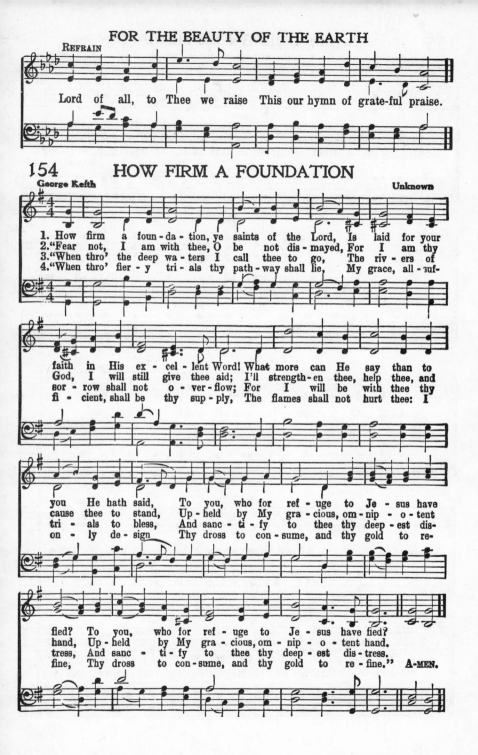

Lord of all, to Thee we raise This our hymn of grate-ful praise.

154   HOW FIRM A FOUNDATION

George Keith   Unknown

1. How firm a foun-da-tion, ye saints of the Lord, Is laid for your
2. "Fear not, I am with thee, O be not dis-mayed, For I am thy
3. "When thro' the deep wa-ters I call thee to go, The riv-ers of
4. "When thro' fier-y tri-als thy path-way shall lie, My grace, all-suf-

faith in His ex-cel-lent Word! What more can He say than to
God, I will still give thee aid; I'll strength-en thee, help thee, and
sor-row shall not o-ver-flow; For I will be with thee thy
fi-cient, shall be thy sup-ply, The flames shall not hurt thee: I

you He hath said, To you, who for ref-uge to Je-sus have
cause thee to stand, Up-held by My gra-cious, om-nip-o-tent
tri-als to bless, And sanc-ti-fy to thee thy deep-est dis-
on-ly de-sign Thy dross to con-sume, and thy gold to re-

fied? To you, who for ref-uge to Je-sus have fled?
hand, Up-held by My gra-cious, om-nip-o-tent hand.
tress, And sanc-ti-fy to thee thy deep-est dis-tress.
fine, Thy dross to con-sume, and thy gold to re-fine." A-MEN.

155 SOME GOLDEN DAYBREAK

C. A. Blackmore

Carl Blackmore

1. Some glo-rious morn-ing sor-row will cease, Some glo-rious morn-ing
2. Sad hearts will glad-den all shall be bright, Good-bye for - ev - er
3. Oh, what a meet-ing, there in the skies, No tears nor cry - ing

all will be peace; Heart-aches all end - ed, school-days all done,
to earth's dark night; Changed in a mo-ment, like Him to be,
shall dim our eyes; Loved ones u - nit - ed e - ter - nal - ly,

rit. CHORUS

Heav - en will o - pen— Je - sus will come.
Oh, glo-rious day-break, Je - sus I'll see. Some gold-en day-break
Oh. what a day-break that morn will be.

Je - sus will come; Some gold-en day-break, bat-tles all won, He'll shout the

vic-t'ry, break thro' the blue, Some gold-en day-break, for me, for you.

156 JUST WHEN I NEED HIM MOST

Rev. Wm. Poole

Chas. H. Gabriel

1. Just when I need Him, Je - sus is near, Just when I fal - ter,
2. Just when I need Him, Je - sus is true, Nev - er for - sak - ing
3. Just when I need Him, Je - sus is strong, Bear-ing my bur - dens
4. Just when I need Him, He is my all, An - swer-ing when up-

just when I fear; Read - y to help me, read - y to cheer,
all the way through; Giv - ing for bur - dens pleas-ures a - new,
all the day long; For all my sor - row giv - ing a song,
on Him I call; Ten - der - ly watch - ing lest I should fall,

Just when I need Him most.

CHORUS

Just when I need Him most, Just when I need Him most; Je - sus is near to com - fort and cheer, Just when I need Him most.

157 ALL HAIL THE POWER OF JESUS' NAME

Edward Perronet

Oliver Holden

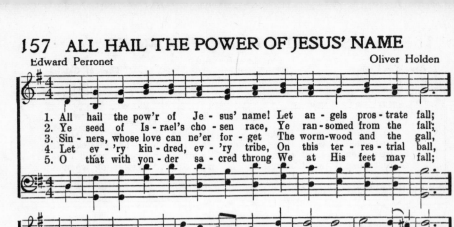

1. All hail the pow'r of Je-sus' name! Let an-gels pros-trate fall;
2. Ye seed of Is-rael's cho-sen race, Ye ran-somed from the fall,
3. Sin-ners, whose love can ne'er for-get The worm-wood and the gall,
4. Let ev-'ry kin-dred, ev-'ry tribe, On this ter-res-trial ball,
5. O that with yon-der sa-cred throng We at His feet may fall;

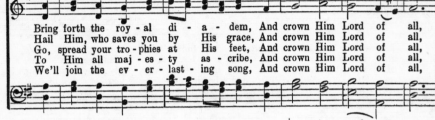

Bring forth the roy-al di-a-dem, And crown Him Lord of all,
Hail Him, who saves you by His grace, And crown Him Lord of all,
Go, spread your tro-phies at His feet, And crown Him Lord of all,
To Him all maj-es-ty as-cribe, And crown Him Lord of all,
We'll join the ev-er-last-ing song, And crown Him Lord of all,

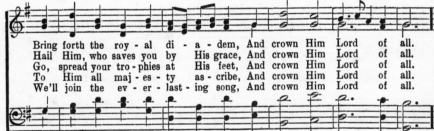

Bring forth the roy-al di-a-dem, And crown Him Lord of all.
Hail Him, who saves you by His grace, And crown Him Lord of all.
Go, spread your tro-phies at His feet, And crown Him Lord of all.
To Him all maj-es-ty as-cribe, And crown Him Lord of all.
We'll join the ev-er-last-ing song, And crown Him Lord of all.

158 ON JORDAN'S STORMY BANKS

Samuel Stennett

Arr. by R. M. McIntosh

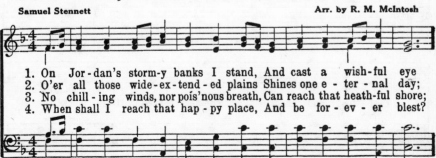

1. On Jor-dan's storm-y banks I stand, And cast a wish-ful eye
2. O'er all those wide-ex-tend-ed plains Shines one e-ter-nal day;
3. No chill-ing winds, nor pois'nous breath, Can reach that heath-ful shore;
4. When shall I reach that hap-py place, And be for-ev-er blest?

ON JORDAN'S STORMY BANKS

To Ca-naan's fair and hap-py land, Where my pos-ses-sions lie.
There God, the Son, for-ev-er reigns, And scat-ters night a-way.
Sick-ness and sor-row, pain and death, Are felt and feared no more.
When shall I see my Fa-ther's face, And in His bos-om rest?

D. S.—*O who will come and go with me? I am bound for the prom-ised land.*

REFRAIN

I am bound for the promised land,.... I am bound for the promised land,
prom-ised land,

159   COME, THOU FOUNT

Robert Robinson

John Wyeth

1. { Come, Thou Fount of ev-'ry bless-ing, Tune my heart to sing Thy grace;
   { Streams of mer-cy, nev-er ceas-ing, Call for songs of loud-est praise.

2. { Here I'll raise my Eb-en-e-zer, Hith-er by Thy help I'm come;
   { And I hope by Thy good pleas-ure, Safe-ly to ar-rive at home.

3. { Oh, to grace how great a debt-or Dai-ly I'm constrained to be!
   { Let Thy good-ness, like a fet-ter, Bind my wand'ring heart to Thee:

D.C.—*Praise the mount, I'm fixed up-on it! Mount of Thy re-deem-ing love.*
D.C.—*He, to res-cue me from dan-ger, In-terposed His pre-cious blood.*
D.C.—*Here's my heart, O take and seal it, Seal it for Thy courts a-bove.*

Teach me some mel-o-dious son-net, Sung by flam-ing tongues a-bove;
Je-sus sought me when a stran-ger, Wand'ring from the fold of God:
Prone to wan-der, Lord, I feel it, Prone to leave the God I love;

160 ONE DAY

Dr. J. Wilbur Chapman

Chas. H. Marsh

1. One day when heav-en was filled with His prais-es, One day when sin
2. One day they led Him up Cal-va-ry's moun-tain, One day they nailed
3. One day they left Him a-lone in the gar-den, One day He rest-
4. One day when full-ness of time was fast dawn-ing, One day the stone
5. One day He's com-ing, for Him I am long-ing; One day the skies

was as black as could be, Je-sus came forth to be
Him for me on the tree; Won-der-ful, Coun-sel-lor
ed from suf-fer-ing free, An-gels came down then to
moved a-way from the door; Then He a-rose, o-ver
with His glo-ry will shine; Won-der-ful day, my be-

born of a vir-gin, Lived, loved, and la-bored—my Teach-er is He.
they had acclaimed Him, Now He is Je-sus—my Je-sus is He.
keep sa-cred vig-il, Weight-ed with sins, my Re-deem-er is He.
death He had conquered, Now He's as-cend-ed, my Lord ev-er-more.
lov-ed ones bring-ing; Hope of the hope-less, this Je-sus is mine.

CHORUS

Liv-ing, He loved me; dy-ing, He saved me; Bur-ied, He car-
ried my sins far a-way; Ris-ing, He jus-ti-fied,

ONE DAY

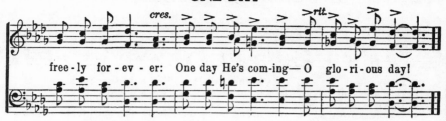

free - ly for - ev - er: One day He's com-ing— O glo - ri - ous day!

161 WHEN WE ALL GET TO HEAVEN

E. E. Hewitt

Mrs. J. G. Wilson

1. Sing the won-drous love of Je - sus, Sing His mer-cy and His grace;
2. While we walk the pil - grim pathway, Clouds will o - ver-spread the sky;
3. Let us then be true and faith-ful, Trust-ing, serv-ing ev - 'ry day;
4. On - ward to the prize be - fore us! Soon His beau-ty we'll be - hold;

In the man-sions bright and blessed, He'll pre-pare for us a place.
But when trav'ling days are o - ver, Not a shad-ow, not a sigh.
Just one glimpse of Him in glo - ry Will the toils of life re - pay.
Soon the pearl - y gates will o - pen, We shall tread the streets of gold.

for us a place.

CHORUS

When we all get to heaven, What a day of re-joicing that will be!
When we all What a day of re-joicing that will be!

When we all see Je-sus, We'll sing and shout the vic-to-ry..........
When we all and shout the vic-to-ry.

162 HE'S A WONDERFUL SAVIOR TO ME

Virgil P. Brock

Blanche Kerr Brock

1. I was lost in sin but Jesus recued me, He's a wonderful Savior to
2. He's a Friend so true, so patient and so kind, He's a wonderful Savior to
3. He is always near to comfort and to cheer, He's a wonderful Savior to
4. Dearer grows the love of Jesus day by day, He's a wonderful Savior to

me; I was bound by fear but Jesus set me free, He's a
me; Ev'rything I need in Him I always find, He's a
me; He forgives my sins, He dries my ev'ry tear, He's a
me; Sweeter is His grace while pressing on my way, He's a

So wonderful!

wonderful Savior to me.............. For He's a wonderful

So wonderful!

Savior to me, He's a wonderful Savior to me; I was

wonderful!

wonderful!

lost in sin, but Jesus took me in, He's a wonderful Savior to me.

163 SAVED, SAVED!

JACK P. SCHOLFIELD

JACK P. SCHOLFIELD

1. I've found a friend who is all to me, His
2. He saves me from ev-ery sin and harm, Se-
3. When poor and need-y and all a-lone, Se-

love is ev-er true; . . . . . I love to tell how He
cures my soul each day; . . . . . I'm lean-ing strong on His
love He said to me, ... "Come un-to Me and I'll

lift-ed me And what His grace can do for you. . . . .
might-y arm; I know He'll guide me all the way. . . . .
lead you home, To live with Me e-ter-nal-ly." . . . .

CHORUS

Saved . . . . by His power di-vine, Saved . . . . to new life sub-lime!
Saved by His power,   Saved to new life,

cres. *rit.*

Life now is sweet and my joy is com-plete, For I'm saved, saved, saved!

164 A SHARE IN THE ATONEMENT

C. A. M.

C. AUSTIN MILES

1. At one with God, how rich is my con - di - tion; At peace with Him where
2. Condemned was He, but I received a pard- on. A sin - ner, I. The
3. He bore the cross, but I received a bless- ing. All that I have, or

ev - er I may be. Between us, then, all bar - ri-ers were broken When
sin- less One was He. To ran - som me, the Son of God was willing To
am, or hope to be,—This do I owe, nor can I e'er re-pay Him Who

Chorus

Je - sus made a- tone-ment on Cal - va - ry.⎫
make a full a- tone-ment, on Cal - va - ry.⎬ I have a share in that a -
made complete a- tone-ment on Cal - va - ry.⎭

tone- ment Which was made on Cal - va - ry. What a treasure is mine,

rit.

This gift so di - vine, That no one can take a - way from me.

165 TRUE HEARTED, WHOLE HEARTED

FRANCES R. HAVERGAL

GEORGE C. STEBBINS

1. True-hearted, whole-hearted, faithful and loy-al, King of our lives by Thy
2. True-hearted, whole-hearted, full-est al-le-giance, Yielding henceforth to our
3. True-hearted, whole-hearted, Sav-ior all-glo-rious! Take Thy great power and

grace we will be; Un-der the stan-dard ex-alt-ed and roy-al, Strong
glo-ri-ous King; Val-iant en-deav-or and lov-ing o-be-dience Free-
reign there a-lone, O-ver our wills and af-fec-tions vic-to-rious, Free-

CHORUS

in Thy strength we will bat-tle for Thee. Peal out the watchword! silence it
ly and joy-ous-ly now we would bring.
ly sur-ren-dered and whol-ly Thine own.

nev-er, Song of our spir-its re-joic-ing and free; Peal out the

watchword! loy-al for-ev-er, King of our lives, by Thy grace we will be.

166 JESUS IS THE JOY OF LIVING

A. H. A.

COPYRIGHT, 1939, BY THE RODEHEAVER CO.
INTERNATIONAL COPYRIGHT SECURED

A. H. Ackley

1. I have found a won-drous Sav-iour, Je-sus Christ, The Soul's De-light;
2. Life is grow-ing rich with beau-ty, Toil has lost its wea-ry strain,
3. Heav'n-ly wis-dom He pro-vides me, Grace to keep my spir-it free;
4. O what splen-dor, O what glo-ry, O what match-less pow'r di-vine,

Ev-'ry bless-ing of His fa-vor Fills my heart with hope so bright.
Now a ha-lo crowns each du-ty, And I sing a glad re-frain.
In His own sweet way He guides me When the path I can-not see.
Is the Christ of Gos-pel sto-ry, Christ, the Sav-iour, who is mine.

CHORUS

Je-sus is the Joy of Liv-ing, He's the King of Life to me; . . . . .
of Life to me;

Un-to Him my all I'm giv-ing, His for-ev-er-more to be (to be).

I will do what He com-mands me, An-y-where He leads I'll go (I'll go);

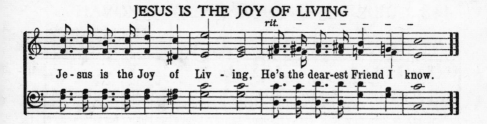

JESUS IS THE JOY OF LIVING

Je-sus is the Joy of Liv-ing, He's the dear-est Friend I know.

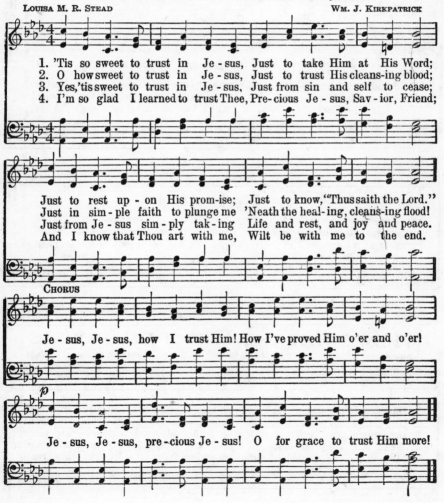

167 'TIS SO SWEET TO TRUST IN JESUS

LOUISA M. R. STEAD   WM. J. KIRKPATRICK

1. 'Tis so sweet to trust in Je-sus, Just to take Him at His Word;
2. O how sweet to trust in Je-sus, Just to trust His cleans-ing blood;
3. Yes,'tis sweet to trust in Je-sus, Just from sin and self to cease;
4. I'm so glad I learned to trust Thee, Pre-cious Je-sus, Sav-ior, Friend;

Just to rest up-on His prom-ise; Just to know, "Thus saith the Lord."
Just in sim-ple faith to plunge me 'Neath the heal-ing, cleans-ing flood!
Just from Je-sus sim-ply tak-ing Life and rest, and joy and peace.
And I know that Thou art with me, Wilt be with me to the end.

CHORUS

Je-sus, Je-sus, how I trust Him! How I've proved Him o'er and o'er!

Je-sus, Je-sus, pre-cious Je-sus! O for grace to trust Him more!

168 GUIDE ME, O THOU GREAT JEHOVAH

William Williams

Thomas Hastings
Har. H. P. M.

1. { Guide me, O Thou great Je - ho - vah, Pil - grim thru this bar - ren land; }
   { I am weak, but Thou art might - y; Hold me with Thy pow'r-ful hand: }

2. { O - pen now the crys - tal foun - tain, Whence the healing wa - ters flow; }
   { Let the fi - er - y, cloud - y pil - lar Lead me all my jour - ney thru: }

3. { When I tread the verge of Jor - dan, Bid my anx - ious fears sub - side; }
   { Bear me thru the swell - ing cur - rent, Land me safe on Ca - naan's side. }

Bread of heav - en, Feed me till I want no more;
Strong De - liv - 'rer, Be Thou still my strength and shield;
Songs of prais - es I will ev - er give to Thee;

sf

Bread of heav - en, Feed me till I want no more.
Strong De - liv - 'rer, Be Thou still my strength and shield.
Songs of prais - es I will ev - er give to Thee.

169 HOW SWEET THE NAME OF JESUS SOUNDS

John Newton

HOLY CROSS C. M.

Arranged by James C. Wade

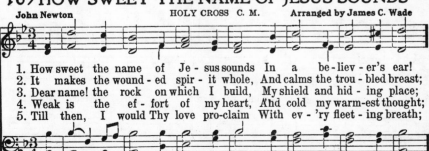

1. How sweet the name of Je - sus sounds In a be - liev - er's ear!
2. It makes the wound - ed spir - it whole, And calms the trou - bled breast;
3. Dear name! the rock on which I build, My shield and hid - ing place;
4. Weak is the ef - fort of my heart, And cold my warm-est thought;
5. Till then, I would Thy love pro-claim With ev - 'ry fleet - ing breath;

HOW SWEET THE NAME OF JESUS SOUNDS

It soothes his sorrows, heals his wounds, And drives away his fear.
'Tis man-na to the hun-gry soul, And to the wea-ry, rest.
My nev-er-fail-ing treas'ry, filled With boundless stores of grace!
But when I see Thee as Thou art, I'll praise Thee as I ought.
And may the mu-sic of Thy name Refresh my soul in death. A-men.

170   O JESUS, THOU ART STANDING

William W. How

Justin H. Knecht

1. O Je-sus, Thou art standing Out-side the fast-closèd door, In low-ly
2. O Je-sus, Thou art knocking; And lo, that hand is scarred, And thorns Thy
3. O Je-sus, Thou art pleading In ac-cents meek and low, "I died for

patience waiting To pass the threshold o'er: Shame on us, Christian brothers, His
brow en-cir-cle, And tears Thy face have marred: O love that passeth knowledge, So
you, my children, And will you treat Me so?" O Lord, with shame and sorrow We

name and sign who bear, O shame, thrice shame upon us, To keep Him standing there!
pa-tient-ly to wait! O sin that hath no e-qual, So fast to bar the gate!
o-pen now the door; Dear Saviour, en-ter, en-ter, And leave us nev-er-more.

171 JESUS TOOK MY BURDEN

Rev. Johnson Oatman, Jr.

Bertha Mae Lillenas

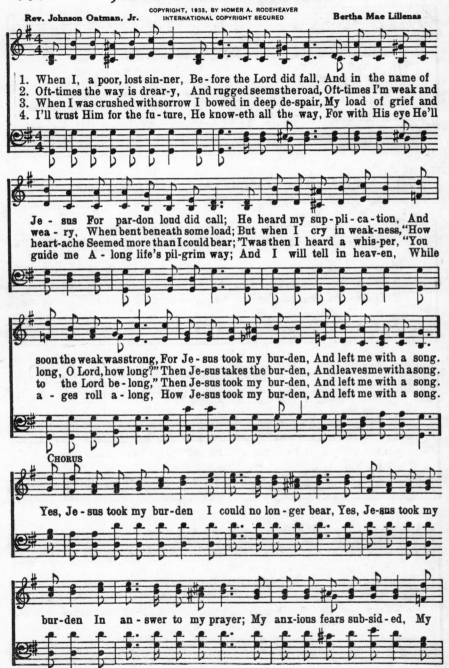

1. When I, a poor, lost sin-ner, Be-fore the Lord did fall, And in the name of
2. Oft-times the way is drear-y, And rugged seems the road, Oft-times I'm weak and
3. When I was crushed with sorrow I bowed in deep de-spair, My load of grief and
4. I'll trust Him for the fu-ture, He know-eth all the way, For with His eye He'll

Je-sus For par-don loud did call; He heard my sup-pli-ca-tion, And
wea-ry, When bent beneath some load; But when I cry in weak-ness, "How
heart-ache Seemed more than I could bear; 'Twas then I heard a whis-per, "You
guide me A-long life's pil-grim way; And I will tell in heav-en, While

soon the weak was strong, For Je-sus took my bur-den, And left me with a song.
long, O Lord, how long?" Then Je-sus takes the bur-den, And leaves me with a song.
to the Lord be-long," Then Je-sus took my bur-den, And left me with a song.
a-ges roll a-long, How Je-sus took my bur-den, And left me with a song.

CHORUS

Yes, Je-sus took my bur-den I could no lon-ger bear, Yes, Je-sus took my

bur-den In an-swer to my prayer; My anx-ious fears sub-sid-ed, My

JESUS TOOK MY BURDEN

spir-it was made strong, For Je-sus took my bur-den, And left me with a song.

172 JESUS SAVES

Priscilla J. Owens

Wm. J. Kirkpatrick

1. We have heard the joy-ful sound, Je-sus saves, Je-sus saves;
2. Waft it on the roll-ing tide, Je-sus saves, Je-sus saves;
3. Sing a-bove the bat-tle's strife, Je-sus saves, Je-sus saves;
4. Give the winds a might-y voice, Je-sus saves, Je-sus saves;

Spread the ti-dings all a-round, Je-sus saves, Je-sus saves;
Tell to sin-ners far and wide, Je-sus saves, Je-sus saves;
By His death and end-less life, Je-sus saves, Je-sus saves;
Let the na-tions now re-joice,— Je-sus saves, Je-sus saves;

Bear the news to ev-'ry land, Climb the steeps and cross the waves,
Sing, ye is-lands of the sea, Ech-o back, ye o-cean caves,
Sing it soft-ly thru the gloom, When the heart for mer-cy craves,
Shout sal-va-tion full and free, High-est hills and deep-est caves,

On-ward!—'tis our Lord's com-mand, Je-sus saves, Je-sus saves.
Earth shall keep her ju-bi-lee, Je-sus saves, Je-sus saves.
Sing in tri-umph o'er the tomb,— Je-sus saves, Je-sus saves.
This our song of vic-to-ry,— Je-sus saves, Je-sus saves.

173 COME, THOU ALMIGHTY KING

Anonymous

Felice De Giardini

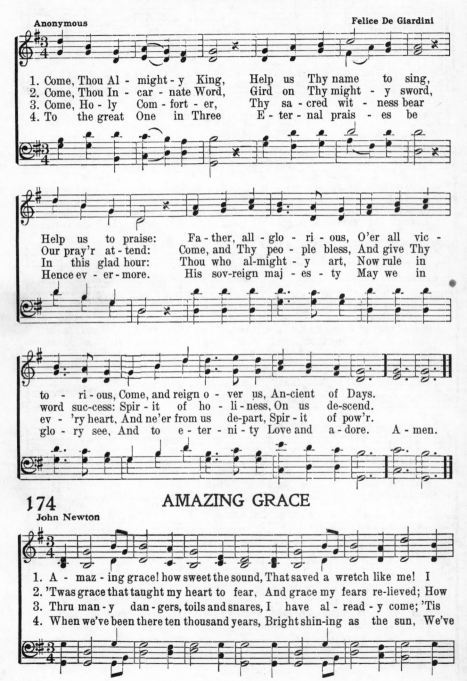

1. Come, Thou Al - might - y King, Help us Thy name to sing,
2. Come, Thou In - car - nate Word, Gird on Thy might - y sword,
3. Come, Ho - ly Com - fort - er, Thy sa - cred wit - ness bear
4. To the great One in Three E - ter - nal prais - es be

Help us to praise: Fa - ther, all - glo - ri - ous, O'er all vic -
Our pray'r at - tend: Come, and Thy peo - ple bless, And give Thy
In this glad hour: Thou who al - might - y art, Now rule in
Hence ev - er - more. His sov-reign maj - es - ty May we in

to - ri - ous, Come, and reign o - ver us, An-cient of Days.
word suc-cess: Spir - it of ho - li - ness, On us de-scend.
ev - 'ry heart, And ne'er from us de-part, Spir - it of pow'r.
glo - ry see, And to e - ter - ni - ty Love and a - dore. A - men.

174 AMAZING GRACE

John Newton

1. A - maz - ing grace! how sweet the sound, That saved a wretch like me! I
2. 'Twas grace that taught my heart to fear, And grace my fears re-lieved; How
3. Thru man - y dan - gers, toils and snares, I have al - read - y come; 'Tis
4. When we've been there ten thousand years, Bright shin-ing as the sun, We've

AMAZING GRACE

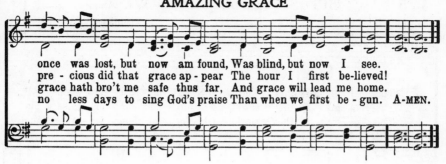

once was lost, but now am found, Was blind, but now I see.
pre - cious did that grace ap - pear The hour I first be-lieved!
grace hath bro't me safe thus far, And grace will lead me home.
no less days to sing God's praise Than when we first be - gun. A-MEN.

175 HOLY, HOLY, HOLY, LORD GOD ALMIGHTY

Reginald Heber   NICÆA 11. 12. 12. 10   John B. Dykes

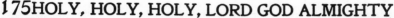

1. Ho - ly, ho - ly, ho - ly, Lord God Al-might - y! Ear - ly in the
2. Ho - ly, ho - ly, ho - ly! all the saints a-dore Thee, Casting down their
3. Ho - ly, ho - ly, ho - ly! tho' the darkness hide Thee, Tho' the eye of
4. Ho - ly, ho - ly, ho - ly, Lord God Al-might - y! All Thy works shall

morn - ing our song shall rise to Thee; Ho - ly, ho - ly, ho - ly,
golden crowns around the glass - y sea; Cher - u - bim and ser - a - phim,
sin - ful man Thy glo - ry may not see; On - ly Thou art ho - ly;
praise Thy name, in earth, and sky, and sea; Ho - ly, ho - ly, ho - ly,

mer - ci - ful and might - y, God in Three Persons, blessed Trin-i - ty.
fall-ing down before Thee, Which wert, and art, and ev-er-more shalt be.
there is none beside Thee, Per - fect in pow'r, in love, and pur-i - ty.
mer - ci - ful and might - y, God in Three Persons, blessed Trin-i - ty! A-men.

176 THIS IS MY FATHER'S WORLD

MALTBIE D. BABCOCK   TERRA BEATA S. M. D.

Traditional English Melody
Arranged by S. F. L.

1. This is my Fa-ther's world, And to my list-'ning ears, All
2. This is my Fa-ther's world, The birds their car-ols raise, The
3. This is my Fa-ther's world, Oh! let me ne'er for-get That

na - ture sings, and round me rings The mu-sic of the spheres.
morn-ing light, the lil-y white, De-clare their Ma-ker's praise.
though the wrong seems oft so strong, God is the Ru-ler yet.

This is my Fa-ther's world, I rest me in the thought Of
This is my Fa-ther's world, He shines in all that's fair; In the
This is my Fa-ther's world, The bat-tle is not done, Je-

rocks and trees, of skies and seas—His hand the won-ders wrought.
rus-tling grass I hear Him pass, He speaks to me ev-'ry-where,
sus who died shall be sat-is-fied, And earth and heav'n be one. A-men.

177 HE KEEPS ME SINGING

L. B. B.

L. B. BRIDGERS

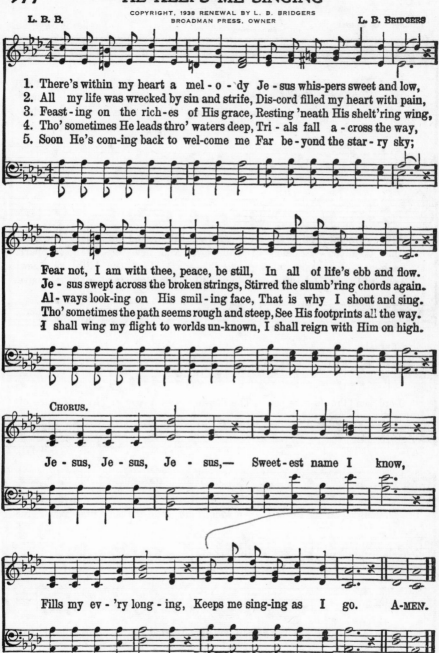

1. There's within my heart a mel-o-dy Je-sus whis-pers sweet and low,
2. All my life was wrecked by sin and strife, Dis-cord filled my heart with pain,
3. Feast-ing on the rich-es of His grace, Resting 'neath His shelt'ring wing,
4. Tho' sometimes He leads thro' waters deep, Tri-als fall a-cross the way,
5. Soon He's com-ing back to wel-come me Far be-yond the star-ry sky;

Fear not, I am with thee, peace, be still, In all of life's ebb and flow.
Je-sus swept across the broken strings, Stirred the slumb'ring chords again.
Al-ways look-ing on His smil-ing face, That is why I shout and sing.
Tho' sometimes the path seems rough and steep, See His footprints all the way.
I shall wing my flight to worlds un-known, I shall reign with Him on high.

CHORUS.

Je-sus, Je-sus, Je-sus,— Sweet-est name I know,

Fills my ev-'ry long-ing, Keeps me sing-ing as I go. A-MEN.

178 PENTECOSTAL POWER

Charlotte G. Homer

Charles H. Gabriel

1. Lord, as of old at Pen - te - cost Thou didst Thy pow'r dis - play,
2. For might - y works for Thee, pre - pare And strengthen ev - 'ry heart;
3. All self con - sume, all sin de - stroy! With earn - est zeal en - due
4. Speak, Lord, be - fore Thy throne we wait, Thy prom - ise we be - lieve,

With cleans-ing, pu - ri - fy - ing flame De - scend on us to - day.
Come, take pos - ses - sion of Thine own, And nev - er - more de - part.
Each wait - ing heart to work for Thee; O Lord, our faith re - new!
And will not let Thee go un - til The bless-ing we re - ceive.

REFRAIN

Lord, send the old-time pow'r, The Pen-te - cos-tal pow'r! Thy floodgates of

blessing on us throw o - pen wide! Lord, send the old - time pow'r, the

Pen - te - cos - tal pow'r, That sinners be converted and Thy name glo - ri-fied!

179 SOME BRIGHT MORNING

CHARLOTTE G. HOMER CHAS. H. GABRIEL

1. Be not a-wea-ry, for la-bor will cease Some glad morn-ing;
2. Wea-ri-some bur-dens will all be laid down, Some glad morn-ing;
3. La-bor well done shall re-ceive its re-ward, Some glad morn-ing;
4. O what a time of re-joic-ing will come, Some glad morn-ing;
5. There with the loved ones who've gone on be-fore, Some glad morn-ing;

Tur-moil will change in-to in-fi-nite peace, Some bright morn-ing.
Then shall our cross be exchanged for a crown, Some bright morn-ing.
Thou who art faith-ful shall be with the Lord, Some bright morn-ing.
When all the ransomed are gathered at home, Some bright morn-ing.
We shall sing praise to the Lamb ev-er-more, Some bright morn-ing.

CHORUS

Some bright morning, Some glad morn-ing, When the sun is shin-ing

in th' e-ter-nal sky;.... Some bright morn-ing, Some glad

cres.

morn-ing.. We shall see the Lord of Har-vest, By and by.

180 GIVE OF YOUR BEST TO THE MASTER

H. B. G.

MRS. CHARLES BARNARD

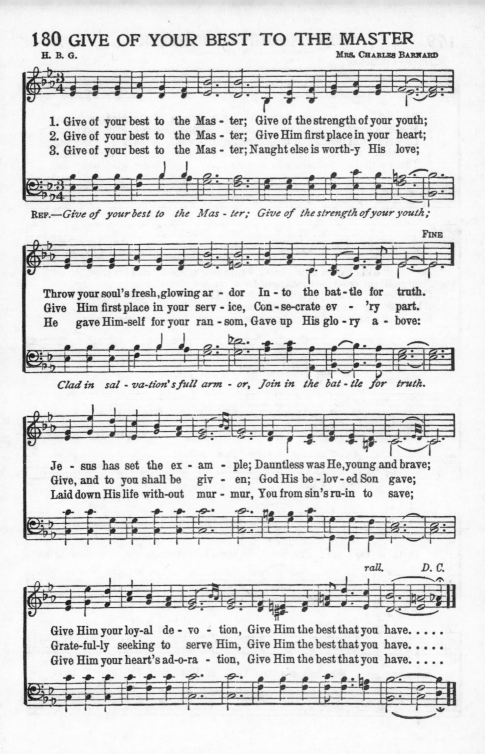

1. Give of your best to the Mas - ter; Give of the strength of your youth;
2. Give of your best to the Mas - ter; Give Him first place in your heart;
3. Give of your best to the Mas - ter; Naught else is worth-y His love;

REF.—*Give of your best to the Mas - ter; Give of the strength of your youth;*

FINE

Throw your soul's fresh, glowing ar - dor In - to the bat - tle for truth.
Give Him first place in your serv - ice, Con - se-crate ev - 'ry part.
He gave Him-self for your ran - som, Gave up His glo - ry a - bove:

Clad in sal - va-tion's full arm - or, Join in the bat - tle for truth.

Je - sus has set the ex - am - ple; Dauntless was He, young and brave;
Give, and to you shall be giv - en; God His be - lov - ed Son gave;
Laid down His life with-out mur - mur, You from sin's ru-in to save;

rall.

D. C.

Give Him your loy-al de - vo - tion, Give Him the best that you have.....
Grate-ful-ly seeking to serve Him, Give Him the best that you have.....
Give Him your heart's ad-o-ra - tion, Give Him the best that you have.....

THE HAVEN OF REST

H. L. GILMOUR   GEORGE D. MOORE

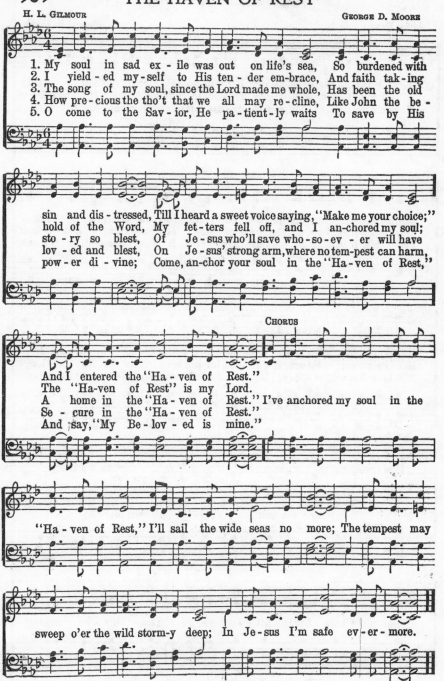

1. My soul in sad ex-ile was out on life's sea, So burdened with
2. I yield-ed my-self to His ten-der em-brace, And faith tak-ing
3. The song of my soul, since the Lord made me whole, Has been the old
4. How pre-cious the tho't that we all may re-cline, Like John the be-
5. O come to the Sav-ior, He pa-tient-ly waits To save by His

sin and dis-tressed, Till I heard a sweet voice saying, "Make me your choice;"
hold of the Word, My fet-ters fell off, and I an-chored my soul;
sto-ry so blest, Of Je-sus who'll save who-so-ev-er will have
lov-ed and blest, On Je-sus' strong arm, where no tem-pest can harm,
pow-er di-vine; Come, an-chor your soul in the "Ha-ven of Rest,"

CHORUS

And I entered the "Ha-ven of Rest."
The "Ha-ven of Rest" is my Lord.
A home in the "Ha-ven of Rest." I've anchored my soul in the
Se-cure in the "Ha-ven of Rest."
And say, "My Be-lov-ed is mine."

"Ha-ven of Rest," I'll sail the wide seas no more; The tempest may

sweep o'er the wild storm-y deep; In Je-sus I'm safe ev-er-more.

182 LOVE LIFTED ME

James Rowe

Howard E. Smith

1. I was sink-ing deep in sin, Far from the peaceful shore, Ver-y deep-ly
2. All my heart to Him I give, Ev-er to Him I'll cling, In His bless-ed
3. Souls in dan-ger, look a-bove, Je-sus com-plete-ly saves; He will lift you

stained with-in, Sink-ing to rise no more; But the Mas-ter of the sea
pres-ence live, Ev-er His prais-es sing. Love so might-y and so true
by His love Out of the an-gry waves. He's the Mas-ter of the sea,

Heard my de-spair-ing cry, From the wa-ters lift-ed me, Now safe am I.
Mer-its my soul's best songs; Faith-ful, lov-ing serv-ice, too, To Him be-longs.
Bil-lows His will o-bey; He your Sav-iour wants to be—Be saved to-day.

CHORUS

Love lift-ed me! .... Love lift-ed me! .... When noth-ing
e - ven me!   e - ven me!

else could help, Love lift-ed me. Love lift-ed me.

183 ALL THE WAY MY SAVIOUR LEADS

Fanny J. Crosby

Robert Lowry

1. All the way my Sav-iour leads me; What have I to ask be-side?
2. All the way my Sav-iour leads me, Cheers each winding path I tread;
3. All the way my Sav-iour leads me; O the ful-ness of His love!

Can I doubt His ten-der mer-cy Who thro' life has been my guide?
Gives me grace for ev-'ry tri-al, Feeds me with the liv-ing bread;
Per-fect rest to me is prom-ised In my Fa-ther's house a-bove;

Heav'nly peace, di-vin-est com-fort, Here by faith in Him to dwell!
Tho' my wea-ry steps may fal-ter, And my soul a-thirst may be,
When my spir-it, clothed, im-mor-tal, Wings its flight to realms of day,

For I know, whate'er be-fall me, Je-sus do-eth all things well;
Gushing from the Rock be-fore me, Lo! a spring of joy I see;
This my song thro' end-less a-ges— Je-sus led me all the way;

For I know, what-e'er be-fall me, Je-sus do-eth all things well.
Gushing from the Rock be-fore me, Lo! a spring of joy I see.
This my song thro' end-less a-ges— Je-sus led me all the way.

184 TRUST AND OBEY

Rev. J. H. Sammis

D. B. Towner

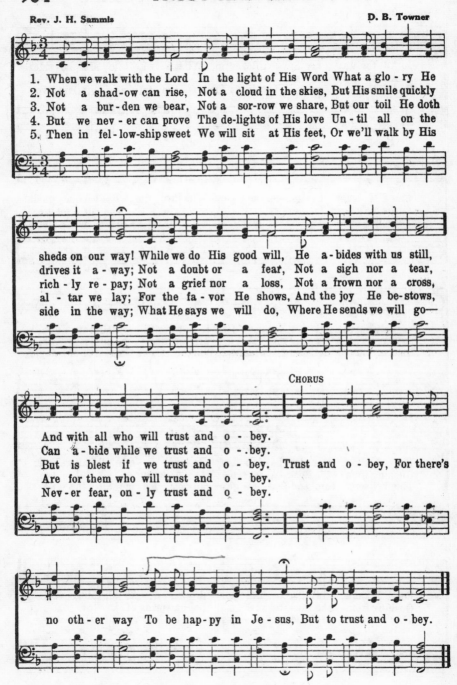

1. When we walk with the Lord In the light of His Word What a glo - ry He
2. Not a shad-ow can rise, Not a cloud in the skies, But His smile quickly
3. Not a bur-den we bear, Not a sor-row we share, But our toil He doth
4. But we nev - er can prove The de-lights of His love Un - til all on the
5. Then in fel - low-ship sweet We will sit at His feet, Or we'll walk by His

sheds on our way! While we do His good will, He a - bides with us still,
drives it a - way; Not a doubt or a fear, Not a sigh nor a tear,
rich - ly re - pay; Not a grief nor a loss, Not a frown nor a cross,
al - tar we lay; For the fa - vor He shows, And the joy He be-stows,
side in the way; What He says we will do, Where He sends we will go—

CHORUS

And with all who will trust and o - bey.
Can a - bide while we trust and o - bey.
But is blest if we trust and o - bey. Trust and o - bey, For there's
Are for them who will trust and o - bey.
Nev - er fear, on - ly trust and o - bey.

no oth - er way To be hap - py in Je - sus, But to trust and o - bey.

IVORY PALACES

H. B.

Henry Barraclough

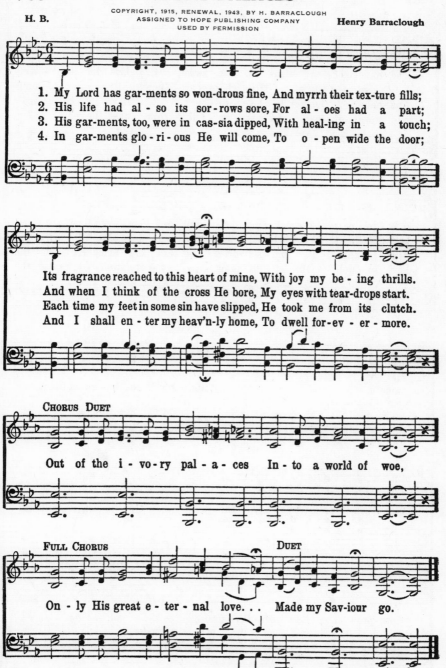

1. My Lord has gar-ments so won-drous fine, And myrrh their tex-ture fills;
2. His life had al - so its sor - rows sore, For al - oes had a part;
3. His gar-ments, too, were in cas-sia dipped, With heal-ing in a touch;
4. In gar-ments glo - ri - ous He will come, To o - pen wide the door;

Its fragrance reached to this heart of mine, With joy my be - ing thrills.
And when I think of the cross He bore, My eyes with tear-drops start.
Each time my feet in some sin have slipped, He took me from its clutch.
And I shall en - ter my heav'n-ly home, To dwell for-ev - er - more.

Chorus Duet

Out of the i - vo - ry pal - a - ces In - to a world of woe,

Full Chorus   **Duet**

On - ly His great e - ter - nal love... Made my Sav-iour go.

186 THE NAME OF JESUS

W. C. MARTIN

E. S. LORENZ

1. The name of Je - sus is so sweet, I love its mu - sic
2. I love the name of Him whose heart Knows all my griefs and
3. That name I fond - ly love to hear, It nev - er fails my
4. No word of man can ev - er tell How sweet the name I

to re - peat; It makes my joys full and com - plete, The pre - cious
bears a part; Who bids all an - xious fears de - part— I love the
heart to cheer, Its mu - sic dries the fall - ing tear; Ex - alt the
love so well, Oh, let its prais - es ev - er swell, Oh, praise the

CHORUS

name of Je - sus. "Je - sus," oh, how sweet the name!
pre - cious name,

"Je - sus," ev - 'ry day the same; "Je - sus," let all

saints pro - claim its wor - thy praise for - ev - er.
Its wor - thy praise

187 SWEET PEACE, THE GIFT OF GOD'S LOVE

Peter P. Bilhorn

Peter P. Bilhorn

1. There comes to my heart one sweet strain, (sweet strain,) A glad and a
2. Thro' Christ on the cross peace was made, (was made,) My debt by His
3. When Je - sus as Lord I had crowned, (had crowned,) My heart with this
4. In Je - sus for peace I a - bide, (a - bide,) And as I keep

joy - ous re-frain; (re-frain;) I sing it a - gain and a - gain,
death was all paid; (all paid;) No oth - er foun - da - tion is laid,
peace did a-bound; (abound;) In Him the rich bless - ing I found,
close to His side; (His side,) There's nothing but peace doth be - tide,

REFRAIN

Sweet peace, the gift of God's love.
For peace, the gift of God's love.   Peace, peace, sweet peace!
Sweet peace, the gift of God's love.
Sweet peace, the gift of God's love.

cres.

Won - der - ful gift from a - bove! (a - bove!) Oh, won - der - ful,

won - der - ful peace! Sweet peace, the gift of God's love!

188 THE WAY OF THE CROSS LEADS HOME

JESSIE BROWN POUNDS

CHAS. H. GABRIEL

1. I must needs go home by the way of the cross, There's no oth-er
2. I must needs go on in the blood-sprinkled way, The path that the
3. Then I bid fare-well to the way of the world, To walk in it

way but this; I shall ne'er get sight of the Gates of Light,
Sav-ior trod, If I ev-er climb to the heights sub-lime,
nev-er-more; For my Lord says "Come," and I seek my home,

CHORUS.

If the way of the cross I miss.
Where the soul is at home with God. The way of the cross leads
Where He waits at the o-pen door.

home, The way of the cross leads home; It is
leads home, leads home;

sweet to know, as I on-ward go, The way of the cross leads home. A-MEN.

189 HAIL, THOU ONCE DESPISED JESUS!

John Bakewell   (AUTUMN)   Francois H. Barthelemon

1. Hail, Thou once de-spis-ed Je-sus! Hail, Thou Gal-i-le-an King!
2. Pas-chal Lamb, by God ap-point-ed, All our sins on Thee were laid:
3. Je-sus, hail! enthroned in glo-ry, There for-ev-er to a-bide;
4. Wor-ship, hon-or, pow'r, and bless-ing, Thou art wor-thy to re-ceive;

Thou didst suf-fer to re-lease us; Thou didst free sal-va-tion bring.
By al-might-y love a-noint-ed, Thou hast full a-tone-ment made.
All the heav'n-ly hosts a-dore Thee; Seat-ed at Thy Fa-ther's side:
Loud-est prais-es, with-out ceas-ing, Meet it is for us to give.

Hail, Thou ag-o-niz-ing Sav-iour, Bear-er of our sin and shame!
All Thy peo-ple are for-giv-en, Thru the vir-tue of Thy blood;
There for sin-ners Thou art plead-ing; There Thou dost our place pre-pare:
Help, ye bright an-gel-ic spir-its, Bring your sweet-est, no-blest lays;

By Thy mer-its we find fa-vor; Life is giv-en thru Thy name.
O-pened is the gate of heav-en; Peace is made 'twixt man and God.
Ev-er for us in-ter-ced-ing Till in glo-ry we ap-pear.
Help to sing our Sav-iour's mer-its; Help to chant Immanuel's praise! A-MEN.

WE HAVE AN ANCHOR

Priscilla J. Owens

Wm. J. Kirkpatrick

1. Will your an-chor hold in the storms of life, When the
2. It is safe-ly moored, 'twill the storm with-stand, For 'tis
3. It will firm-ly hold in the straits of fear, When the
4. When our eyes be-hold thru the gath-'ring night The

clouds un-fold their wings of strife? When the strong tides lift, and the
well se-cured by the Sav-iour's hand; And the ca-bles, passed from His
breakers have told the reef is near; Though the tem-pest rage and the
cit-y of gold, our har-bor bright, We shall an-chor fast by the

ca-bles strain, Will your an-chor drift, or firm re-main?
heart to mine, Can de-fy the blast, thru strength di-vine.
wild winds blow, Not an an-gry wave shall our bark o'er-flow.
heav'n-ly shore, With the storms all past for-ev-er-more.

REFRAIN

We have an an-chor that keeps the soul Steadfast and sure while the billows roll,

Fastened to the Rock which cannot move, Grounded firm and deep in the Saviour's love.

191 HE IS SO PRECIOUS TO ME

C. H. G.

Chas. H. Gabriel

1. So pre-cious is Je-sus, my Sav-iour, my King, His praise all the
2. He stood at my heart's door 'mid sun shine and rain, And pa-tient-ly
3. I stand on the moun-tain of bless-ing at last, No cloud in the
4. I praise Him be-cause He ap-point-ed a place Where, some day, thru

day long with rap-ture I sing; To Him in my weak-ness for
wait-ed an en-trance to gain; What shame that so long He en-
heav-ens a shad-ow to cast; His smile is up-on me, the
faith in His won-der-ful grace. I know I shall see Him—shall

CHORUS *Faster*

strength I can cling, For He is so pre-cious to me.
treat-ed in vain, For He is so pre-cious to me.   For He is so
val-ley is past, For He is so pre-cious to me.
look on His face, For He is so pre-cious to me.

pre-cious to me, . . . For He is so pre-cious to me; . . . 'Tis
so pre-cious to me,   so pre-cious to me;

rit.

heav-en be-low My Re-deem-er to know, For He is so pre-cious to me.

192 AN EVENING PRAYER

C. M. Battersby
Arr. by C. H. G.

Chas. H. Gabriel

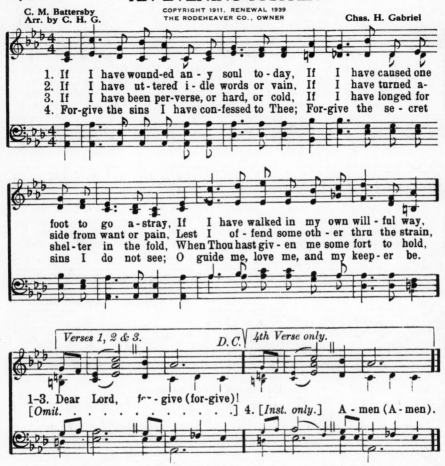

1. If I have wound-ed an - y soul to - day, If I have caused one
2. If I have ut - tered i - dle words or vain, If I have turned a-
3. If I have been per-verse, or hard, or cold, If I have longed for
4. For-give the sins I have con-fessed to Thee; For-give the se - cret

foot to go a - stray, If I have walked in my own will - ful way,
side from want or pain, Lest I of - fend some oth - er thru the strain,
shel - ter in the fold, When Thou hast giv - en me some fort to hold,
sins I do not see; O guide me, love me, and my keep - er be.

Verses 1, 2 & 3.   *D.C.* | *4th Verse only.*

1-3. Dear Lord, for - give (for-give)!
[*Omit* . . . .] 4. [*Inst. only.*] A - men (A - men).

193 PRAYER IS THE SOUL'S SINCERE DESIRE

James Montgomery   LAMBETH C. M.   Anonymous

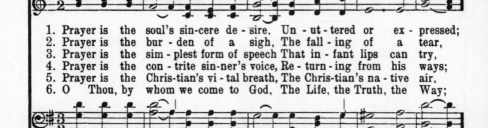

1. Prayer is the soul's sin-cere de - sire, Un - ut - tered or ex - pressed;
2. Prayer is the bur - den of a sigh, The fall - ing of a tear,
3. Prayer is the sim - plest form of speech That in - fant lips can try,
4. Prayer is the con - trite sin-ner's voice, Re - turn - ing from his ways;
5. Prayer is the Chris-tian's vi - tal breath, The Chris-tian's na - tive air,
6. O Thou, by whom we come to God, The Life, the Truth, the Way;

PRAYER IS THE SOUL'S SINCERE DESIRE

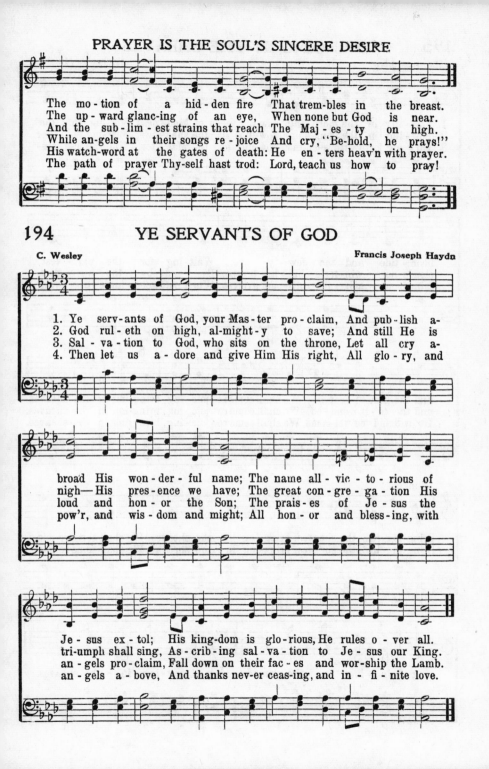

The mo-tion of a hid-den fire That trem-bles in the breast.
The up-ward glanc-ing of an eye, When none but God is near.
And the sub-lim-est strains that reach The Maj-es-ty on high.
While an-gels in their songs re-joice And cry, "Be-hold, he prays!"
His watch-word at the gates of death: He en-ters heav'n with prayer.
The path of prayer Thy-self hast trod: Lord, teach us how to pray!

194   YE SERVANTS OF GOD

C. Wesley

Francis Joseph Haydn

1. Ye serv-ants of God, your Mas-ter pro-claim, And pub-lish a-
2. God rul-eth on high, al-might-y to save; And still He is
3. Sal-va-tion to God, who sits on the throne, Let all cry a-
4. Then let us a-dore and give Him His right, All glo-ry, and

broad His won-der-ful name; The name all-vic-to-rious of
nigh—His pres-ence we have; The great con-gre-ga-tion His
loud and hon-or the Son; The prais-es of Je-sus the
pow'r, and wis-dom and might; All hon-or and bless-ing, with

Je-sus ex-tol; His king-dom is glo-rious, He rules o-ver all.
tri-umph shall sing, As-crib-ing sal-va-tion to Je-sus our King.
an-gels pro-claim, Fall down on their fac-es and wor-ship the Lamb.
an-gels a-bove, And thanks nev-er ceas-ing, and in-fi-nite love.

195 BRINGING IN THE SHEAVES

Knowles Shaw

George A. Minor

1. Sow-ing in the morn-ing, sow-ing seeds of kind-ness, Sow-ing in the
2. Sow-ing in the sun-shine, sow-ing in the shad-ows, Fear-ing nei - ther
3. Go - ing forth with weep-ing, sow-ing for the Mas - ter, Tho' the loss sus-

noon - tide and the dew - y eve; Wait-ing for the har - vest,
clouds nor win-ter's chill-ing breeze; By and by the har - vest,
tained our spir - it oft - en grieves; When our weep-ing's o - ver,

and the time of reap-ing, We shall come re - joic-ing, bring-ing in the sheaves.
and the la - bor end - ed, We shall come re - joic-ing, bring-ing in the sheaves.
He will bid us wel-come, We shall come re - joic-ing, bring-ing in the sheaves.

CHORUS

Bring-ing in the sheaves, bring-ing in the sheaves, We shall come re-joic-
Bring-ing in the sheaves, bring-ing in the sheaves, We shall come re-joic-

1

ing, bring - ing in the sheaves; ing, bring-ing in the sheaves.

2

196 THE EVERLASTING ARMS

A. H. A.   A. H. Ackley

1. Un-der-neath us are the arms e-ter-nal, O what con-fi-dence it
2. Un-der-neath us are the arms e-ter-nal, God sees all the hid-den
3. Un-der-neath us are the arms e-ter-nal, For temp-ta-tion we are
4. Un-der-neath us are the arms e-ter-nal, Naught can sep-a-rate us

gives to know, That the might-y Sov-'reign of cre-a-tion Is sus-
griefs we bear, He knows all a-bout our heav-y bur-dens, And sup-
for-ti-fied, Safe-ly shel-tered in the time of trou-ble, All we
from His love, Life, nor death, nor an-y oth-er crea-ture Shall His

CHORUS

tain-ing us where-e'er we go.
ports us by His lov-ing care. Un-der-neath are the ev-er-last-ing arms,
need we find in Him sup-plied.
nev-er-fail-ing help re-move.

God is might-i-er than all, He will nev-er let us fall, He has promised to de-

fend from all that harms, Un-der-neath are the ev-er-last-ing arms.

197 JESUS, I MY CROSS HAVE TAKEN

Henry F. Lyte   ELLESDIE 8. 7. 8. 7. D.   Johann C. W. A. Mozart

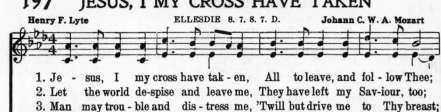

1. Je - sus, I my cross have tak - en, All to leave, and fol - low Thee;
2. Let the world de-spise and leave me, They have left my Sav-iour, too;
3. Man may trou - ble and dis - tress me, 'Twill but drive me to Thy breast;
4. Haste thee on from grace to glo - ry, Armed by faith and winged by pray'r;

Des - ti-tute, despised, for - sak - en, Thou, from hence, my all shalt be:
Hu - man hearts and looks de-ceive me; Thou art not, like man, un - true;
Life with tri - als hard may press me, Heav'n will bring me sweet-er rest.
Heav'n's e-ter - nal day's be - fore thee, God's own hand will keep thee there.

Per - ish ev - 'ry fond am - bi - tion, All I've sought, and hoped, and known;
And, while Thou shalt smile up-on me, God of wis - dom, love, and might,
Oh! 'tis not in grief to harm me, While Thy love is left to me;
Soon shall close thy earth-ly mis-sion, Swift shall pass thy pil - grim days,

Yet how rich is my con-di - tion, God and heav'n are still my own!
Foes may hate, and friends may shun me; Show thy face, and all is bright.
Oh! 'twere not in joy to charm me, Were that joy unmixed with Thee.
Hope shall change to glad fru-i-tion, Faith to sight, and pray'r to praise. A - men.

198 GLORIOUS THINGS OF THEE ARE SPOKEN

John Newton   AUSTRIA 8. 7. 8. 7. D.   Francis J. Haydn

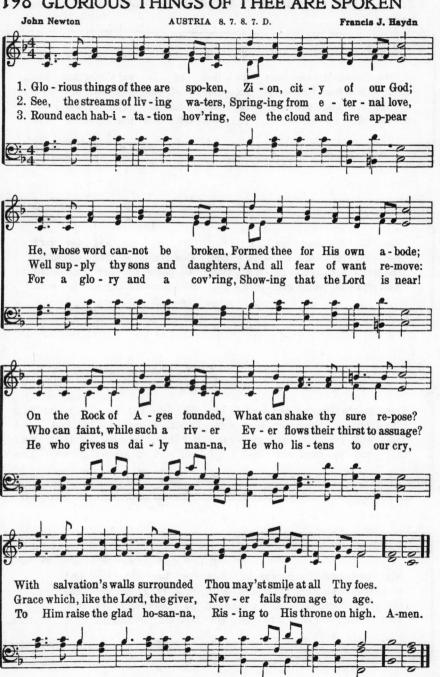

1. Glo - rious things of thee are spo-ken, Zi - on, cit - y of our God;
2. See, the streams of liv - ing wa-ters, Spring-ing from e - ter - nal love,
3. Round each hab-i - ta - tion hov'ring, See the cloud and fire ap-pear

He, whose word can-not be broken, Formed thee for His own a - bode;
Well sup - ply thy sons and daughters, And all fear of want re-move:
For a glo - ry and a cov'ring, Show-ing that the Lord is near!

On the Rock of A - ges founded, What can shake thy sure re-pose?
Who can faint, while such a riv - er Ev - er flows their thirst to assuage?
He who gives us dai - ly man-na, He who lis - tens to our cry,

With salvation's walls surrounded Thou may'st smile at all Thy foes.
Grace which, like the Lord, the giver, Nev - er fails from age to age.
To Him raise the glad ho-san-na, Ris - ing to His throne on high. A-men.

199 THE CHURCH'S ONE FOUNDATION

SAMUEL J. STONE

SAMUEL S. WESLEY

1. The Church-'s one foun - da - tion Is Je - sus Christ her Lord;
2. E - lect from ev - 'ry na - tion, Yet one o'er all the earth,
3. 'Mid toil and trib - u - la - tion, And tu - mult of her war,
4. Yet she on earth hath un - ion With God the Three in One,

She is His new cre - a - tion By wa - ter and the word:
Her char - ter of sal - va - tion, One Lord, one faith, one birth;
She waits the con - sum - ma - tion Of peace for ev - er - more;
And mys - tic sweet com - mun - ion With those whose rest is won:

From heav'n He came and sought her To be His ho - ly bride; With
One ho - ly name she bless - es, Par-takes one ho - ly food, And
Till, with the vis - ion glo - rious, Her long - ing eyes are blest, And
O hap - py ones and ho - ly! Lord, give us grace that we, Like

His own blood He bought her, And for her life He died.
to one hope she press - es, With ev - 'ry grace en - dued.
the great church vic - to - rious Shall be the church at rest.
them, the meek and low - ly, On high may dwell with Thee. A - men.

200 GOD WILL TAKE CARE OF YOU

C. D. Martin

W. S. Martin

1. Be not dis-mayed what-e'er be-tide, God will take care of you;
2. Thru days of toil when heart doth fail, God will take care of you;
3. All you may need He will pro-vide, God will take care of you;
4. No mat-ter what may be the test, God will take care of you;

Be-neath His wings of love a-bide, God will take care of you.
When dan-gers fierce your path as-sail, God will take care of you.
Noth-ing you ask will be de-nied, God will take care of you.
Lean, wea-ry one, up-on His breast, God will take care of you.

CHORUS

God will take care of you, Thru ev-'ry day, O'er all the way;

He will take care of you, God will take care of you. . . . .
take care of you.

201 YOU MAY HAVE THE JOY-BELLS

J. Edward Ruark

Wm. J. Kirkpatrick

1. You may have the joy bells ring-ing in your heart, And a peace that
2. Love of Je-sus in its full-ness you may know, And this love to
3. You will meet with tri-als as you jour-ney home; Grace suf-fi-cient
4. Let your life speak well of Je-sus ev-'ry day; Own His right to

from you nev-er will de-part; Walk the straight and nar-row way,
those a-round you sweet-ly show; Words of kind-ness al-ways say,
He will give to o-ver-come; Tho' un-seen by mor-tal eye,
ev-'ry serv-ice you can pay; Sin-ners you can help to win

Live for Je-sus ev-'ry day, He will keep the joy-bells ringing in your heart.
Deeds of mer-cy do each day, Then He'll keep the joy-bells ringing in your heart.
He is with you ev-er nigh, And He'll keep the joy-bells ringing in your heart.
If your life is pure and clean, If you keep the joy-bells ringing in your heart.

FINE.

CHORUS

D. S.—*He will keep the joy-bells ring-ing in your heart.*

Joy - - - - bells ring-ing in your heart, Joy - - - - bells
Ring-ing in your heart; You may have the joy-bells

D. S.

ringing in your heart; Take the Sav-iour here below With you ev'ry where you go;

FACE TO FACE

Mrs. Frank A. Breck
Moderato.

Grant Colfax Tullar

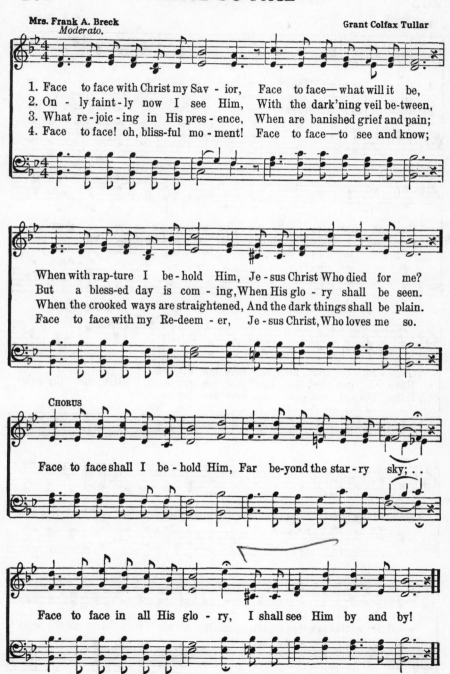

1. Face to face with Christ my Sav - ior, Face to face—what will it be,
2. On - ly faint-ly now I see Him, With the dark'ning veil be-tween,
3. What re-joic-ing in His pres-ence, When are banished grief and pain;
4. Face to face! oh, bliss-ful mo-ment! Face to face—to see and know;

When with rap-ture I be-hold Him, Je - sus Christ Who died for me?
But a bless-ed day is com - ing, When His glo - ry shall be seen.
When the crooked ways are straightened, And the dark things shall be plain.
Face to face with my Re-deem - er, Je - sus Christ, Who loves me so.

CHORUS

Face to face shall I be - hold Him, Far be-yond the star - ry sky; . .

Face to face in all His glo - ry, I shall see Him by and by!

GIVE ME THY HEART

Eliza E. Hewitt

Annie F. Bourne

1. "Give me thy heart," says the Fa - ther a - bove, No gift so pre - cious to
2. "Give me thy heart," says the Sav - ior of men, Call - ing in mer - cy a-
3. "Give me thy heart," says the Spir - it di - vine, "All that thou hast, to my

Him as our love, Soft - ly He whis-pers wher - ev - er thou art,
gain and a - gain; "Turn now from sin, and from e - vil de - part,
keep - ing re - sign; Grace more a - bound-ing is mine to im - part,

CHORUS

"Grate - ful - ly trust me, and give me thy heart."
Have I not died for thee? give me thy heart." "Give me thy heart,
Make full sur - ren - der and give me thy heart."

Give me thy heart," Hear the soft whisper, wher-ev - er thou art; From this dark

rit.

world He would draw thee a-part, Speak-ing so ten-der-ly, "Give me thy heart."

204 GROWING DEARER EACH DAY

C. H. G.

Chas. H. Gabriel

1. How sweet is the love of my Sav-iour! 'Tis bound-less and deep as the sea;
2. I know He is ev-er be-side me! E-ter-ni-ty on-ly will prove
3. Wher-ev-er He leads I will fol-low, Thru sor-row, or shad-ow, or sun;
4. Some day face to face I shall see Him, And oh, what a joy it will be

And best of it all, it is dai-ly Grow-ing sweeter and sweeter to me.
The height and the depth of His mercy, And the breadth of His in-fi-nite love.
And though I be tried in the fur-nace, I can say, "Lord, Thy will be it done."
To know that His love, now so precious, Will for-ev-er grow sweeter to me!

CHORUS

Sweet - - er and sweet-er to me, ... Dear - - er and
Sweet-er to me, grow - ing sweet-er to me, Dear-er each day,

dear - er each day; . . . . Oh, won - - der-ful love of my
grow - ing dear - er each day; Oh, won-der-ful love, love of my

Sav - iour, Grow - ing dear - - - er each step of my way!
Sav - iour, Grow - ing dear - er and dear - er each step of my way!

205   BACK OF THE CLOUDS

C. R. F.   Carolyn R. Freeman

DUET. Soprano and Alto

1. Nev - er fear tho' shad-ows dark a-round your path may fall; Do not let your
2. Win - ter long is o - ver and the spring has gone her way, Oft - en have the
3. Keep the light of hope e - ter - nal dwell-ing in your heart, Rest up -on the

heart be trou - - bled; From His throne in heav - en, God is
storm-clouds gath - - ered, But the rain has on - ly made the
Fa - ther's prom - - ise, And you'll find that care and trou - ble

watch-ing one and all, .. He will ev - er care for you. . . . .
blos-soms look more gay, .. Giv - en earth a bright - er hue. . . . .
quick-ly will de - part, .. Heaven's peace will en - ter in.. . . .

care for you,

CHORUS *All, in two parts*

Back of the clouds the sun is al-ways shin-ing, Aft - er the

(Simile)

Four Parts

storms your skies will all be blue; God has pre - pared a

pre-pared

BACK OF THE CLOUDS

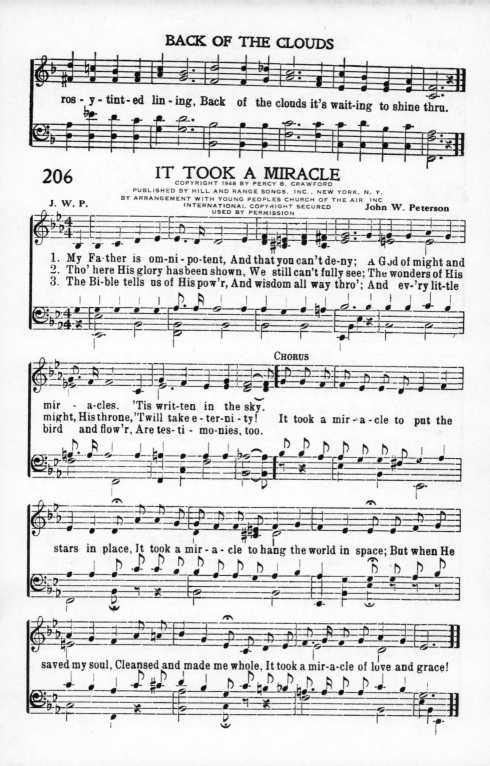

ros-y-tint-ed lin-ing, Back of the clouds it's wait-ing to shine thru.

206 IT TOOK A MIRACLE

J. W. P.   John W. Peterson

1. My Fa-ther is om-ni-po-tent, And that you can't de-ny; A God of might and
2. Tho' here His glory has been shown, We still can't fully see; The wonders of His
3. The Bi-ble tells us of His pow'r, And wisdom all way thro'; And ev-'ry lit-tle

Chorus

mir - a-cles. 'Tis writ-ten in the sky.
might, His throne, 'Twill take e-ter-ni-ty! It took a mir-a-cle to put the
bird and flow'r, Are tes-ti-mo-nies, too.

stars in place, It took a mir-a-cle to hang the world in space; But when He

saved my soul, Cleansed and made me whole, It took a mir-a-cle of love and grace!

207 OH, IT IS WONDERFUL

C. H. G. Chas. H. Gabriel

1. I stand all amazed at the love Je-sus of-fers me, Confused at the
2. I mar-vel that He would descend from His throne divine, To res-cue a
3. I think of his hands pierced and bleeding to pay the debt! Such mercy, such

grace that so ful-ly He proffers me; I tremble to know that for me He was
soul so re-bel-lious and proud as mine; That He should extend His great love unto
love and de-vo-tion can I forget? No, no! I will praise and a-dore at the

rit.

cru-ci-fied—That for me, a sin-ner, He suf-fered, He bled, and died.
such as I; Suf-fi-cient to own, to re-deem, and to jus-ti-fy.
mer-cy-seat, Un-til at the glo-ri-fied throne I kneel at His feet.

REFRAIN.

Oh, it is won-der-ful that He should care for me! E-nough to
won-der-ful!

die for me! Oh, it is won-der-ful, won-der-ful to me!
won-der-ful!

UNDER HIS WINGS

W. O. CUSHING

IRA D. SANKEY

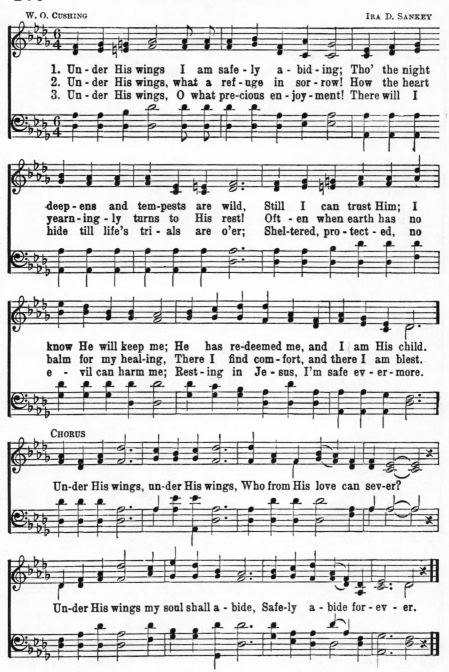

1. Un-der His wings I am safe-ly a-bid-ing; Tho' the night
2. Un-der His wings, what a ref-uge in sor-row! How the heart
3. Un-der His wings, O what pre-cious en-joy-ment! There will I

deep-ens and tem-pests are wild, Still I can trust Him; I
yearn-ing-ly turns to His rest! Oft-en when earth has no
hide till life's tri-als are o'er; Shel-tered, pro-tect-ed, no

know He will keep me; He has re-deemed me, and I am His child.
balm for my heal-ing, There I find com-fort, and there I am blest.
e-vil can harm me; Rest-ing in Je-sus, I'm safe ev-er-more.

CHORUS

Un-der His wings, un-der His wings, Who from His love can sev-er?

Un-der His wings my soul shall a-bide, Safe-ly a-bide for-ev-er.

209 A NEW NAME IN GLORY

C. A. M.

C. Austin Miles

1. I was once a sin-ner, but I came Par-don to re-ceive from my
2. I was humbly kneeling at the cross, Fearing naught but God's an-gry
3. In the Book 'tis written "Saved by Grace," O the joy that came to my

Lord: This was free-ly giv-en, and I found That He al-ways kept His
frown; When the heavens opened and I saw That my name was writ-ten
soul! Now I am for-giv-en and I know By the blood I am made

word (kept His word).
down (writ-ten down). There's a new name writ-ten down in glo-ry,
whole (am made whole).

And it's mine, O yes, it's mine! And the white-robed angels sing the
And it's mine, yes, it's mine!

CHORUS

sto-ry, "A sin-ner has come home." For there's a
has come home.

A NEW NAME IN GLORY

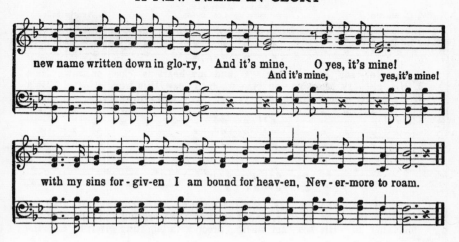

new name written down in glo-ry, And it's mine, O yes, it's mine!
And it's mine, yes, it's mine!

with my sins for-giv-en I am bound for heav-en, Nev-er-more to roam.

210 HEAVENLY SUNSHINE

Dedicated to Old Fashioned Revival Hour

ARRANGEMENT COPYRIGHT, 1942, BY CHARLES E. FULLER

Arr. by C. E. F.   Arr. by Charles E. Fuller

Heav-en-ly sun-shine, heav-en-ly sun-shine, Flood-ing my

soul with glo-ry di-vine; Heav-en-ly sun-shine, heav-en-ly

sun-shine, Hal-le-lu-jah! Je-sus is mine!

211 STILL SWEETER EVERY DAY

W. C. Martin   C. Austin Miles

1. To Je - sus ev - 'ry day I find my heart is clos - er drawn; He's
2. His glo - ry broke up - on me when I saw Him from a - far: He's
3. My heart is some-times heav - y, but He comes with sweet re - lief; He

fair - er than the glo - ry of the gold and pur - ple dawn; He's all my
fair - er than the lil - y, bright - er than the morn-ing star; He fills and
folds me to His bos - om when I droop with blighting grief; I love the

fan - cy pic - tures in its fair-est dreams, and more; Each day He grows still
sat - is - fies my long-ing spir - it o'er and o'er; Each day He grows still
Christ who all my bur - dens in His bod - y bore; Each day He grows still

CHORUS

sweet-er than He was the day be-fore. The half. . . . . can not be
sweet-er than He was the day be-fore.
sweet-er than He was the day be-fore. The half can not be fan - cied on this

fan - cied   this side. . . . . the gold-en shore;   O
side the gold-en shore, The half can not be fan-cied on this side the golden shore; O

STILL SWEETER EVERY DAY

there........ He'll be still sweet-er than He ev-er was be-fore.
there he'll be still sweeter than he ev-er was be-fore, than he

212 HOLD FAST TO JESUS

A. H. A.   A. H. Ackley

1. Hold fast to Je - sus, Cling to Him al - way. He be-
2. Hold fast to Je - sus, He a - lone can save, Not some
3. Hold fast to Je - sus Till you reach the goal, If you
4. Hold fast to Je - sus, O to Him be true, And re-

lieves in you, you must trust Him, too, If you win the day.
law or creed, or some no - ble deed, But the life He gave.
cher - ish doubt, till your faith gives out, You will lose your soul.
mem - ber, friend, to the ver - y end He will hold fast you.

CHORUS

Hold fast to Je - sus; Hold fast to Je - sus, With a

might - y grip that will not slip, And He will hold fast to you.

213 JESUS IS ALL THE WORLD TO ME

W. L. T.

Will L. Thompson

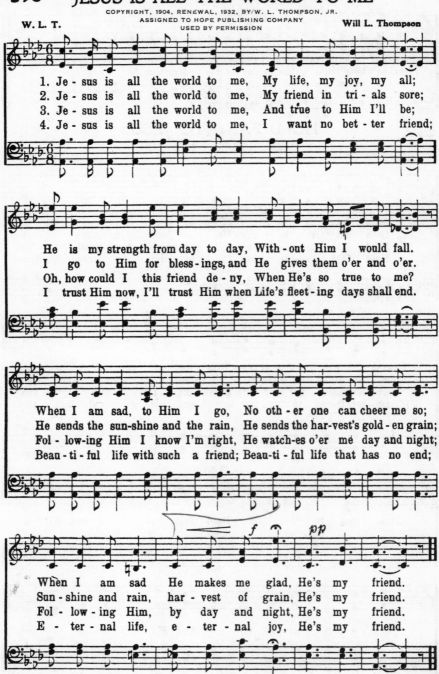

1. Je-sus is all the world to me, My life, my joy, my all;
2. Je-sus is all the world to me, My friend in tri-als sore;
3. Je-sus is all the world to me, And true to Him I'll be;
4. Je-sus is all the world to me, I want no bet-ter friend;

He is my strength from day to day, With-out Him I would fall.
I go to Him for bless-ings, and He gives them o'er and o'er.
Oh, how could I this friend de-ny, When He's so true to me?
I trust Him now, I'll trust Him when Life's fleet-ing days shall end.

When I am sad, to Him I go, No oth-er one can cheer me so;
He sends the sun-shine and the rain, He sends the har-vest's gold-en grain;
Fol-low-ing Him I know I'm right, He watch-es o'er me day and night;
Beau-ti-ful life with such a friend; Beau-ti-ful life that has no end;

f *pp*

When I am sad He makes me glad, He's my friend.
Sun-shine and rain, har-vest of grain, He's my friend.
Fol-low-ing Him, by day and night, He's my friend.
E-ter-nal life, e-ter-nal joy, He's my friend.

214 DEARER THAN ALL

COPYRIGHT, 1915, RENEWAL, 1943
THE RODEHEAVER CO. OWNER

A. H. A

Alfred H. Ackley

1. Ye who the love of a moth-er have known, There is a love sweet-er
2. Je-sus en-treats you in Him to con-fide, Make Him your constant com-
3. Heav-en, with all of its beau-ty so rare, With my Re-deem-er can

far you may own, Love all suf-fi-cient for sin to a-tone;
pan-ion and guide; He can do more than the whole world be-side;
nev-er com-pare; He is the glo-ry tran-scend-ent up there;

Chorus

Je-sus is dear-er than all. Dear-er than all, yes, dear-er than all,

He is my King, be-fore Him I fall; No friend like Je-sus my

soul can en-thrall, Je-sus is dear-er, far dear-er than all.

215 FAITH IS THE VICTORY

John H. Yates

Ira D. Sankey

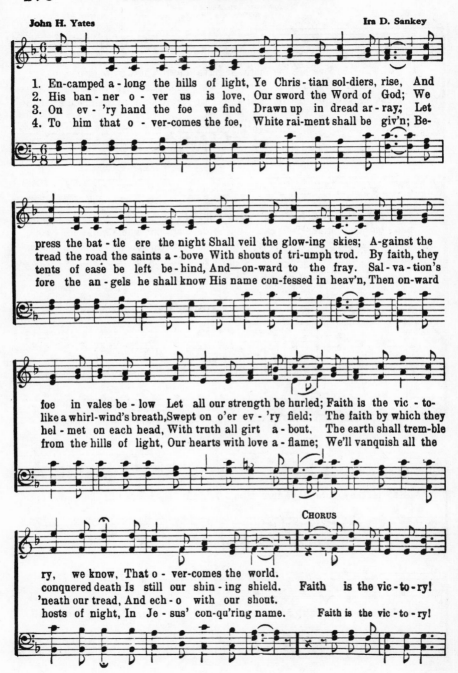

1. En-camped a-long the hills of light, Ye Chris-tian sol-diers, rise, And
2. His ban-ner o-ver us is love, Our sword the Word of God; We
3. On ev-'ry hand the foe we find Drawn up in dread ar-ray; Let
4. To him that o-ver-comes the foe, White rai-ment shall be giv'n; Be-

press the bat-tle ere the night Shall veil the glow-ing skies; A-gainst the
tread the road the saints a-bove With shouts of tri-umph trod. By faith, they
tents of ease be left be-hind, And—on-ward to the fray. Sal-va-tion's
fore the an-gels he shall know His name con-fessed in heav'n, Then on-ward

foe in vales be-low Let all our strength be hurled; Faith is the vic-to-
like a whirl-wind's breath, Swept on o'er ev-'ry field; The faith by which they
hel-met on each head, With truth all girt a-bout, The earth shall trem-ble
from the hills of light, Our hearts with love a-flame; We'll vanquish all the

CHORUS

ry, we know, That o-ver-comes the world.
conquered death Is still our shin-ing shield. Faith is the vic-to-ry!
'neath our tread, And ech-o with our shout.
hosts of night, In Je-sus' con-qu'ring name. Faith is the vic-to-ry!

FAITH IS THE VICTORY

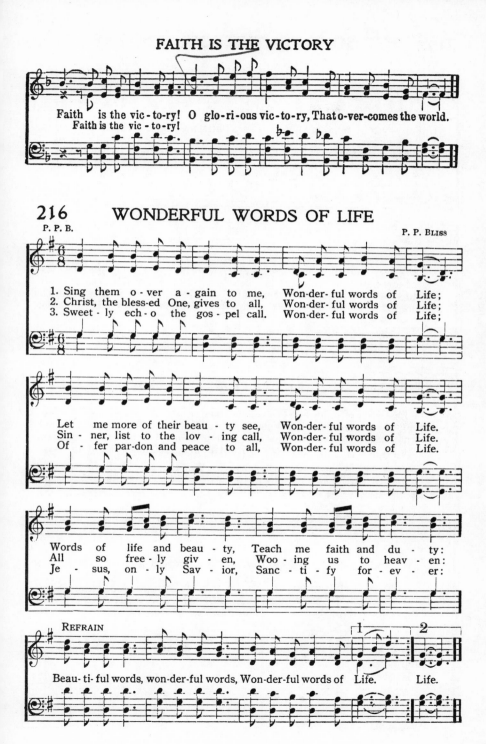

Faith is the vic-to-ry! O glo-ri-ous vic-to-ry, That o-ver-comes the world.
Faith is the vic - to - ry!

216   WONDERFUL WORDS OF LIFE

P. P. B.

P. P. BLISS

1. Sing them o - ver a - gain to me, Won-der- ful words of Life;
2. Christ, the bless-ed One, gives to all, Won-der- ful words of Life;
3. Sweet - ly ech - o the gos - pel call. Won-der- ful words of Life;

Let me more of their beau - ty see, Won-der- ful words of Life.
Sin - ner, list to the lov - ing call, Won-der- ful words of Life.
Of - fer par-don and peace to all, Won-der- ful words of Life.

Words of life and beau - ty, Teach me faith and du - ty:
All so free - ly giv - en, Woo - ing us to heav - en:
Je - sus, on - ly Sav - ior, Sanc - ti - fy for - ev - er:

REFRAIN

Beau- ti- ful words, won-der-ful words, Won-der-ful words of Life. Life.

217 THE SONG OF THE SOUL SET FREE

Oswald J. Smith   A. H. Ackley

1. Fair - est of ten thousand, Is Je-sus Christ my Saviour, The Li - ly of the
2. Once my heart was burdened, But now I am for -giv- en, And with a song of
3. When He came to save me, He set the joy bells ring-ing And now I'm ev-er
5. An - gels can-not sing it, This song of joy and freedom, For mor-tals only

Val - ley, The bright and Morning Star, ... He is all my glo - ry And
glad - ness, I'm on my way to heav'n; . . Christ is my Re-deem-er, My
sing - ing, For Christ has ransomed me; . . . . Once I lived in dark-ness The
know it, The ran-somed and the free: . . . . Slaves were they in bondage, And

in this heart of mine, For-ev-er-more I'm sing-ing, A song of love di-vine.
Song of songs is He, My Sav-iour, Lord and Master, To Him my praise shall be.
light I could not see. But now I sing His prais-es, For He has set me free.
deep-est mis - er - y, But now they sing tri-umphant, Their song of lib-er-ty.

CHORUS

'Tis the song of the soul set free, (set free,) And its mel - o - dy is ring-ing;

'Tis the song of the soul set free, (set free,) Joy and peace to me it's bringing,

THE SONG OF THE SOUL SET FREE

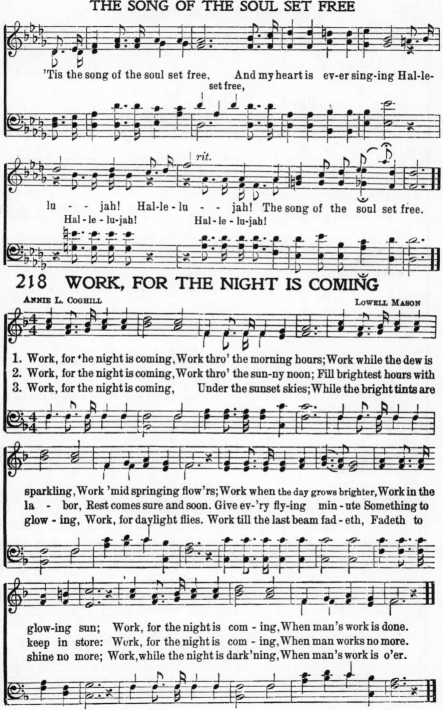

'Tis the song of the soul set free, And my heart is ev-er sing-ing Hal-le-
set free,

lu - - jah! Hal-le-lu - - jah! The song of the soul set free.
Hal - le - lu-jah!   Hal - le - lu-jah!

218 WORK, FOR THE NIGHT IS COMING

ANNIE L. COGHILL

LOWELL MASON

1. Work, for the night is coming, Work thro' the morning hours; Work while the dew is
2. Work, for the night is coming, Work thro' the sun-ny noon; Fill brightest hours with
3. Work, for the night is coming, Under the sunset skies; While the bright tints are

sparkling, Work 'mid springing flow'rs; Work when the day grows brighter, Work in the
la - bor, Rest comes sure and soon. Give ev-'ry fly-ing min-ute Something to
glow - ing, Work, for daylight flies. Work till the last beam fad - eth, Fadeth to

glow-ing sun;   Work, for the night is com - ing, When man's work is done.
keep in store: Work, for the night is com - ing, When man works no more.
shine no more; Work, while the night is dark'ning, When man's work is o'er.

219 HE HIDETH MY SOUL

Fanny J. Crosby   Wm. J. Kirkpatrick

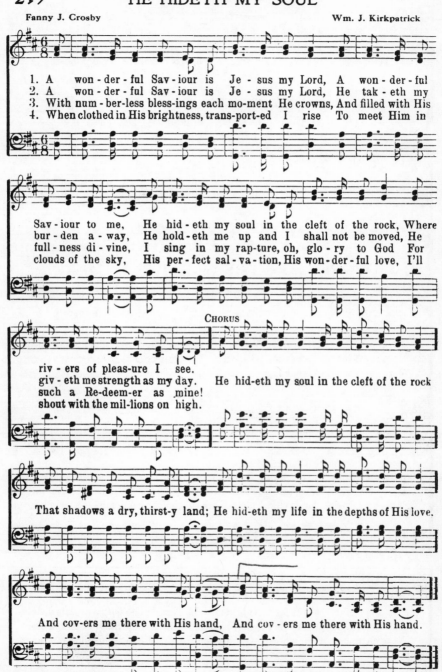

1. A won-der-ful Sav-iour is Je-sus my Lord, A won-der-ful
2. A won-der-ful Sav-iour is Je-sus my Lord, He tak-eth my
3. With num-ber-less bless-ings each mo-ment He crowns, And filled with His
4. When clothed in His brightness, trans-port-ed I rise To meet Him in

Sav-iour to me, He hid-eth my soul in the cleft of the rock, Where
bur-den a-way, He hold-eth me up and I shall not be moved, He
full-ness di-vine, I sing in my rap-ture, oh, glo-ry to God For
clouds of the sky, His per-fect sal-va-tion, His won-der-ful love, I'll

CHORUS

riv-ers of pleas-ure I see.
giv-eth me strength as my day.   He hid-eth my soul in the cleft of the rock
such a Re-deem-er as mine!
shout with the mil-lions on high.

That shadows a dry, thirst-y land; He hid-eth my life in the depths of His love.

And cov-ers me there with His hand, And cov-ers me there with His hand.

220 JESUS IS ALWAYS THERE

B. M. L.

Bertha Mae Lillenas

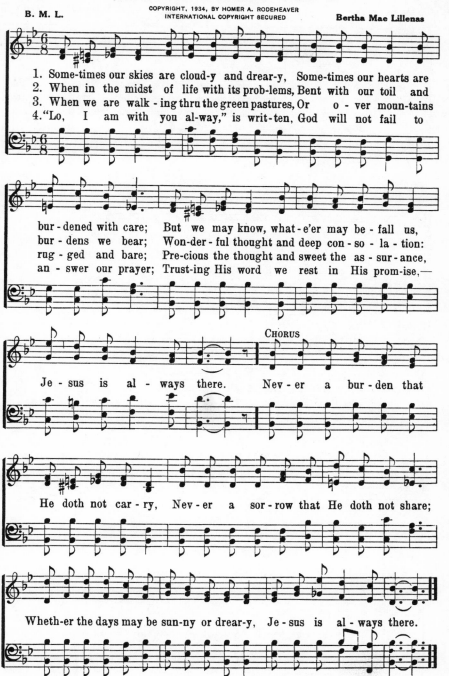

1. Some-times our skies are cloud-y and drear-y, Some-times our hearts are
2. When in the midst of life with its prob-lems, Bent with our toil and
3. When we are walk-ing thru the green pastures, Or o-ver moun-tains
4. "Lo, I am with you al-way," is writ-ten, God will not fail to

bur-dened with care; But we may know, what-e'er may be-fall us,
bur-dens we bear; Won-der-ful thought and deep con-so-la-tion:
rug-ged and bare; Pre-cious the thought and sweet the as-sur-ance,
an-swer our prayer; Trust-ing His word we rest in His prom-ise,—

CHORUS

Je-sus is al-ways there. Nev-er a bur-den that
He doth not car-ry, Nev-er a sor-row that He doth not share;
Wheth-er the days may be sun-ny or drear-y, Je-sus is al-ways there.

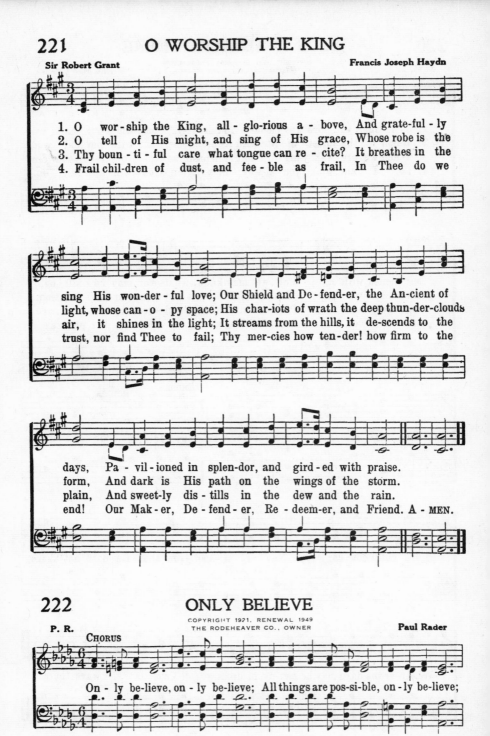

221 O WORSHIP THE KING

Sir Robert Grant

Francis Joseph Haydn

1. O wor-ship the King, all - glo-rious a - bove, And grate-ful - ly
2. O tell of His might, and sing of His grace, Whose robe is the
3. Thy boun - ti - ful care what tongue can re - cite? It breathes in the
4. Frail chil-dren of dust, and fee - ble as frail, In Thee do we

sing His won-der - ful love; Our Shield and De-fend-er, the An-cient of
light, whose can - o - py space; His char-iots of wrath the deep thun-der-clouds
air, it shines in the light; It streams from the hills, it de-scends to the
trust, nor find Thee to fail; Thy mer-cies how ten-der! how firm to the

days, Pa - vil - ioned in splen-dor, and gird - ed with praise.
form, And dark is His path on the wings of the storm.
plain, And sweet-ly dis - tills in the dew and the rain.
end! Our Mak - er, De - fend - er, Re - deem-er, and Friend. A - MEN.

222 ONLY BELIEVE

P. R.

Paul Rader

Chorus

On - ly be-lieve, on - ly be-lieve; All things are pos-si-ble, on - ly be-lieve;

ONLY BELIEVE

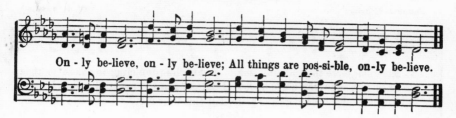

On - ly be-lieve, on - ly be-lieve; All things are pos-si-ble, on-ly be-lieve.

223 LET THE LOWER LIGHTS BE BURNING

P. P. B.

P. P. Bliss

1. Bright-ly beams our Fa-ther's mer-cy From His lighthouse ev - er - more;
2. Dark the night of sin has set-tled, Loud the an - gry bil-lows roar;
3. Trim your fee - ble lamp, my brother! Some poor sea - man, tempest-tossed,

But to us He gives the keep-ing Of the lights a - long the shore.
Ea - ger eyes are watching, long-ing, For the lights a - long the shore.
Try - ing now to make the har-bor, In the dark-ness may be lost.

CHORUS

Let the low - er lights be burning! Send a gleam a-cross the wave!

Some poor fainting, struggling sea-man You may res - cue, you may save.

224 SAVIOUR, MORE THAN LIFE

Fanny J. Crosby

W. H. Doane

1. Sav - iour, more than life to me. I am cling-ing, cling-ing close to thee;
2. Thru this changing world be-low, Lead me gen-tly, gen-tly as I go;
3. Let me love Thee more and more, Till this fleet-ing, fleet-ing life is o'er,

Let Thy pre-cious blood ap-plied; Keep me ev - er. ev - er near Thy side.
Trust-ing Thee, I can not stray, I can nev - er, nev - er lose my way.
Till my soul is lost in love, In a bright-er, bright-er world above.

D. S.—*May Thy ten - der love to me Bind me clos - er, clos - er, Lord, to Thee.*

REFRAIN

Ev - 'ry day, ev - 'ry hour, Let me feel Thy cleansing pow'r;
Ev - 'ry day and hour, Ev - 'ry day and hour,

225 MY SOUL, BE ON THY GUARD

George Heath

LABAN S. M.

Lowell Mason

1. My soul, be on thy guard; Ten thous-and foes a - rise;
2. Oh! watch, and fight, and pray; The bat - tle ne'er give o'er;
3. Ne'er think the vic - t'ry won, Nor lay thine ar - mor down;
4. Fight on, my soul, till death Shall bring thee to thy God;

MY SOUL, BE ON THY GUARD

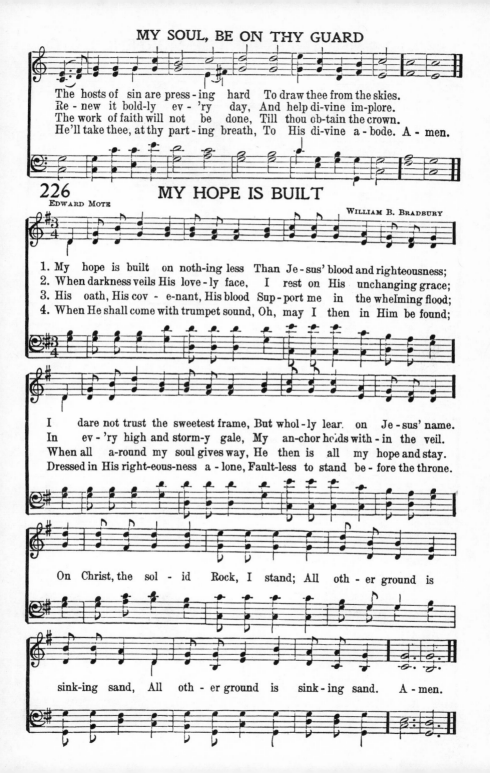

The hosts of sin are press-ing hard To draw thee from the skies.
Re - new it bold-ly ev - 'ry day, And help di-vine im-plore.
The work of faith will not be done, Till thou ob-tain the crown.
He'll take thee, at thy part-ing breath, To His di-vine a - bode. A - men.

226 MY HOPE IS BUILT

Edward Mote

William B. Bradbury

1. My hope is built on noth-ing less Than Je - sus' blood and righteousness;
2. When darkness veils His love - ly face, I rest on His unchanging grace;
3. His oath, His cov - e-nant, His blood Sup-port me in the whelming flood;
4. When He shall come with trumpet sound, Oh, may I then in Him be found;

I dare not trust the sweetest frame, But whol - ly lean on Je - sus' name.
In ev - 'ry high and storm-y gale, My an-chor holds with - in the veil.
When all a-round my soul gives way, He then is all my hope and stay.
Dressed in His right-eous-ness a - lone, Fault-less to stand be - fore the throne.

On Christ, the sol - id Rock, I stand; All oth - er ground is

sink-ing sand, All oth - er ground is sink-ing sand. A - men.

227 WE PRAISE THEE FOR THE MORNING LIGHT

A. H. Ackley

B. D. Ackley

1. We praise Thee for the morn-ing light, The glo-ry of this day,
2. For grant-ing us Thy gifts to share, Thy knowledge and Thy love,
3. O may Thy Spir-it make us strong, And loy-al to the best,

And bless-ed be Thy ho-ly Name, Who or-ders all our way.
Thy work, Thy joy, we thank Thee, Lord, And worth-y we would prove.
Like Je-sus, hum-ble, brave and true, And faith-ful in each test.

228 THINE IS THE KINGDOM

A. H. A.

A. H. Ackley

1. Thine is the King-dom of good-ness and mer-cy, Thou art the
2. Thine is the Pow'r, ev-er-last-ing, e-ter-nal, Nor can Thy
3. Thine is the Glo-ry, tran-scend-ent, su-per-nal, Thy love a-

King we ac-knowl-edge and a-dore:
gran-deur our fee-ble minds ex-plore: Thine is the King-dom,
lone shall this wan-d'ring world re-store:

Thine the Pow'r and Glo-ry, Praise be to Thee, O God for-ev-er-more.

229 HE IS MINE

I. H. M.

I. H. Meredith

Je - sus, Je - sus, Ev - er bless-ed Sav-iour, Son of God di - vine.
Bless-ed Je-sus,

Je - sus, Je - sus, And this bless - ed Sav - iour, He is mine.
Je-sus, Je-sus, bless-ed Je-sus,

230 LET THE BEAUTY OF JESUS

*Affectionately dedicated to my friend. Gipsy Smith, as a token of appreciation
for his loyal friendship thru many years.* —B. D. A.

Albert Osborn

B. D. Ackley

Let the beau-ty of Je-sus be seen in me (in me), All His

won-der-ful pas-sion and pu - ri - ty; O Thou Spir-it di-vine, All my

rall.

na-ture re-fine Till the beau-ty of Je-sus my Sav-iour be seen in me.

231 FAIR SON OF GOD, THY SHINING LIGHT

A. H. Ackley

B. D. Ackley

1. Fair Son of God, Thy shin-ing light Il-lu-mines this new day,
2. With char-i-ty toward all man-kind, Helps us to walk in peace,
3. De-fend our souls in per-il's hour, In trou-bles, com-fort give,

Shine in our hearts till all is bright, And shad-ows flee a-way.
From sel-fish pride and an-ger's wave, Grant us a sure re-lease.
A-bound-ing, Lord, in all good works, Help us this day to live.

232 DEEPER, LORD, STILL DEEPER

Virgil P. Brock

Blanche Kerr Brock

1. Deep-er, Lord, still deep-er, help me go (still deep-er go), More of Thine own
2. Deep-er, Lord, still deep-er, help me go (still deep-er go), That true serv-ice

like-ness would I know(Thy like-ness know);Cru-ci-fied with Thee,
from my life may flow (true serv-ice flow); Read-y thus to share,

From all self set free, Deep-er, Lord, still deeper, help me go.
Mak-ing life a prayer; Deep-er, Lord, still deeper, help me go. A-MEN.

233 JESUS, MY RIGHTEOUSNESS

A. H. A.

A. H. Ackley

Joyously and in moderate time

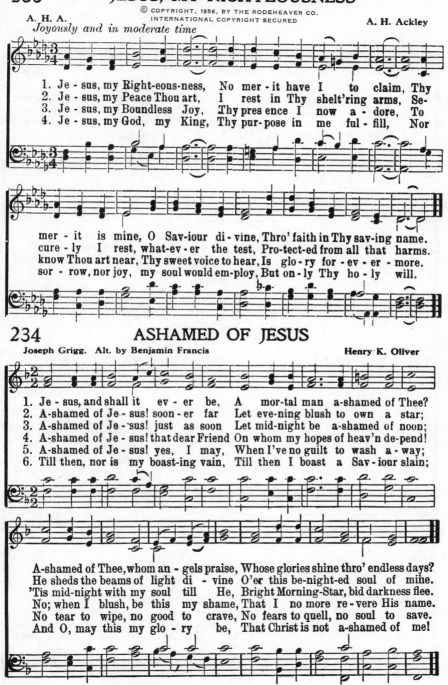

1. Je - sus, my Right-eous-ness, No mer - it have I to claim, Thy
2. Je - sus, my Peace Thou art, I rest in Thy shelt'ring arms, Se -
3. Je - sus, my Boundless Joy, Thy pres ence I now a - dore, To
4. Je - sus, my God, my King, Thy pur - pose in me ful - fill, Nor

mer - it is mine, O Sav-iour di - vine, Thro' faith in Thy sav-ing name.
cure - ly I rest, what-ev - er the test, Pro-tect-ed from all that harms.
know Thou art near, Thy sweet voice to hear, Is glo - ry for - ev - er - more.
sor - row, nor joy, my soul would em-ploy, But on - ly Thy ho - ly will.

234 ASHAMED OF JESUS

Joseph Grigg. Alt. by Benjamin Francis

Henry K. Oliver

1. Je - sus, and shall it ev - er be, A mor-tal man a-shamed of Thee?
2. A-shamed of Je - sus! soon-er far Let eve-ning blush to own a star;
3. A-shamed of Je - sus! just as soon Let mid-night be a-shamed of noon;
4. A-shamed of Je - sus! that dear Friend On whom my hopes of heav'n de-pend!
5. A-shamed of Je - sus! yes, I may, When I've no guilt to wash a - way;
6. Till then, nor is my boast-ing vain, Till then I boast a Sav - iour slain;

A-shamed of Thee, whom an - gels praise, Whose glories shine thro' endless days?
He sheds the beams of light di - vine O'er this be-night-ed soul of mine.
'Tis mid-night with my soul till He, Bright Morning-Star, bid darkness flee.
No; when I blush, be this my shame, That I no more re - vere His name.
No tear to wipe, no good to crave, No fears to quell, no soul to save.
And O, may this my glo - ry be, That Christ is not a-shamed of me!

235 LIFT UP THY COUNTENANCE ON US

A. H. Ackley

B. D. Ackley

1. Lift up Thy coun-ten-ance on us, Rule in our hearts with peace,
2. Keep us in Thine om-nis-cient care, From sin and shame set free,
3. In ho-ly love so let us dwell, What-ev-er life may bring;
4. Give us the grace of self-de-nial, That we our cross may take

Be Thou our strength, our song this day, Un-til its light shall cease.
Put Thou a seal up-on our lips, And may we think of Thee.
What-ev-er comes of weal or woe, Teach us Thy praise to sing.
And fol-low in the steps of Christ, Who died for oth-ers' sake.

236 WE BLESS THEE FOR THIS HOLY DAY

A. H. Ackley

B. D. Ackley

1. We bless Thee for this ho-ly day, From world-ly toil and care,
2. En-a-ble us to wor-ship Thee, And for the com-ing week
3. May sin-ners hear and heed Thy Word, Per-fect Thy saints in Thee,
4. Now may Thy prom-ise be ful-filled, That where Thy peo-ple meet

Grant us, O Lord, a-bid-ing peace, In this Thy house of prayer.
Pre-pare us, may we here re-ceive The bless-ing that we seek.
Fill us with faith and ho-ly zeal, And keep our spir-its free.
There Thou wilt be, and may we rest Se-rene-ly at Thy feet.

237 GOD WALKS WITH ME

Rollin Pease

B. D. Ackley

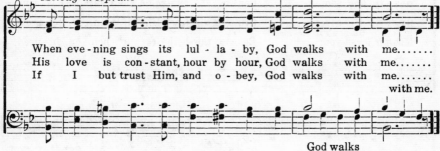

1. When morning wings a - cross the sky, When noontide blaz-es warm and high,
2. I see His pur-pose in the flow'r, The thun-der tells me of His pow'r,
3. In ev - ery com-mon sim-ple day His hand is nev - er far a - way,

Melody in tenor

Melody in soprano

When eve - ning sings its lul - la - by, God walks with me.......
His love is con - stant, hour by hour, God walks with me.......
If I but trust Him, and o - bey, God walks with me.......

with me.

God walks

238 O CHRIST THE GLORY OF THE CHURCH

A. H. Ackley

B. D. Ackley

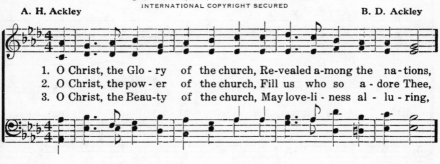

1. O Christ, the Glo - ry of the church, Re-vealed a-mong the na - tions,
2. O Christ, the pow - er of the church, Fill us who so a - dore Thee,
3. O Christ, the Beau - ty of the church, May love-li - ness al - lu - ring,

May we pre-serve with stead-fast faith, Thy love in all re - la - tions.
With Thy great pow'r that we may walk In low - li - ness be - fore Thee.
Re - flect Thy pres-ence in our hearts, The love-li - ness en - dur - ing.

239 MAKE ME A BLESSING

(To the Moody Memorial Church Choir)

Ira B. Wilson

Geo. S. Schuler

Slowly

1. Out in the high-ways and by-ways of life, Man-y are
2. Tell the sweet sto-ry of Christ and His love, Tell of His
3. Give as 'twas giv-en to you in your need, Love as the

wea-ry and sad; .... Car-ry the sun-shine where darkness is rife,
are wea-ry and sad;
pow'r to for-give; .... Oth-ers will trust Him if on-ly you prove
His pow'r to for-give;
Mas-ter loved you; .... Be to the help-less a help-er in-deed,
the Mas-ter loved you;

rit.

CHORUS *Men or Unison*

Mak-ing the sor-row-ing glad.... Make me a bless-ing,
True, ev-'ry mo-ment you live. ...
Un-to your mis-sion be true. ...

Women

Make me a bless-ing, Out of my life .... may Je-
Out of my life
Men

rit.

Unison

Women

sus shine; ... Make me a bless-ing, O Sav-ior,

MAKE ME A BLESSING

I pray, ... Make me a bless-ing to some one to-day.
I pray Thee, my Sav - ior.

Tenors

240 NEARER, STILL NEARER

C. H. M.

Mrs. C. H. Morris

1. Nearer, still nearer, close to Thy heart, Draw me, my Sav-ior, so precious Thou
2. Nearer, still nearer, noth-ing I bring, Naught as an of-f'ring to Je-sus my
3. Nearer, still nearer, Lord, to be Thine, Sin, with its fol-lies, I glad-ly re-
4. Nearer, still nearer, while life shall last, Till safe in glo-ry my an-chor is

art; Fold me, O fold me close to Thy breast, Shel-ter me safe in that
King; On-ly my sin-ful, now contrite heart, Grant me the cleansing Thy
sign; All of its pleasures, pomp and its pride, Give me but Je-sus, my
cast; Thro' endless a-ges, ev-er to be, Near-er, my Sav-ior, still

"Ha-ven of Rest," Shel-ter me safe in that "Ha-ven of Rest."
blood doth im-part, Grant me the cleansing Thy blood doth im-part.
Lord cru-ci-fied, Give me but Je-sus, my Lord cru-ci-fied.
near-er to Thee, Near-er, my Sav-ior, still near-er to Thee.

241 A SHELTER IN THE TIME OF STORM!

F. J. C.

Ira D. Sankey

1. The Lord's our Rock, in Him we hide, A shel-ter in the time of storm;
2. A shade by day, de-fense by night, A shel-ter in the time of storm;
3. The rag-ing storms may round us beat, A shel-ter in the time of storm;
4. O Rock di-vine, O Ref-uge dear, A shel-ter in the time of storm;

Se-cure what-ev-er ill be-tide, A shel-ter in the time of storm.
No fears a-larm, no foes af-fright, A shel-ter in the time of storm.
We'll nev-er leave our safe re-treat, A shel-ter in the time of storm.
Be Thou our help-er ev-er near, A shel-ter in the time of storm.

CHORUS

Oh, Je-sus is a Rock in a wea-ry land, A

wea-ry land, a wea-ry land; Oh, Je-sus is a

Rock in a wea-ry land! A shel-ter in the time of storm.

242 THERE SHALL BE SHOWERS OF BLESSING

El Nathan

J. McGranahan

1. There shall be show-ers of bless - ing: This is the prom-ise of love;
2. There shall be show-ers of bless - ing— Pre-cious re - viv-ing a - gain;
3. There shall be show-ers of bless - ing: Send them up-on us, O Lord!
4. There shall be show-ers of bless - ing: O that to-day they might fall,
5. There shall be show-ers of bless - ing, If we but trust and o - bey;

There shall be sea - sons re-fresh-ing, Sent from the Sav - iour a - bove.
O - ver the hills and the val - leys. Sound of a - bun-dance of rain.
Grant to us now a re - fresh-ing; Come, and now hon - or Thy Word.
Now as to God we're con - fess-ing, Now as on Je - sus we call!
There shall be sea - sons re - fresh-ing, If we let God have His way.

CHORUS

Show - ers of bless - ing, Show-ers of bless-ing we need;
Show - ers, show-ers

Mer - cy-drops round us are fall - ing, But for the show-ers we plead.

243 WHERE THE GATES SWING OUTWARD NEVER

C. H. G.

CHAS. H. GABRIEL

1. Just a few more days to be filled with praise, And to tell the
2. Just a few more years with their toil and tears, And the jour - ney
3. Tho' the hills be steep and the val - leys deep, With no flow'rs my
4. What a joy 'twill be when I wake to see Him for whom my

old, old sto - ry; Then, when twi - light falls, and my Sav - ior calls,
will be end - ed; Then I'll be with Him, where the tide of time
way a - dorn - ing; Tho' the night be lone and my rest a stone,
heart is burn - ing! Nev - er - more to sigh, nev - er - more to die—

CHORUS

I shall go to Him in glo - ry.
With e - ter - ni - ty is blend - ed. I'll exchange my cross for a
Joy a - waits me in the morn - ing.
For that day my heart is yearn - ing.

star - ry crown, Where the gates swing outward nev - er; At His feet I'll

lay ev - 'ry bur - den down, And with Je - sus reign for - ev - er.

244 GREAT IS THY FAITHFULNESS

T. O. Chisholm

William M. Runyan

1. "Great is Thy faith-ful-ness," O God my Fa-ther, There is no shad-ow of
2. Sum-mer and winter, and spring-time and harvest, Sun, moon and stars in their
3. Par-don for sin and a peace that en-dur-eth, Thine own dear presence to

turning with Thee; Thou changest not, Thy compassions, they fail not, As Thou hast
cours-es a-bove, Join with all na-ture in man-i-fold wit-ness, To Thy great
cheer and to guide; Strength for to-day and bright hope for to-morrow, Blessings all

CHORUS

been Thou for-ev-er wilt be."
faith-ful-ness, mer-cy and love. "Great is Thy faith-ful-ness! Great is Thy
mine, with ten thou-sand be-side!

faith-ful-ness!" Morn-ing by morn-ing new mer-cies I see; All I have

rall.

need-ed Thy hand hath provided,—"Great is Thy faithfulness," Lord, un-to me!

245 LEAD, KINDLY LIGHT

JOHN H. NEWMAN   LUX BENIGNA 10. 4. 10. 4. 10. 10   JOHN B. DYKES

1. Lead, kindly Light, amid th'encircling gloom, Lead Thou me on! The night is
2. I was not ev-er thus, nor pray'd that Thou Should'st lead me on; I loved to
3. So long Thy pow'r hath blest me, sure it still Will lead me on O'er moor and

dark, and I am far from home; Lead Thou me on! Keep Thou my feet; I
choose and see my path; but now Lead Thou me on! I loved the gar - ish
fen, o'er crag and torrent, till The night is gone; And with the morn those

do not ask to see The dis-tant scene; one step e-nough for me.
day and, spite of fears, Pride ruled my will. Remember not past years.
an - gel fac - es smile, Which I have loved long since and lost a - while.

246 HOLY BIBLE, BOOK DIVINE

John Burton   Wm. B. Bradbury

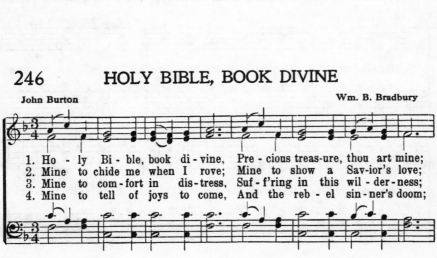

1. Ho - ly Bi - ble, book di - vine, Pre - cious treas-ure, thou art mine;
2. Mine to chide me when I rove; Mine to show a Sav-ior's love;
3. Mine to com - fort in dis - tress, Suf - f'ring in this wil - der-ness;
4. Mine to tell of joys to come, And the reb - el sin-ner's doom;

Mine to tell me whence I came; Mine to teach me what I am;
Mine thou art to guide and guard; Mine to pun-ish or re-ward;
Mine to show by liv-ing faith, Man can tri-umph o-ver death;
O thou ho-ly book di-vine, Pre-cious treas-ure, thou art mine. A-MEN.

247 JESUS SPREADS HIS BANNER O'ER US

Roswell Park   AUTUMN   Louis von Esch

1. Je-sus spreads His ban-ner o'er us, Cheers our famished souls with food;
2. In Thy ho-ly in-car-na-tion, When the an-gels sang Thy birth;

He the ban-quet spreads be-fore us Of His mys-tic flesh and blood.
In Thy fast-ing and temp-ta-tion, In Thy la-bors on the earth,

Precious ban-quet, bread of heav-en, Wine of glad-ness, flow-ing free;
In Thy tri-al and re-jec-tion, In Thy suf-f'rings on the tree,

May we taste it, kind-ly giv-en, In re-mem-brance, Lord, of Thee.
In Thy glo-rious res-ur-rec-tion, May we, Lord, re-mem-ber Thee.

248   SINCE I HAVE BEEN REDEEMED

E. O. E.

E. O Excell

1. I have a song I love to sing, Since I have been re-deemed,
2. I have a Christ that sat-is-fies, Since I have been re-deemed,
3. I have a Wit-ness bright and clear, Since I have been re-deemed,
4. I have a joy I can't ex-press, Since I have been re-deemed,
5. I have a home pre-pared for me, Since I have been re-deemed,

Of my Re-deem-er, Sav-ior, King, Since I have been re-deemed.
To do His will my high-est prize, Since I have been re-deemed.
Dis-pel-ling ev-'ry doubt and fear, Since I have been re-deemed.
All thro' His blood and right-eous-ness, Since I have been re-deemed.
Where I shall dwell e-ter-nal-ly, Since I have been re-deemed.

CHORUS.

Since I . . . . have been re-deemed,   Since I have been re-
Since I have been redeemed, Since   I have been redeemed,

deemed, I will glo-ry in His name; Since I . . . . . have been re-
Since I have been redeemed, Since

deemed,   I will glo-ry in my Sav-ior's name. A-MEN.
I have been re-deemed,

249 I SHALL SEE THE KING

W. C. Poole

B. D. Ackley

1. I shall see the King Where the an - gels sing, I shall see the
2. In the land of song, In the glo - ry-throng, Where there nev - er
3. I shall see the King, All my trib - utes bring, And shall look up-

King some day, In the bet - ter land, On the gold - en strand,
comes a night, With my Lord once slain I shall ev - er reign
on His face; Then my song shall be How He ran-somed me

And with Him shall ev - er stay.
In the glo - ry land of light.
And has kept me by His grace.

REFRAIN

In His glo - ry, I shall see the King, And for - ev - er end - less prais - es sing; 'Twas on

Cal - va - ry Je - sus died for me; I shall see the King some day.

250 I'LL GO WHERE YOU WANT ME TO GO

Mary Brown

Carrie E. Rounsefell

1. It may not be on the mountain height, Or o-ver the storm-y sea,
2. Per-haps to-day there are lov-ing words Which Jesus would have me speak;
3. There's sure-ly somewhere a low-ly place In earth's harvest fields so wide,

It may not be at the bat-tle's front My Lord will have need of me;
There may be now in the paths of sin Some wand'rer whom I should seek:
Where I may la-bor thru life's short day For Je-sus, the Cru-ci-fied;

But if, by a still, small voice He calls To paths that I do not know,
O Sav-iour, if Thou wilt be my guide, Tho' dark and rug-ged the way,
So trust-ing my all to Thy ten-der care, And knowing Thou lov-est me,

I'll answer, dear Lord, with my hand in Thine, I'll go where you want me to go,
My voice shall ech-o the mes-sage sweet, I'll say what you want me to say.
I'll do Thy will with a heart sin-cere, I'll be what you want me to be.

REFRAIN

I'll go where you want me to go, dear Lord, O-ver mountain, or plain, or sea;

I'LL GO WHERE YOU WANT ME TO GO

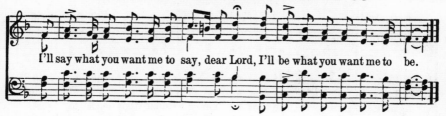

I'll say what you want me to say, dear Lord, I'll be what you want me to be.

251 O THOU, IN WHOSE PRESENCE

Joseph Swain   MEDITATION 11. 8. 11. 8.   Freeman Lewis

1. O Thou in whose pres-ence my soul takes de-light, On
2. Where dost Thou, dear Shep-herd, re-sort with Thy sheep, To
3. Oh! why should I wan-der an a-lien from Thee, Or
4. Re-store, my dear Sav-iour, the light of Thy face; Thy
5. He looks! and ten thous-ands of an-gels re-joice, And

whom in af-flic-tion I call, My com-fort by day, and my
feed them in pas-tures of love? Say, why in the val-ley of
cry in the des-ert for bread? Thy foes will re-joice when my
soul-cheer-ing com-fort im-part; And let the sweet to-kens of
myr-i-ads wait for His word; He speaks! and e-ter-ni-ty,

song in the night, My hope, my sal-va-tion, my all!
death should I weep, Or a-lone in this wil-der-ness rove?
sor-rows they see, And smile at the tears I have shed.
par-don-ing grace Bring joy to my des-o-late heart.
filled with His voice, Re-ech-oes the praise of the Lord. A-men.

252 LOVE OPENED WIDE THE DOOR

A. H. Ackley

B. D. Ackley

1. Love o-pened wide the door for me, The door that leads to God;
2. Love o-pened wide the door for me, The door to par-d'ning grace,
3. Love o-pened wide the door for me, The door that leads to rest,
4. Love o-pened wide the door for me, The door that leads to pow'r,

The hand of Je - sus turned the key, And marked that door with blood.
And clothed my soul with right-eous-ness, To stand be - fore His face.
My troub - led soul found sweet re - lief From bur-dens that op-pressed.
My weak-ness changed to glo-rious strength, In-creas-ing hour by hour.

Chorus

Love o - pened wide the door for me, Re - stored my soul, and

set me free; His life He free - ly gave, my life to save,

'Twas Love that o - pened wide the door for me.

THE PALMS

253

Arr. by C. H. G.

1. O'er all the way green palms and blossoms gay Are strewn this day in festival
2. His word goes forth, and peo-ple by its might Once more their freedom gain from
3. Sing and re-joice, O blest Je - ru - sa - lem, Of all thy songs sing the e-

prep - a - ra - tion, Where Je - sus comes, to wipe our tears a - way;
deg - ra - da - tion; Hu - man - i - ty doth give to each his right,
man - ci - pa - tion; Thro' bound-less love, the Christ of Beth - le - hem

RESPONSE

E'en now the throng to welcome Him prepare. Join, sing His name di-vine,
While those in darkness find restored the light.
Brings forth the hope to thee for - ev - er-more. Join all, and sing Ho - san - na!

Let ev - 'ry voice resound with u - nit - ed ac - cla-ma - tion, Ho-san - -
Praised be the

na! Praised be the Lord, Bless Him who cometh to bring us sal-va - tion.
Lord, Ho-san na!

254 ARISE, MY SOUL, ARISE

Charles Wesley   (LENOX)   Lewis Edson

1. A - rise, my soul, a- rise; Shake off thy guilt-y fears; The bleeding Sac-ri-
2. He ev-er lives a-bove, For me to in-ter-cede; His all-re-deem-ing
3. Five bleeding wounds He bears, Re-ceived on Cal-va-ry, They pour ef-fec-tual
4. The Fa-ther hears Him pray, His dear a-noint-ed One; He can not turn a-
5. My God is rec-on-ciled; His pard'ning voice I hear, He owns me for His

fice In my be-half ap-pears: Be - fore the throne my Surety stands, Be-
love, His pre-cious blood to plead; His blood a-toned for all our race, His
prayers, They strongly plead for me: "For-give him, O for-give," they cry, "For-
way The pres-ence of His Son; His Spir-.it an-swers to the blood, His
child, I can no long-er fear; With con - fi-dence I now draw nigh, With

fore the throne my Sure-ty stands My name is writ-ten on His hands.
blood a-toned for all our race, And sprinkles now the throne of grace.
give him, O for-give," they cry, "Nor let that ransomed sin - ner die!"
Spir - it an-swers to the blood, And tells me I am born of God.
con - fi-dence I now draw nigh, And, "Fa-ther, Ab-ba, Fa - ther," cry.

255 O THOU GOD OF MY SALVATION

Thomas Olivers   REGENT SQUARE 8. 7. 6 lines   Henry Smart

1. O Thou God of my sal - va - tion, My Re-deem - er from all sin;
2. Though unseen, I love the Sav - iour; He hath bro't sal - va - tion near;
3. While the an - gel choirs are cry - ing, "Glo - ry to the great I AM,"
4. An - gels now are hov'ring 'round us, Un - per-ceived a - mid the throng;

O THOU GOD OF MY SALVATION

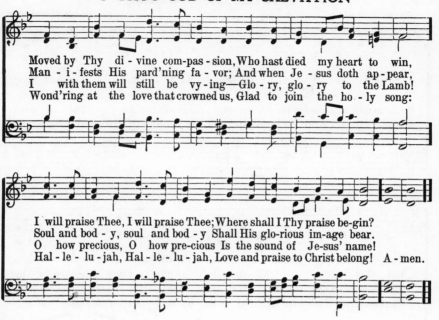

Moved by Thy di - vine com-pas - sion, Who hast died my heart to win,
Man - i - fests His pard'ning fa - vor; And when Je - sus doth ap - pear,
I with them will still be vy - ing—Glo - ry, glo - ry to the Lamb!
Wond'ring at the love that crowned us, Glad to join the ho - ly song:

I will praise Thee, I will praise Thee; Where shall I Thy praise be-gin?
Soul and bod - y, soul and bod - y Shall His glo-rious im-age bear.
O how precious, O how pre-cious Is the sound of Je-sus' name!
Hal - le - lu - jah, Hal - le - lu - jah, Love and praise to Christ belong! A - men.

256   BREATHE ON ME, BREATH OF GOD

EDWIN HATCH   (TRENTHAM)   ROBERT JACKSON

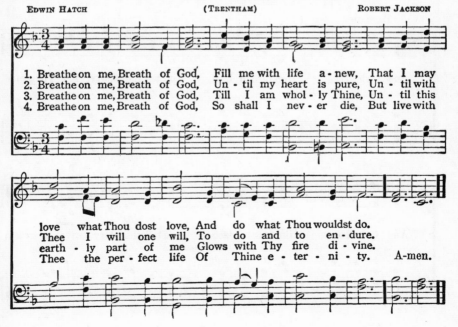

1. Breathe on me, Breath of God, Fill me with life a - new, That I may
2. Breathe on me, Breath of God, Un - til my heart is pure, Un - til with
3. Breathe on me, Breath of God, Till I am whol - ly Thine, Un - til this
4. Breathe on me, Breath of God, So shall I nev - er die, But live with

love what Thou dost love, And do what Thou wouldst do.
Thee I will one will, To do and to en - dure.
earth - ly part of me Glows with Thy fire di - vine.
Thee the per - fect life Of Thine e - ter - ni - ty.   A - men.

257   SAVED BY GRACE

Fanny J. Crosby

George C. Stebbins

1. Some day the sil-ver cord will break, And I no more as now shall sing;
2. Some day my earth-ly house will fall, I can-not tell how soon 'twill be,
3. Some day, when fades the golden sun Beneath the ros-y-tint-ed west,
4. Some day: till then I'll watch and wait, My lamp all trimmed and burning bright,

But Oh! the joy when I shall wake With-in the pal-ace of the King!
But this I know, my All-in-all Has now a place in heav'n for me.
My blessed Lord will say,"Well done!" And I shall en-ter in-to rest.
That when my Sav-iour opes the gate, My soul to Him may take its flight.

REFRAIN

And I shall see Him face to face, And tell the sto-ry, saved by grace;
shall see   to face,

rit.

And I shall see Him face to face, And tell the story, saved by grace.
shall see   to face,

258 CHRIST RECEIVETH SINFUL MEN

Arr. from NEUMASTER, 1671

JAMES McGRANAHAN

1. Sin - ners Je - sus will re - ceive; Sound this word of grace to all
2. Come, and He will give you rest; Trust Him, for His word is plain;
3. Now my heart condemns me not, Pure be - fore the law I stand;
4. Christ re - ceiv - eth sin - ful men, E - ven me with all my sin;

Who the heav'n - ly path - way leave, All who lin - ger, all who fall.
He will take the sin - ful - est; Christ re - ceiv - eth sin - ful men.
He who cleansed me from all spot, Sat - is - fied its last de - mand.
Purged from ev - 'ry spot and stain, Heav'n with Him I en - ter in.

REFRAIN

Sing it o'er and o'er a - gain; Christ re -
Sing it o'er a - gain, Sing it o'er a - gain; Christ re -

ceiv - eth sin - ful men; Make the mes - sage
ceiv-eth sin - ful men, Christ re - ceiv- eth sin-ful men; Make the message plain,

clear and plain; Christ re - ceiv - eth sin - ful men. A - men.
Make the message plain;

259 WONDERFUL GRACE OF JESUS

H. L.

Haldor Lillenas

1. Won - der - ful grace of Je - sus, Great - er than all my sin; . .
2. Won - der - ful grace of Je - sus, Reach-ing to all the lost, . .
3. Won - der - ful grace of Je - sus, Reach-ing the most de - filed, . .

How shall my tongue de - scribe it, Where shall its praise be - gin? . . .
By it I have been pardoned, Saved to the ut - ter - most, . .
By its trans-form-ing pow - er, Mak - ing him God's dear child, . .

Tak - ing a - way my bur - den, Set - ting my spir - it free; . .
Chains have been torn a - sun - der, Giv - ing me lib - er - ty; . . .
Pur - chas-ing peace and heav - en, For all e - ter - ni - ty; . . .

For the won - der - ful grace of Je - sus reach - es me.
For the won - der - ful grace of Je - sus reach - es me.
And the won - der - ful grace of Je - sus reach - es me.

CHORUS

the matchless grace of Je-sus,
Won-der-ful the matchless grace of Je - - - sus, Deep-er than the

WONDERFUL GRACE OF JESUS

might-y roll-ing sea;............. Won - - - der-ful
the roll-ing sea;
Higher than the mountain,

grace, all - suf - fi - - - cient for
spar-kling like a foun-tain, All - suf-fi-cient grace for e - ven

me, for e - ven me, Broad-er than the scope of my trans-
me,.................

gres - sions, Great-er far than all my sin and shame,.........
gres-sions, sing it! my sin and shame,

O mag-ni-fy the pre-cious name of Je-sus, Praise His name!

260 AWAKENING CHORUS

Charlotte G. Homer

Chas. H. Gabriel

1. A - wake! A-wake! a - wake! a-wake! and sing the bless - ed sto - ry;

2. Ring out! Ring out! ring out! ring out! O bells of joy and glad - ness!

A-wake! A-wake! a-wake! a-wake! and let your song of praise a - rise; A-

Re-peat, Re-peat, re-peat re-peat a - new the sto - ry o'er a - gain, Till

wake! A-wake! a - wake! a-wake! the earth is full of glo - ry, And light is

all Till all the earth the earth shall lose its weight of sad-ness, And shout And shout a-

Male voices in Unison

beam - ing is beam-ing from the ra-diant skies; The rocks and rills, the vales and

new a-new the glo - ri - ous re-frain; With an - gels in the heights sing

hills re-sound with glad-ness, All na - ture joins to sing the tri-umph

of the great sal - va - tion He wrest - ed from the hand of sin and

AWAKENING CHORUS

Full harmony

song. The Lord Je - ho - vah reigns and sin is back-ward hurled!
death. The Lord Je - ho - vah reigns and sin is back-ward hurled!
sin is backward hurled!

Unison

Re-joice, re - joice! Lift heart and voice; Je - ho - vah reigns!

Full harmony

Pro-claim His sov-'reign pow'r to all the world, And let His
pow'r to all the world, And let the

glo - rious ban-ner be un-furled! Je - ho - vah reigns!
grand and glo-rious ban-ner be un-furled! Je-ho-vah reigns! Je-ho-vah reigns!

Re-joice! re - joice! re - joice! Je - ho - vah reigns!
Re-joice! re - joice! re - joice!

261 THE VOICE OF MY SAVIOUR

A. H. A.

A. H. Ackley

SOPRANO OBLIGATO

1. Soft and low, soft and low, Mur-m'ring
2. When He speaks, when He speaks, Ac - cent
3. "Come to Me," Je - sus calls, Shel - t'ring

1. Soft and low, soft and low, is the voice that I hear, Like a mur-mur-ing
2. When He speaks, when He speaks, O how gentle the tone, Ev -'ry ac-cent is
3. "Come to Me, come to Me," Je-sus lov-ing-ly calls, In His shel-ter-ing

zeph-yr of spring, of spring; To my heart,
ten - der and mild, and mild; Ev -'ry word,
arms I find rest, find rest; Per-fect peace,

zeph-yr of spring; .... To my heart, to my heart, it brings
ten - der and mild; .... Ev -'ry word, ev -'ry word, has a
arms I find rest; .... Per-fect peace, per-fect peace, all my

to my heart, Christ .... my King. ..
ev -'ry word, Voice .... to her child. ..
per - fect peace, I .... am blest. ..

com - fort and cheer, 'Tis the voice of Christ Je-sus my King. ..
charm all its own, Like a moth-er's kind voice to her child. ..
be - ing en-thralls, With an in - fi - nite calm I am blest. ..

THE VOICE OF MY SAVIOUR

CHORUS.

O the voice of my Sav-iour no tongue can de-scribe, On earth or in

*Humming. . . . . .

heav-en a-bove; . . . . So en-tranc-ing-ly sweet, And with
in heav-en a-bove;

. . . . Voice . . . . of love. . . .

joy so re-plete, Is the voice of my Sav-iour's great love. . .

*Add one voice for every twelve singers in humming.

262 LEANING ON THE EVERLASTING ARMS

REV. E. A. HOFFMAN

A. J. SHOWALTER

1. What a fel-low-ship, what a joy Di-vine, Lean-ing
2. O how sweet to walk in this pil-grim way, Lean-ing
3. What have I to dread, what have I to fear, Lean-ing

on the Ev-er-last-ing Arms! What a bless-ed-ness, what a peace is min.
on the Ev-er-last-ing Arms! O how bright the path grows from day to day,
on the Ev-er-last-ing Arms! I have peace complete with my Lord so near,

REFRAIN

Lean-ing on the Ev-er-last-ing Arms! Lean - - ing,
Lean-ing on Je-sus,

lean - - ing, Safe and secure from all a-larms; Lean - - ing,
Lean-ing on Je-sus, Lean-ing on Je-sus,

lean - - ing, Lean-ing on the Ev-er-last-ing Arms.
Lean-ing on Je-sus,

263 I AM COMING HOME

A. H. ACKLEY

B. D. ACKLEY

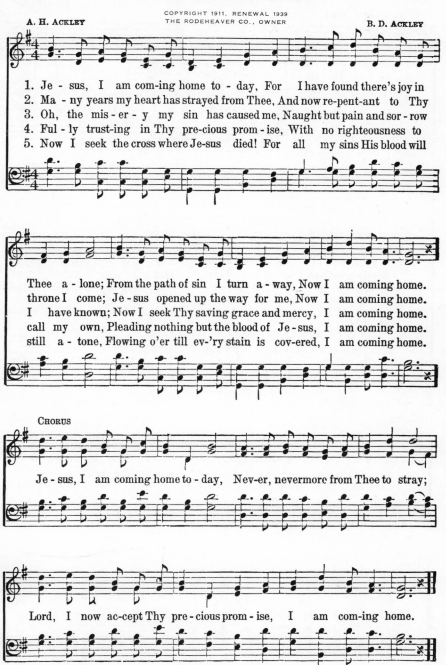

1. Je - sus, I am com-ing home to - day, For I have found there's joy in
2. Ma - ny years my heart has strayed from Thee, And now re-pent-ant to Thy
3. Oh, the mis-er - y my sin has caused me, Naught but pain and sor - row
4. Ful - ly trust-ing in Thy pre-cious prom - ise, With no righteousness to
5. Now I seek the cross where Je-sus died! For all my sins His blood will

Thee a - lone; From the path of sin I turn a - way, Now I am coming home.
throne I come; Je - sus opened up the way for me, Now I am coming home.
I have known; Now I seek Thy saving grace and mercy, I am coming home.
call my own, Pleading nothing but the blood of Je - sus, I am coming home.
still a - tone, Flowing o'er till ev-'ry stain is cov-ered, I am coming home.

CHORUS

Je - sus, I am coming home to - day, Nev-er, nevermore from Thee to stray;

Lord, I now ac-cept Thy pre - cious prom - ise, I am com-ing home.

264 I SURRENDER ALL

J. W. Van Deventer   W. S. Weeden

1. All to Je-sus I sur-ren-der, All to Him I free-ly give;
2. All to Je-sus I sur-ren-der, Hum-bly at His feet I bow,
3. All to Je-sus I sur-ren-der, Make me, Sav-ior, whol-ly Thine.
4. All to Je-sus I sur-ren-der, Lord, I give my-self to Thee;
5. All to Je-sus I sur-ren-der, Now I feel the sa-cred flame;

I will ev-er love and trust Him, In His pres-ence dai-ly live.
World-ly pleas-ures all for-sak-en, Take me, Je-sus, take me now.
Let me feel the Ho-ly Spir-it,—Tru-ly know that Thou art mine.
Fill me with Thy love and pow-er, Let Thy bless-ing fall on me.
Oh, the joy of full sal-va-tion! Glo-ry, glo-ry to His name!

CHORUS

I sur-ren-der all, I sur-ren-der all,
I sur-ren-der all, I sur-ren-der all,
All to Thee, my bless-ed Sav-ior, I sur-ren-der all.

265   I AM PRAYING FOR YOU

S. O'MALEY CLUFF

IRA D. SANKEY

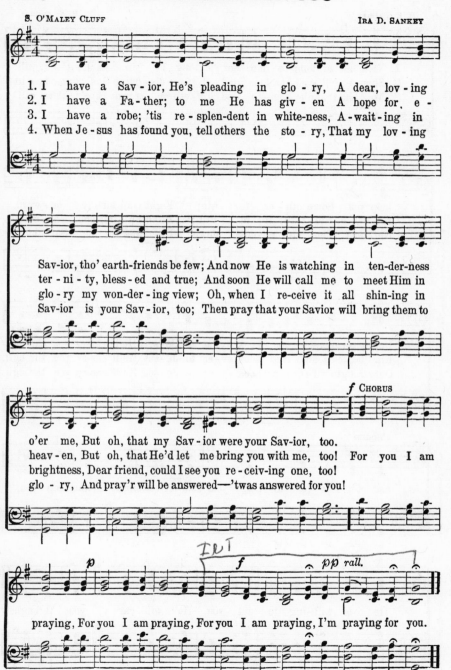

1. I have a Sav - ior, He's pleading in glo - ry, A dear, lov - ing
2. I have a Fa - ther; to me He has giv - en A hope for e -
3. I have a robe; 'tis re - splen-dent in white-ness, A - wait - ing in
4. When Je - sus has found you, tell others the sto - ry, That my lov - ing

Sav-ior, tho' earth-friends be few; And now He is watching in ten-der-ness
ter - ni - ty, bless - ed and true; And soon He will call me to meet Him in
glo - ry my won-der - ing view; Oh, when I re-ceive it all shin-ing in
Sav-ior is your Sav - ior, too; Then pray that your Savior will bring them to

_f_ CHORUS

o'er me, But oh, that my Sav - ior were your Sav-ior, too.
heav - en, But oh, that He'd let me bring you with me, too! For you I am
brightness, Dear friend, could I see you re - ceiv-ing one, too!
glo - ry, And pray'r will be answered—'twas answered for you!

_p_   _f_   _pp_ rall.

praying, For you I am praying, For you I am praying, I'm praying for you.

266 YIELD NOT TO TEMPTATION

H. R. Palmer

H. R. Palmer

1. Yield not to temp-ta-tion, For yield-ing is sin; Each vic-t'ry will
2. Shun e-vil com-pan-ions, Bad lan-guage dis-dain; God's name hold in
3. To him that o'er-com-eth, God giv-eth a crown; Thro' faith we will

help you Some oth-er to win; Fight man-ful-ly on-ward,
rev-'rence, Nor take it in vain; Be thought-ful and ear-nest,
con-quer, Tho' oft-en cast down; He who is our Sav-ior,

Dark pas-sions sub-due; Look ev-er to Je-sus, He'll car-ry you through.
Kind-heart-ed and true; Look ev-er to Je-sus, He'll car-ry you through.
Our strength will re-new; Look ev-er to Je-sus, He'll car-ry you through.

CHORUS

Ask the Sav-ior to help you, Com-fort, strength-en, and keep you;

He is will-ing to aid you, He will car-ry you through.

267 SOFTLY AND TENDERLY

W. L. T.

WILL L. THOMPSON

1. Soft - ly and ten-der - ly Je - sus is call-ing, Call - ing for you and for me;
2. Why should we tarry when Jesus is plead-ing, Pleading for you and for me?
3. Time is now fleeting, the moments are passing, Passing from you and from me;
4. Oh! for the won-der-ful love He has promised, Promised for you and for me;

See, on the portals He's waiting and watching, Watching for you and for me.
Why should we linger and heed not His mercies, Mer-cies for you and for me?
Shadows are gathering, death-beds are coming, Com-ing for you and for me.
Tho' we have sinned, He has mercy and pardon, Par-don for you and for me.

CHORUS m

Come home,.. come home,..... Ye who are wear-y, come home;...
Come home, come home,

Ear-nest-ly, ten-der-ly, Je - sus is call-ing, Call-ing, O sin-ner, come home!

268 JESUS IS CALLING

Fanny J. Crosby

George C. Stebbins

1. Je-sus is ten-der-ly call-ing thee home—Call-ing to-day, call-ing to-day;
2. Je-sus is call-ing the wea-ry to rest— Call-ing to-day, call-ing to-day;
3. Je-sus is wait-ing, O come to Him now—Waiting to-day, wait-ing to-day;
4. Je-sus is pleading, O list to His voice—Hear Him to-day, hear Him to-day;

Why from the sun-shine of love wilt thou roam Far-ther and far-ther a-way?
Bring Him thy bur-den and thou shalt be blest; He will not turn thee a-way.
Come with thy sins, at His feet low-ly bow; Come, and no lon-ger de-lay.
They who be-lieve on His name shall re-joice; Quick-ly a-rise and a-way.

Chorus

Call - - ing to-day! . . . Call - - ing to-day! . . .
Call-ing, call-ing to-day, to-day! Call-ing, call-ing to-day, to-day!

Je - - sus is call - - ing, Is ten-der-ly call-ing to-day.
Je-sus is ten-der-ly call-ing to-day,

269 THANK YOU, LORD

S. S.

Copyright, 1940, by Seth Sykes

Mr. and Mrs. SETH SYKES

Thank you, Lord, for sav-ing my soul, Thank you, Lord, for mak-ing me whole,

THANK YOU, LORD

Thank you, Lord, for giv-ing to me Thy great sal-va-tion so rich and free.

270 THE CLEANSING WAVE

Mrs. Phœbe Palmer

Mrs. Joseph F. Knapp

1. Oh, now I see the crim-son wave, The foun-tain deep and wide;
2. I see the new cre-a-tion rise, I hear the speak-ing blood;
3. I rise to walk in heav'n's own light, A-bove the world and sin;
4. A-maz-ing grace! 'tis heav'n be-low, To feel the blood ap-plied;

Je-sus, my Lord, might-y to save, Points to His wound-ed side.
It speaks! pol-lut-ed na-ture dies—Sinks 'neath the crim-son flood.
With hearts made pure and garments white, And Christ enthroned with-in.
And Je-sus, on-ly Je-sus know, My Je-sus cru-ci-fied.

CHORUS

The cleans-ing stream I see, I see! I plunge, and oh, it cleans-eth me;

Oh, praise the Lord, it cleans-eth me, It cleans-eth me, yes, cleans-eth me.

271 YOU MUST OPEN THE DOOR

Ina Duley Ogdon

Homer A. Rodeheaver

1. There's a Sav-ior who stands at the door of your heart, He is
2. He has come from the Fa-ther sal-va-tion to bring, And His
3. He is lov-ing and kind, full of in-fi-nite grace, In your
4. He will lead you at last to that bless-ed a-bode, To the

long-ing to en-ter—why let Him de-part? He has pa-tient-ly
name is called Je-sus, Re-deem-er and King; To save you and
heart, in your life, will you give Him a place? He is wait-ing to
cit-y of God, at the end of the road, Where the night nev-er

called you so oft-en be-fore, But you must o-pen the door.
keep you He pleads ev-er-more, But you must o-pen the door.
bless you, your soul to re-store, But you must o-pen the door.
falls, when life's jour-ney is o'er, But you must o-pen the door.

CHORUS

You must o-pen the door, You must o-pen the door, When

Je-sus comes in, He will save you from sin, But you must o-pen the door.

272 JUST AS I AM

Charlotte Elliott

William B. Bradbury

1. Just as I am, with-out one plea, But that Thy blood was shed for me,
2. Just as I am, and wait-ing not To rid my soul of one dark blot,
3. Just as I am, though tossed a-bout With many a con-flict, many a doubt,
4. Just as I am—poor, wretched, blind; Sight, rich-es, heal-ing of the mind,
5. Just as I am—Thou wilt re-ceive, Wilt welcome, pardon, cleanse, relieve,

And that Thou bidd'st me come to Thee, O Lamb of God, I come! I come!
To Thee whose blood can cleanse each spot, O Lamb of God, I come! I come!
Fightings and fears with-in, with-out, O Lamb of God, I come! I come!
Yea, all I need in Thee to find, O Lamb of God, I come! I come!
Be-cause Thy prom-ise I be-lieve, O Lamb of God, I come! I come!

273 FIGHT THE GOOD FIGHT

John S. B. Monsell

PENTECOST L. M.

William Boyd

1. Fight the good fight with all thy might, Christ is thy strength, and Christ thy right;
2. Run the straight race thro' God's good grace, Lift up thine eyes, and seek His face;
3. Cast care a-side, lean on thy Guide; His boundless mer-cy will pro-vide;
4. Faint not, nor fear, His arms are near; He changeth not, and thou art dear;

Lay hold on life, and it shall be Thy joy and crown e-ter-nal-ly.
Life with its way before us lies, Christ is the path, and Christ the prize.
Trust, and thy trusting soul shall prove Christ is its life, and Christ its love.
On-ly believe, and thou shalt see That Christ is all in all to thee. A-men.

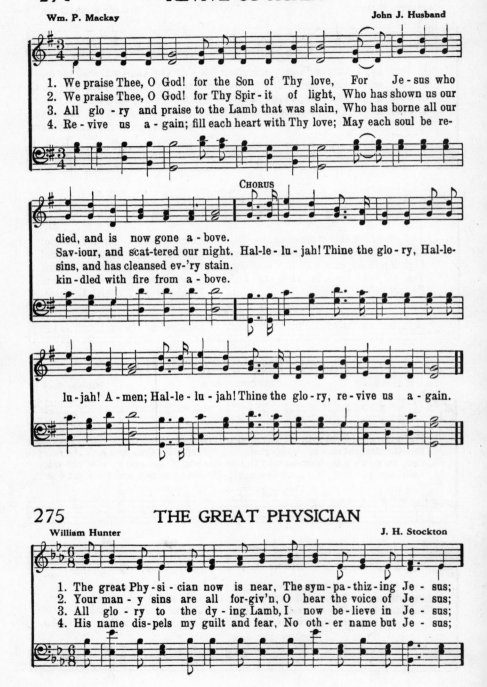

274 REVIVE US AGAIN

Wm. P. Mackay

John J. Husband

1. We praise Thee, O God! for the Son of Thy love, For Je-sus who
2. We praise Thee, O God! for Thy Spir-it of light, Who has shown us our
3. All glo-ry and praise to the Lamb that was slain, Who has borne all our
4. Re-vive us a-gain; fill each heart with Thy love; May each soul be re-

CHORUS

died, and is now gone a-bove.
Sav-iour, and scat-tered our night. Hal-le-lu-jah! Thine the glo-ry, Hal-le-
sins, and has cleansed ev-'ry stain.
kin-dled with fire from a-bove.

lu-jah! A-men; Hal-le-lu-jah! Thine the glo-ry, re-vive us a-gain.

275 THE GREAT PHYSICIAN

William Hunter

J. H. Stockton

1. The great Phy-si-cian now is near, The sym-pa-thiz-ing Je-sus;
2. Your man-y sins are all for-giv'n, O hear the voice of Je-sus;
3. All glo-ry to the dy-ing Lamb, I now be-lieve in Je-sus;
4. His name dis-pels my guilt and fear, No oth-er name but Je-sus;

THE GREAT PHYSICIAN

He speaks the droop-ing heart to cheer, O hear the voice of Je - sus.
Go on your way in peace to heav'n, And wear a crown with Je - sus.
I love the bless - ed Sav-ior's name, I love the name of Je - sus.
Oh! how my soul de-lights to hear The charming name of Je - sus.

D. S.—*Sweet-est car - ol ev - er sung,* Je - sus, bless-ed Je - sus

REFRAIN

Sweet-est note in ser - aph song, Sweet-est name on mor - tal tongue,

---

276   I'LL LIVE FOR HIM

R. E. HUDSON   C. R. DUNBAR

1. My life, my love I give to Thee, Thou Lamb of God who died for me;
2. I now be-lieve Thou dost re-ceive, For Thou hast died that I might live;
3. O Thou who died on Cal - va - ry, To save my soul and make me free,

CHO.—*I'll live for Him who died for me, How hap-py then my life shall be!*

D. C. CHORUS

Oh, may I ev - er faith-ful be, My Sav - ior and my God!
And now henceforth I'll trust in Thee, My Sav - ior and my God!
I'll con - se-crate my life to Thee, My Sav - ior and my God!

I'll live for Him who died for me, My Sav - ior and my God!

277 O HAPPY DAY

Philip Doddridge

E. F. Rimbault

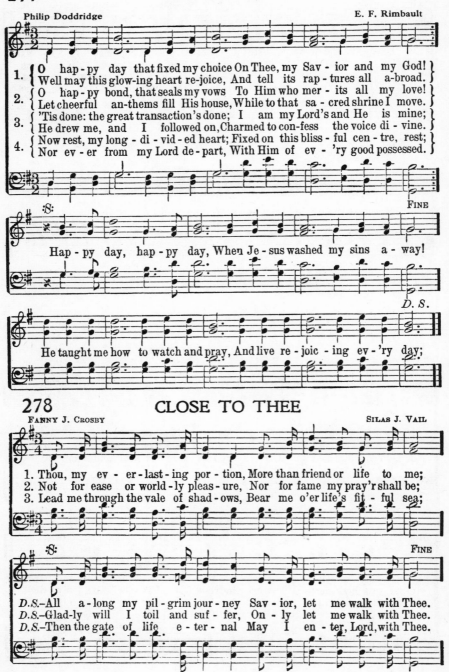

1. { O hap-py day that fixed my choice On Thee, my Sav-ior and my God!
Well may this glow-ing heart re-joice, And tell its rap-tures all a-broad. }

2. { O hap-py bond, that seals my vows To Him who mer-its all my love!
Let cheerful an-thems fill His house, While to that sa-cred shrine I move. }

3. { 'Tis done: the great transaction's done; I am my Lord's and He is mine;
He drew me, and I followed on, Charmed to con-fess the voice di-vine. }

4. { Now rest, my long-di-vid-ed heart; Fixed on this bliss-ful cen-tre, rest;
Nor ev-er from my Lord de-part, With Him of ev-'ry good possessed. }

FINE

Hap-py day, hap-py day, When Je-sus washed my sins a-way!

D. S.

He taught me how to watch and pray, And live re-joic-ing ev-'ry day;

278 CLOSE TO THEE

FANNY J. CROSBY

SILAS J. VAIL

1. Thou, my ev-er-last-ing por-tion, More than friend or life to me;
2. Not for ease or world-ly pleas-ure, Nor for fame my pray'r shall be;
3. Lead me through the vale of shad-ows, Bear me o'er life's fit-ful sea;

FINE

D.S.—All a-long my pil-grim jour-ney Sav-ior, let me walk with Thee.
D.S.—Glad-ly will I toil and suf-fer, On-ly let me walk with Thee.
D.S.—Then the gate of life e-ter-nal May I en-ter, Lord, with Thee.

CLOSE TO THEE

REFRAIN

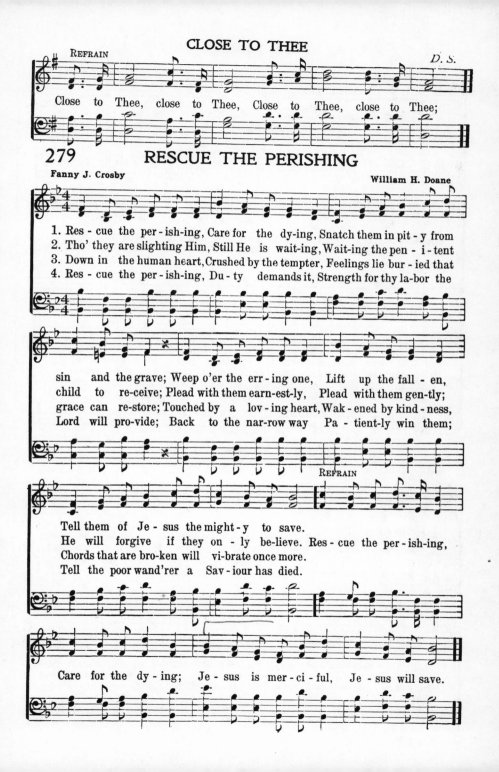

Close to Thee, close to Thee, Close to Thee, close to Thee;

279 RESCUE THE PERISHING

Fanny J. Crosby

William H. Doane

1. Res - cue the per - ish-ing, Care for the dy-ing, Snatch them in pit - y from
2. Tho' they are slighting Him, Still He is wait-ing, Wait-ing the pen - i - tent
3. Down in the human heart, Crushed by the tempter, Feelings lie bur - ied that
4. Res - cue the per - ish-ing, Du - ty demands it, Strength for thy la-bor the

sin and the grave; Weep o'er the err - ing one, Lift up the fall - en,
child to re-ceive; Plead with them earn-est-ly, Plead with them gen-tly;
grace can re-store; Touched by a lov - ing heart, Wak - ened by kind - ness,
Lord will pro-vide; Back to the nar-row way Pa - tient-ly win them;

REFRAIN

Tell them of Je - sus the might - y to save.
He will forgive if they on - ly be-lieve. Res - cue the per - ish-ing,
Chords that are bro-ken will vi-brate once more.
Tell the poor wand'rer a Sav - iour has died.

Care for the dy - ing; Je - sus is mer - ci - ful, Je - sus will save.

280 ALMOST PERSUADED

P. P. Bliss

P. P. Bliss

1. "Al - most per-suad - ed," now to be - lieve; "Al - most per-suad - ed,"
2. "Al - most per-suad - ed," come, come to - day; "Al - most per-suad - ed,"
3. "Al - most per-suad - ed," har-vest is past! "Al - most per-suad - ed,"

Christ to re - ceive; Seems now some soul to say, "Go, Spir - it,
turn not a - way; Je - sus in - vites you here, An - gels are
doom comes at last! "Al - most" can - not a - vail; "Al - most" is

go Thy way, Some more con-ven - ient day On Thee I'll call."
lin-g'ring near, Prayers rise from hearts so dear, O wan - d'rer, come.
but to fail! Sad, sad, that bit - ter wail, "Al - most," but lost!

281 ONLY TRUST HIM

J. H. S.

J. H. Stockton

1. Come, ev - 'ry soul by sin oppressed,There's mer - cy with the Lord,
2. For Je - sus shed His pre - cious blood,Rich bless-ings to be - stow;
3. Yes, Je - sus is the Truth, the Way, That leads you in - to rest:

And He will sure - ly give you rest By trust - ing in His Word.
Plunge now in - to the crim - son flood That wash - es white as snow.
Be - lieve in Him with - out de - lay, And you are ful - ly blest.

ONLY TRUST HIM

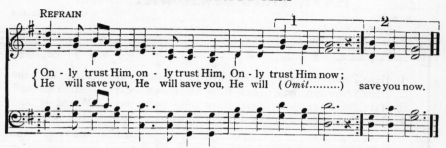

REFRAIN

{ On - ly trust Him, on - ly trust Him, On - ly trust Him now;
{ He will save you, He will save you, He will (*Omit.........*) save you now.

282 LORD, I'M COMING HOME

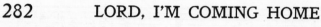

W. J. K.

Wm. J. Kirkpatrick

With feeling

1. I've won - dered far a - way from God, Now I'm com - ing home;
2. I've wast - ed man - y pre - cious years, Now I'm com - ing home;
3. I'm tired of sin and stray - ing, Lord, Now I'm com - ing home;
4. My soul is sick, my heart is sore, Now I'm com - ing home;
5. I need His cleans - ing blood, I know, Now I'm com - ing home;

FINE

The paths of sin too long I've trod, Lord, I'm com - ing home.
I now re - pent with bit - ter tears, Lord, I'm com - ing home.
I'll trust Thy love, be - lieve Thy word, Lord, I'm com - ing home.
My strength re - new, my hope re - store, Lord, I'm com - ing home.
Oh, wash me whit - er than the snow, Lord, I'm com - ing home.

D. S.—*O - pen wide Thine arms of Love, Lord, I'm com - ing home.*

CHORUS

D. S.

Com - ing home, com - ing home, Nev - er - more to roam;

283 HAVE THINE OWN WAY, LORD

A. A. P.

Slowly

Geo. C. Stebbins

1. Have Thine own way, Lord! Have Thine own way! Thou art the
2. Have Thine own way, Lord! Have Thine own way! Search me and
3. Have Thine own way, Lord! Have Thine own way! Wound-ed and
4. Have Thine own way, Lord! Have Thine own way! Hold o'er my

Pot - ter; I am the clay Mould me and make me Aft-er Thy
try me, Mas-ter, to - day! Whit - er than snow, Lord, Wash me just
wea - ry, Help me, I pray! Pow - er—all pow - er—Sure-ly is
be - ing Ab-so-lute sway! Fill with Thy Spir - it Till all shall

will, While I am wait - ing, Yield - ed and still.
now, As in Thy pres - ence Hum - bly I bow.
Thine! Touch me and heal me, Sav - ior di - vine!
see. Christ on - ly, al - ways, Liv - ing in me!

284 WHERE HE LEADS ME

E. W. Blandly

J. S. Norris

1. I can hear my Sav-ior call-ing, I can hear my Sav-ior call-ing,
2. I'll go with Him thru the gar-den, I'll go with Him thru the gar-den,
3. I'll go with Him thru the judg-ment, I'll go with Him thru the judg-ment,
4. He will give me grace and glo - ry, He will give me grace and glo-ry,

REF.—*Where He leads me I will fol - low, Where He leads me I will fol - low,*

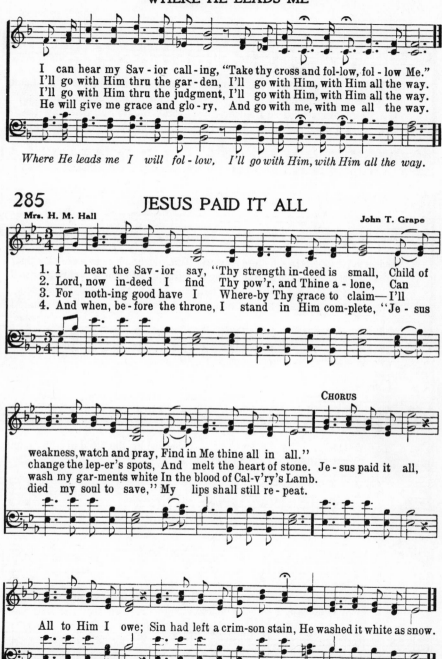

WHERE HE LEADS ME

I can hear my Sav-ior call-ing, "Take thy cross and fol-low, fol-low Me."
I'll go with Him thru the gar-den, I'll go with Him, with Him all the way.
I'll go with Him thru the judgment, I'll go with Him, with Him all the way.
He will give me grace and glo-ry, And go with me, with me all the way.

Where He leads me I will fol-low, I'll go with Him, with Him all the way.

285

JESUS PAID IT ALL

Mrs. H. M. Hall

John T. Grape

1. I hear the Sav-ior say, "Thy strength in-deed is small, Child of
2. Lord, now in-deed I find Thy pow'r, and Thine a-lone, Can
3. For noth-ing good have I Where-by Thy grace to claim—I'll
4. And when, be-fore the throne, I stand in Him com-plete, "Je - sus

CHORUS

weakness, watch and pray, Find in Me thine all in all."
change the lep-er's spots, And melt the heart of stone. Je-sus paid it all,
wash my gar-ments white In the blood of Cal-v'ry's Lamb.
died my soul to save," My lips shall still re-peat.

All to Him I owe; Sin had left a crim-son stain, He washed it white as snow.

REDEEMED

Fanny J. Crosby

Wm. J. Kirkpatrick

1. Redeemed—how I love to pro-claim it! Redeemed by the blood of the Lamb;
2. Redeemed and so happy in Je - sus, No language my rap-ture can tell;
3. I think of my bless-ed Re-deem-er, I think of Him all the day long;
4. I know I shall see in His beau-ty The King in whose law I de - light;

Redeemed thro' His in - fi - nite mer-cy, His child, and for - ev - er, I am.
I know that the light of His presence With me doth con-tin - ual - ly dwell.
I sing, for I can-not be si - lent; His love is the theme of my song.
Who lov - ing - ly guardeth my footsteps, And giv-eth me songs in the night.

CHORUS

Re - deemed, .. re - deemed, .. Redeemed by the blood of the Lamb;
re-deemed, re-deemed,

Re - deemed, .. re - deemed, .. His child, and for - ev - er, I am.
re-deemed, re-deemed,

287 AT THE CROSS

Isaac Watts

Ralph E. Hudson

1. A - las! and did my Sav - ior bleed? And did my Sov'reign die?
2. Was it for crimes that I had done, He groaned up-on the tree?
3. Well might the sun in dark-ness hide, And shut his glo - ries in,
4. But drops of grief can ne'er re - pay The debt of love I owe:

Would He de - vote that sa - cred head For such a worm as I?
A - maz-ing pit - y! grace unknown! And love be-yond de - gree!
When Christ, the mighty Mak - er, died For man the crea-ture's sin.
Here, Lord, I give my - self a - way,—'Tis all that I can do.

Chorus

At the cross, at the cross where I first saw the light, And the

bur-den of my heart rolled a - way, rolled a - way, It was there by

faith I received my sight, And now I am hap - py all the day.

GLORY TO HIS NAME

TAKE MY LIFE, AND LET IT BE

let them move At the im-pulse of Thy love, At the im-pulse of Thy love.
let me sing Al-ways, on - ly, for my King, Al-ways, on-ly, for my King.
and my days, Let them flow in cease-less praise, Let them flow in ceaseless praise.
is Thine own, It shall be Thy roy - al throne, It shall be Thy roy - al throne.

290   NOTHING BUT THE BLOOD

R. L.

Robert Lowry

1. What can wash a - way my sin? Noth-ing but the blood of Je - sus;
2. For   my par - don this I   see— Noth-ing but the blood of Je - sus;
3. Noth-ing can for sin a - tone— Noth-ing but the blood of Je - sus;
4. This is   all my hope and peace—Noth-ing but the blood of Je - sus;

What can make me whole a - gain? Noth-ing but the blood of Je - sus.
For   my cleans-ing this my   plea— Noth-ing but the blood of Je - sus.
Naught of good that I have done—Noth-ing but the blood of Je - sus.
This is   all my right-eous - ness—Noth-ing but the blood of Je - sus.

Oh! pre - cious is the flow That makes me white as snow;

No oth - er fount I know, Noth-ing but the blood of Je - sus.

291 ARE YOU WASHED IN THE BLOOD?

E. A. H.

Rev. Elisha A. Hoffman

1. Have you been to Je-sus for the cleansing pow'r? Are you washed in the blood
2. Are you walk-ing dai-ly by the Sav-iour's side? Are you washed in the blood
3. When the Bridegroom cometh will your robes be white? Are you washed in the blood
4. Lay a-side the garments that are stained with sin, And be washed in the blood

S:

of the Lamb? Are you ful-ly trust-ing in His grace this hour? Are you
of the Lamb? Do you rest each mo-ment in the Cru-ci-fied? Are you
of the Lamb? Will your soul be read-y for the mansions bright, And be
of the Lamb? There's a fountain flow-ing for the soul un-clean, O be

D.S.—Are they white as snow? Are you

FINE CHORUS

washed in the blood of the Lamb? Are you washed   in the blood,
Are you washed   in the blood.

washed in the blood of the Lamb?

D.S.

In the soul-cleansing blood of the Lamb?   Are your garments spotless?
of the Lamb?

292 PRAY ON

Copyright, 1938, by The Rodeheaver Co.
International Copyright Secured

OSWALD J. SMITH
DUET

CLARENCE KOHLMANN

1. Pray on, O soul of mine, pray on! This night of sin will soon be gone,
2. Pray on, O soul of mine, pray on! Tempta-tions can-not last for long,
3. Pray on, O soul of mine, pray on! The Lord will keep thee true and strong

PRAY ON

The break of day will come ere long Till then, my soul, pray on!.........
Thou soon shalt sing the victor's song, With faith, my soul, pray on!.........
And an-swer all thy pray'rs ere long With joy my soul, pray on!.........

293   SAVED THROUGH JESUS' BLOOD

J. W. Van de Venter

J. W. Van de Venter

1. Some-time we'll stand be-fore the judgment bar, The quick, the ris-en dead;
2. I'll then re-ceive a bright and star-ry crown, As on-ly God can give;
3. Then we shall meet to nev-er part a-gain, Our toil will then be o'er;

The Lord will then make known the rec-ord there; Our names will all be read.

And when I've been with Him ten thousand years, I'll have no less to live.

We'll lay our bur-dens down at Je-sus' feet, And rest for ev-er-more.

CHORUS

I'll be present when the roll is called, Pure and spotless thro' the

I'll be present, I'll be

I'll be pure

crim-son flood;   I will answer when they call my name; Saved thro' Jesus' blood.

I will answer, I will

294 THERE IS POWER IN THE BLOOD

L. E. J.

L. E. JONES

1. Would you be free from the bur-den of sin? There's pow'r in the blood,
2. Would you be free from your pas-sion and pride? There's pow'r in the blood,
3. Would you be whit-er, much whiter than snow? There's pow'r in the blood,
4. Would you do serv-ice for Je-sus your King? There's pow'r in the blood,

pow'r in the blood; Would you o'er e-vil a vic-to-ry win? There's
pow'r in the blood; Come for a cleans-ing to Cal-va-ry's tide; There's
pow'r in the blood; Sin-stains are lost in its life-giv-ing flow; There's
pow'r in the blood; Would you live dai-ly His prais-es to sing? There's

CHORUS.

won-der-ful pow'r in the blood. There is pow'r, pow'r, Wonder-working pow'r
there is

In the blood of the Lamb; There is pow'r, pow'r,
In the blood of the Lamb; there is

Won-der-work-ing pow'r In the pre-cious blood of the Lamb. A-MEN.

295 SAVED BY THE BLOOD

S. J. Henderson

D. B. Towner

1. Saved by the blood of the Cru-ci-fied One! Ran-somed from
2. Saved by the blood of the Cru-ci-fied One! The an-gels re-
3. Saved by the blood of the Cru-ci-fied One! The Fa-ther He
4. Saved by the blood of the Cru-ci-fied One! All hail to the

sin and a new work be-gun, Sing praise to the Fa-ther and
joic-ing be-cause it is done; A child of the Fa-ther, joint-
spake, and His will it was done; Great price of my par-don, His
Fa-ther, all hail to the Son, All hail to the Spir-it, the

praise to the Son, Saved by the blood of the Cru-ci-fied One!
heir with the Son, Saved by the blood of the Cru-ci-fied One!
own pre-cious Son; Saved by the blood of the Cru-ci-fied One!
great Three in One! Saved by the blood of the Cru-ci-fied One!

CHORUS

Saved! . . saved! . . My sins are all pardoned my guilt is all gone!
Glo-ry, I'm saved! glo-ry, I'm saved!

Saved! . . saved! . . I am saved by the blood of the Cru-ci-fied One!
Glo-ry, I'm saved! glo-ry, I'm saved!

296 WHITER THAN SNOW

JAMES NICHOLSON

WM. G. FISCHER

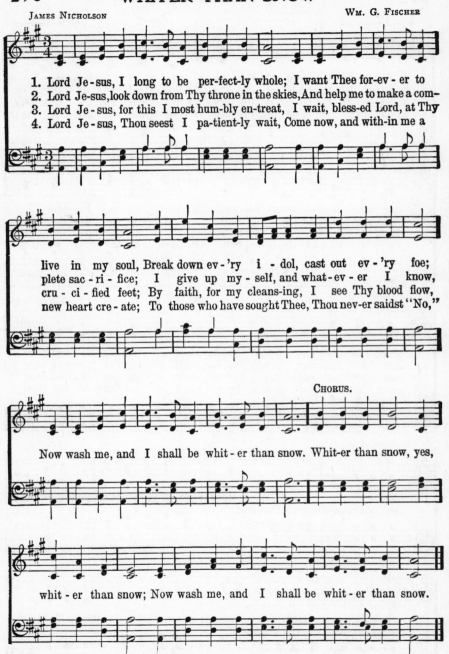

1. Lord Je-sus, I long to be per-fect-ly whole; I want Thee for-ev - er to
2. Lord Je-sus, look down from Thy throne in the skies, And help me to make a com-
3. Lord Je-sus, for this I most hum-bly en-treat, I wait, bless-ed Lord, at Thy
4. Lord Je-sus, Thou seest I pa-tient-ly wait, Come now, and with-in me a

live in my soul, Break down ev-'ry i - dol, cast out ev-'ry foe;
plete sac - ri - fice; I give up my - self, and what-ev - er I know,
cru - ci - fied feet; By faith, for my cleans-ing, I see Thy blood flow,
new heart cre - ate; To those who have sought Thee, Thou nev-er saidst "No,"

CHORUS.

Now wash me, and I shall be whit - er than snow. Whit-er than snow, yes,

whit - er than snow; Now wash me, and I shall be whit - er than snow.

297 THERE IS A FOUNTAIN

William Cowper

Lowell Mason

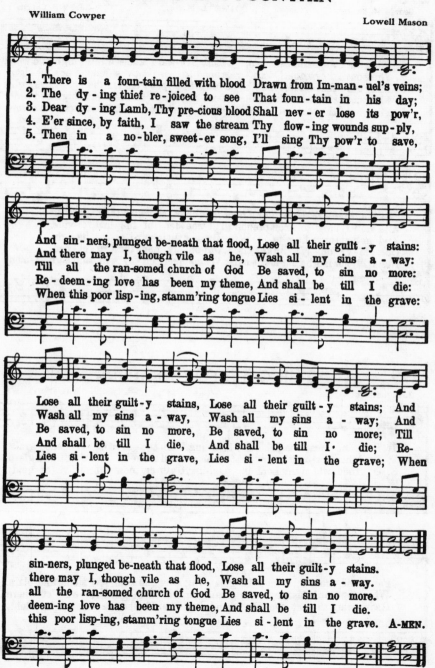

1. There is a foun-tain filled with blood Drawn from Im-man-uel's veins;
2. The dy-ing thief re-joiced to see That foun-tain in his day;
3. Dear dy-ing Lamb, Thy pre-cious blood Shall nev-er lose its pow'r,
4. E'er since, by faith, I saw the stream Thy flow-ing wounds sup-ply,
5. Then in a no-bler, sweet-er song, I'll sing Thy pow'r to save,

And sin-ners, plunged be-neath that flood, Lose all their guilt-y stains:
And there may I, though vile as he, Wash all my sins a-way:
Till all the ran-somed church of God Be saved, to sin no more:
Re-deem-ing love has been my theme, And shall be till I die:
When this poor lisp-ing, stamm'ring tongue Lies si-lent in the grave:

Lose all their guilt-y stains, Lose all their guilt-y stains; And
Wash all my sins a-way, Wash all my sins a-way; And
Be saved, to sin no more, Be saved, to sin no more; Till
And shall be till I die, And shall be till I die; Re-
Lies si-lent in the grave, Lies si-lent in the grave; When

sin-ners, plunged be-neath that flood, Lose all their guilt-y stains.
there may I, though vile as he, Wash all my sins a-way.
all the ran-somed church of God Be saved, to sin no more.
deem-ing love has been my theme, And shall be till I die.
this poor lisp-ing, stamm'ring tongue Lies si-lent in the grave. A-MEN.

298 FLING OUT THE BANNER!

George W. Doane

DOANE L. M.

John B. Calkin

1. Fling out the banner! let it float Sky-ward and seaward, high and wide;
2. Fling out the banner! an-gels bend In anx-ious si-lence o'er the sign,
3. Fling out the banner! heath-en lands Shall see from far the glo-rious sight,
4. Fling out the banner! let it float Sky-ward and seaward, high and wide,
5. Fling out the banner! wide and high, Seaward and skyward, let it shine;

The sun, that lights its shining folds, The cross, on which the Saviour died.
And vain-ly seek to comprehend The won-der of the love di-vine.
And nations crowding to be born, Baptize their spir-its in its light.
Our glo-ry, on-ly in the cross; Our on-ly hope the Cru-ci-fied.
Nor skill, nor might, nor merit ours; We conquer on-ly in that sign. A-men.

299 THE CALL FOR REAPERS

J. O. Thompson

J. B. O. Clemm

1. Far and near the fields are teem-ing With the waves of ri-pened grain;
2. Send them forth with morn's first beaming; Send them in the noontide's glare;
3. O thou, whom thy Lord is send-ing, Gath-er now the sheaves of gold;

FINE.

Far and near their gold is gleam-ing O'er the sun-ny slope and plain.
When the sun's last rays are gleam-ing, Bid them gath-er ev-'ry-where.
Heav'nward then at eve-ning wend-ing, Thou shalt come with joy un-told.

D. S.—*Send them now the sheaves to gath-er, Ere the har-vest-time pass by.*

THE CALL FOR REAPERS

CHORUS

D. S.

Lord of har-vest, send forth reapers! Hear us. Lord, to Thee we cry;

300   O COULD I SPEAK

Samuel Medley

Dr. Lowell Mason

1. O could I speak the matchless worth, O could I sound the glories forth Which
2. I'd sing the pre-cious blood He spilt, My ransom from the dreadful guilt Of
3. I'd sing the char-ac-ters He bears, And all the forms of love He wears, Ex-
4. Well, the de-light-ful day will come When my dear Lord will bring me home, And

in my Sav-ior shine, I'd soar and touch the heav'nly strings, And vie with Ga-briel
sin, and wrath di-vine; I'd sing His glorious righteousness, In which all-per-fect,
alt-ed on His throne; In loftiest songs of sweetest praise, I would to ev-er-
I shall see His face; Then with my Savior, Brother, Friend, A blest e-ter-ni-

while he sings In notes al-most di-vine, In notes al-most di-vine.
heav'n-ly dress My soul shall ev-er shine, My soul shall ev-er shine.
last-ing days Make all His glo-ries known, Make all His glo-ries known.
ty I'll spend, Tri-um-phant in His grace, Tri-um-phant in His grace.

301 THE KINGDOM IS COMING

MARY B. C. SLADE

ROBERT M. McINTOSH

1. From all the dark pla - ces Of earth's hea-then ra - ces, O
2. The sun - light is glanc - ing O'er ar - mies ad - vanc - ing To
3. With shout - ing and sing - ing, And ju - bi-lant ring - ing, Their

see how the thick shadows fly! The voice of sal - va - tion A -
con - quer the king - doms of sin; Our Lord shall pos-sess them, His
arms of re - bel - lion cast down, At last ev - 'ry na - tion, The

wakes ev - 'ry na - tion, "Come o - ver and help us," they cry.
pres - ence shall bless them, His beau - ty shall en - ter them in.
Lord of sal - va - tion Their King and Re - deem - er shall crown!

REFRAIN

The kingdom is coming, O tell ye the story, God's banner ex-alt-ed shall be!

The earth shall be full of His knowledge and glory, As waters that cover the sea!

302 TILL THE WHOLE WORLD KNOWS

Rev. A. H. Ackley

B. D. Ackley

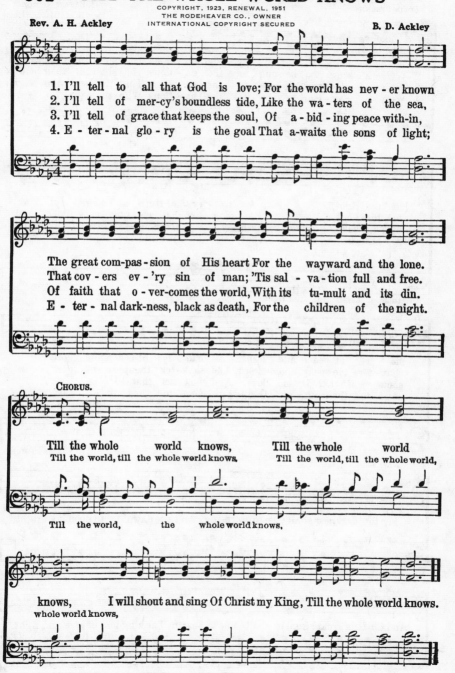

1. I'll tell to all that God is love; For the world has nev - er known
2. I'll tell of mer-cy's boundless tide, Like the wa - ters of the sea,
3. I'll tell of grace that keeps the soul, Of a - bid - ing peace with-in,
4. E - ter - nal glo - ry is the goal That a-waits the sons of light;

The great com-pas-sion of His heart For the wayward and the lone.
That cov - ers ev - 'ry sin of man; 'Tis sal - va - tion full and free.
Of faith that o - ver-comes the world, With its tu-mult and its din.
E - ter - nal dark-ness, black as death, For the children of the night.

CHORUS.

Till the whole world knows, Till the whole world
Till the world, till the whole world knows, Till the world, till the whole world,
Till the world, the whole world knows,

knows, I will shout and sing Of Christ my King, Till the whole world knows.
whole world knows,

303 WE'VE A STORY TO TELL TO THE NATIONS

Colin Sterne   H. Ernest Nichol

1. We've a sto-ry to tell to the na-tions That shall turn their hearts
2. We've a song to be sung to the na-tions That shall lift their hearts
3. We've a mes-sage to give to the na-tions, That the Lord who reign-
4. We've a Sav-iour to show to the na-tions Who the path of sor-

1. That shall turn

to the right,   A sto-ry of truth and mer-cy,   A
to the Lord,   A song that shall con-quer e-vil   And
eth a-bove   Hath sent us His Son to save us,   And
row hath trod,   That all of the world's great peo-ples Might

their hearts to the right,

sto-ry of peace and light, A sto-ry of peace and light.
shat-ter the spear and sword, And shat-ter the spear and sword.
show us that God is love, And show us that God is love.
come to the truth of God, Might come to the truth of God.

A sto-ry of peace and light.

REFRAIN

For the darkness shall turn to dawn-ing, And the dawning to noonday bright,

rall.

And Christ's great kingdom shall come to earth, The kingdom of love and light.

304 THE MORNING LIGHT IS BREAKING

S. F. Smith   WEBB 7. 6. 7. 6. D.   G. J. Webb

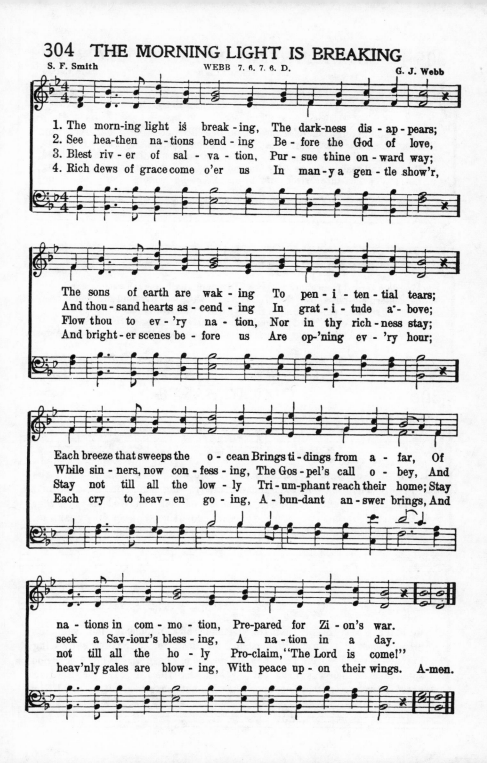

1. The morn-ing light is break-ing, The dark-ness dis-ap-pears;
2. See hea-then na-tions bend-ing Be-fore the God of love,
3. Blest riv-er of sal-va-tion, Pur-sue thine on-ward way;
4. Rich dews of grace come o'er us In man-y a gen-tle show'r,

The sons of earth are wak-ing To pen-i-ten-tial tears;
And thou-sand hearts as-cend-ing In grat-i-tude a-bove;
Flow thou to ev-'ry na-tion, Nor in thy rich-ness stay;
And bright-er scenes be-fore us Are op-'ning ev-'ry hour;

Each breeze that sweeps the o-cean Brings ti-dings from a-far, Of
While sin-ners, now con-fess-ing, The Gos-pel's call o-bey, And
Stay not till all the low-ly Tri-um-phant reach their home; Stay
Each cry to heav-en go-ing, A-bun-dant an-swer brings, And

na-tions in com-mo-tion, Pre-pared for Zi-on's war.
seek a Sav-iour's bless-ing, A na-tion in a day.
not till all the ho-ly Pro-claim, "The Lord is come!"
heav'nly gales are blow-ing, With peace up-on their wings. A-men.

305 JESUS SHALL REIGN WHERE'ER THE SUN

Isaac Watts　　　　　DUKE STREET L. M.　　　　　John Hatton

1. Je - sus shall reign where'er the sun Does his successive jour-neys run;
2. From north to south the prin-ces meet To pay their homage at His feet;
3. To Him shall endless pray'r be made, And endless praises crown His head;
4. Peo-ple and realms of ev - 'ry tongue Dwell on His love with sweetest song,
5. Let ev-'ry crea-ture rise and bring Pe-cu-liar honors to our King;

His kingdom spread from shore to shore, Till moons shall wax and wane no more.
While western em-pires own their Lord, And savage tribes attend His word.
His name like sweet per-fume shall rise With ev'ry morn-ing sac-ri - fice.
And infant voic-es shall pro-claim Their early blessings on His name.
An - gels descend with songs a - gain, And earth repeat the loud A - men. A-men.

306 O ZION, HASTE

Mary A. Thomson　　　　　　　　　　　　　James Walch

1. O Zi - on, haste, Thy mission high ful-fill - ing, To tell to all the
2. Be - hold how ma - ny thousands still are ly - ing Bound in the dark-some
3. Pro-claim to ev - 'ry people, tongue and na-tion That God in whom they
4. Give of Thy sons to bear the message glo - rious; Give of thy wealth to
5. He comes a - gain; O Zi - on, ere thou meet Him Make known to ev - 'ry

world that God is Light; That He who made all nations is not will - ing
pris-on-house of sin, With none to tell them of the Saviour's dy - ing,
live and move is love: Tell how He stooped to save His lost cre - a - tion,
speed them on their way; Pour out thy soul for them in pray'r vic - to - rious;
heart His saving grace; Let none whom He hath ransomed fail to greet Him,

O ZION, HASTE

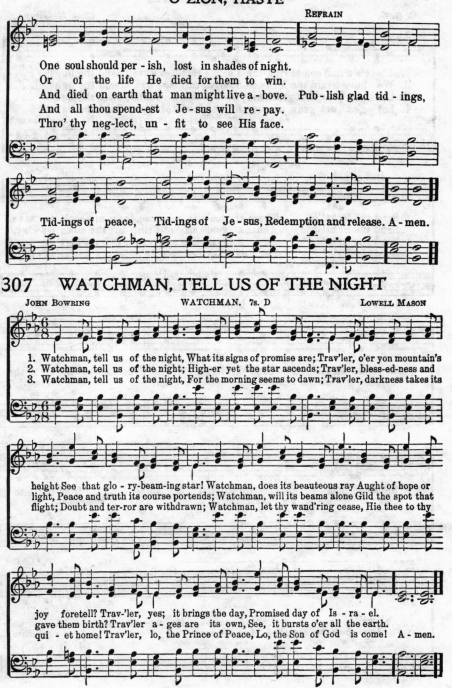

REFRAIN

One soul should per - ish, lost in shades of night.
Or of the life He died for them to win.
And died on earth that man might live a - bove. Pub - lish glad tid - ings,
And all thou spend-est Je - sus will re - pay.
Thro' thy neg-lect, un - fit to see His face.

Tid-ings of peace, Tid-ings of Je - sus, Redemption and release. A - men.

307 WATCHMAN, TELL US OF THE NIGHT

JOHN BOWRING   WATCHMAN. 7s. D   LOWELL MASON

1. Watchman, tell us of the night, What its signs of promise are; Trav'ler, o'er yon mountain's
2. Watchman, tell us of the night; High-er yet the star ascends; Trav'ler, bless-ed-ness and
3. Watchman, tell us of the night, For the morning seems to dawn; Trav'ler, darkness takes its

height See that glo - ry-beam-ing star! Watchman, does its beauteous ray Aught of hope or
light, Peace and truth its course portends; Watchman, will its beams alone Gild the spot that
flight; Doubt and ter-ror are withdrawn; Watchman, let thy wand'ring cease, Hie thee to thy

joy foretell? Trav'ler, yes; it brings the day, Promised day of Is - ra - el.
gave them birth? Trav'ler a - ges are its own, See, it bursts o'er all the earth.
qui - et home! Trav'ler, lo, the Prince of Peace, Lo, the Son of God is come! A - men.

308 SEND THE LIGHT

C. H. G.

Chas. H. Gabriel

1. There's a call comes ring-ing o'er the rest-less wave, "Send the light! . . . .
2. We have heard the Mac-e-do-nian call to-day, "Send the light! . . . .
3. Let us pray that grace may ev-'ry-where a-bound; Send the light! . . . .
4. Let us not grow wea-ry in the work of love, Send the light! . . . .

Send the light!

Send the light!" There are souls to res-cue, there are souls to save,
Send the light!" And a gold-en of-f'ring at the cross we lay,
Send the light! And a Christ-like spir-it ev-'ry-where be found,
Send the light! Let us gath-er jew-els for a crown a-bove,

Send the light!

REFRAIN

Send the light! . . . . Send the light! . . . . Send the light! . . . . the
Send the light! Send the light! Send the light!

bless-ed gos-pel light; Let it shine . . . . from shore to
the bless-ed gos-pel light; Let it shine

shore! . . . . shine . . . . for-ev-er-more. . . . . .
from shore to shore! Let it shine for-ev-er-more.

309 IT CAME UPON THE MIDNIGHT CLEAR

EDMUND H. SEARS   RICHARD S. WILLIS

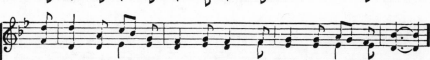

1. It came up - on the mid-night clear, That glo-rious song of old,
2. Still thro' the clo-ven skies they come, With peaceful wings un - furled,
3. And ye, be - neath life's crushing load, Whose forms are bending low,
4. For lo, the days are has - t'ning on, By prophet bards fore-told,

From an - gels bending near the earth To touch their harps of gold:
And still their heav'nly mu - sic floats O'er all the wea - ry world:
Who toil a - long the climb - ing way With pain - ful steps and slow,
When with the ev - er - cir - cling years Comes 'round the age of gold:

"Peace on the earth, good-will to men, From heav'ns all-gracious King:" The
A - bove its sad and low - ly plains They bend on hov'ring wing: And
Look now! for glad and gold - en hours Come swift-ly on the wing; O
When peace shall o - ver all the earth Its an - cient splendors fling, And

world in sol - emn still-ness lay To hear the an - gels sing.
ev - er o'er its Ba - bel sounds The bless-ed an - gels sing.
rest be - side the wea - ry road, And hear the an - gels sing.
the whole world give back the song Which now the an - gels sing. A - men.

310 O LITTLE TOWN OF BETHLEHEM

Phillips Brooks   ST. LOUIS 8. 6. 8. 6. D. Irregular   Lewis H. Redner

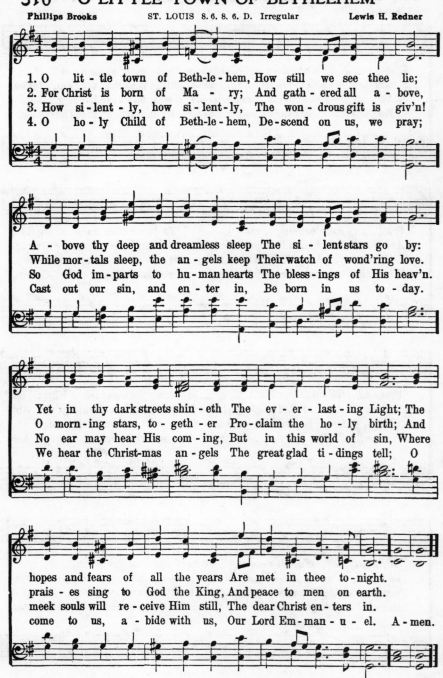

1. O lit - tle town of Beth-le - hem, How still we see thee lie;
2. For Christ is born of Ma - ry; And gath - ered all a - bove,
3. How si - lent - ly, how si - lent - ly, The won - drous gift is giv'n!
4. O ho - ly Child of Beth-le - hem, De - scend on us, we pray;

A - bove thy deep and dreamless sleep The si - lent stars go by:
While mor - tals sleep, the an - gels keep Their watch of wond'ring love.
So God im - parts to hu - man hearts The bless - ings of His heav'n.
Cast out our sin, and en - ter in, Be born in us to - day.

Yet in thy dark streets shin - eth The ev - er - last - ing Light; The
O morn - ing stars, to - geth - er Pro - claim the ho - ly birth; And
No ear may hear His com - ing, But in this world of sin, Where
We hear the Christ-mas an - gels The great glad ti - dings tell; O

hopes and fears of all the years Are met in thee to - night.
prais - es sing to God the King, And peace to men on earth.
meek souls will re - ceive Him still, The dear Christ en - ters in.
come to us, a - bide with us, Our Lord Em - man - u - el. A - men.

311 JOY TO THE WORLD

Isaac Watts · ANTIOCH C. M. · George F. Handel

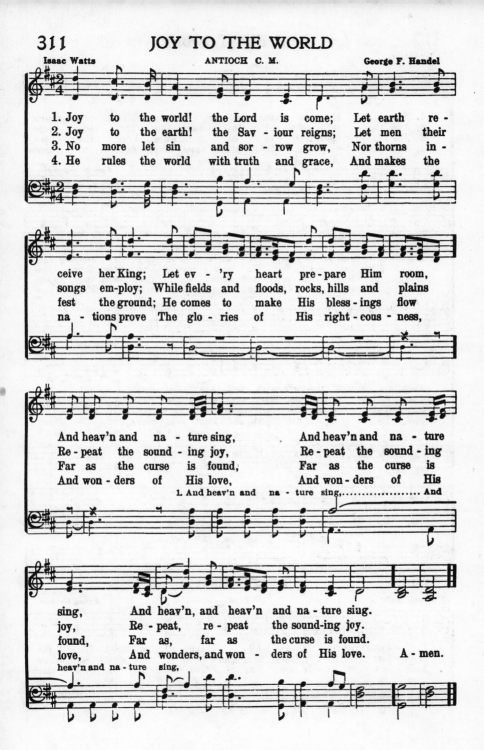

1. Joy to the world! the Lord is come; Let earth re-
2. Joy to the earth! the Sav-iour reigns; Let men their
3. No more let sin and sor-row grow, Nor thorns in-
4. He rules the world with truth and grace, And makes the

ceive her King; Let ev-'ry heart pre-pare Him room,
songs em-ploy; While fields and floods, rocks, hills and plains
fest the ground; He comes to make His bless-ings flow
na-tions prove The glo-ries of His right-eous-ness,

And heav'n and na-ture sing,
Re-peat the sound-ing joy,
Far as the curse is found,
And won-ders of His love,

And heav'n and na-ture
Re-peat the sound-ing
Far as the curse is
And won-ders of His

1. And heav'n and na-ture sing,.................... And

sing, And heav'n, and heav'n and na-ture sing.
joy, Re-peat, re-peat the sound-ing joy.
found, Far as, far as the curse is found.
love, And wonders, and won-ders of His love. A-men.

heav'n and na-ture sing,

312 THE FIRST NOEL

Traditional

Traditional

313 SILENT NIGHT

Joseph Mohr

P. M.

Franz Gruber

SILENT NIGHT

vir - gin moth - er and Child! Ho - ly In - fant, so ten - der and mild,
stream from heav-en a - far, Heav'n-ly hosts sing Al - le - lu - ia;
beams from Thy ho - ly face, With the dawn of re - deem - ing grace,

Sleep in heav - en - ly peace, Sleep in heav - en - ly peace.
Christ, the Sav-iour, is born, Christ, the Sav-iour, is born.
Je - sus, Lord, at Thy birth, Je - sus, Lord, at Thy birth. A - MEN.

314 AWAY IN A MANGER

M. L.

Martin Luther

1. A - way in a man - ger, No crib for a bed, The lit - tle Lord
2. The cat - tle are low - ing, The Ba - by a-wakes, But lit - tle Lord
3. Be near me, Lord Je - sus, I ask Thee to stay Close by me for-

Je - sus Laid down His sweet head; The stars in the sky Looked
Je - sus, No cry - ing He makes; I love Thee, Lord Je - sus! Look
ev - er, And love me, I pray; Bless all the dear chil - dren In

down where He lay,—The lit - tle Lord Je - sus, A - sleep on the hay.
down from the sky, And stay by my cra - dle, Till morn-ing is nigh.
Thy ten - der care, Pre - pare us for heav - en, To live with Thee there.

315 HARK! THE HERALD ANGELS SING

MENDELSSOHN 7. 7. 7. 7. D. With Refrain

Charles Wesley   Felix Mendelssohn Bartholdy

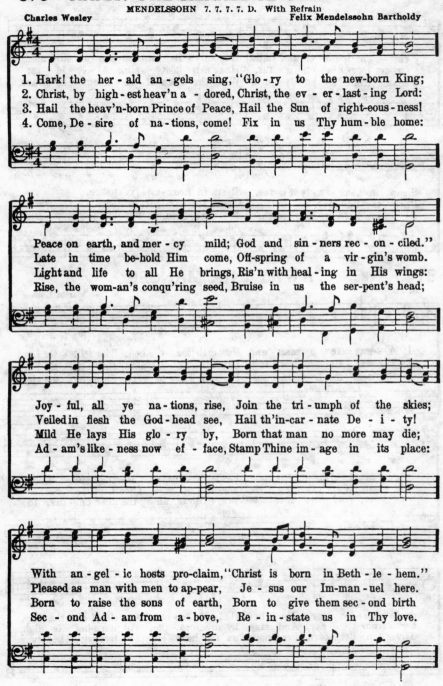

1. Hark! the her-ald an-gels sing, "Glo-ry to the new-born King;
2. Christ, by high-est heav'n a - dored, Christ, the ev-er-last-ing Lord:
3. Hail the heav'n-born Prince of Peace, Hail the Sun of right-eous-ness!
4. Come, De-sire of na-tions, come! Fix in us Thy hum-ble home:

Peace on earth, and mer-cy mild; God and sin-ners rec-on-ciled."
Late in time be-hold Him come, Off-spring of a vir-gin's womb.
Light and life to all He brings, Ris'n with heal-ing in His wings:
Rise, the wom-an's conqu'ring seed, Bruise in us the ser-pent's head;

Joy-ful, all ye na-tions, rise, Join the tri-umph of the skies;
Veiled in flesh the God-head see, Hail th'in-car-nate De - i - ty!
Mild He lays His glo-ry by, Born that man no more may die;
Ad-am's like-ness now ef - face, Stamp Thine im-age in its place:

With an-gel-ic hosts pro-claim, "Christ is born in Beth-le-hem."
Pleased as man with men to ap-pear, Je-sus our Im-man-uel here.
Born to raise the sons of earth, Born to give them sec-ond birth
Sec-ond Ad-am from a-bove, Re-in-state us in Thy love.

HARK! THE HERALD ANGELS SING

Hark! the her-ald an-gels sing, "Glo-ry to the new-born King." Amen.

316   O COME, ALL YE FAITHFUL

Tr. by Frederick Oakeley   PORTUGUESE HYMN P. M.   Wade's Cantus Diversi

1. O come, all ye faith-ful, joy-ful and tri-um-phant, O
2. Sing, choirs of an-gels, sing in ex-ul-ta-tion, O
3. Yea, Lord, we greet Thee, born this hap-py morn-ing,

come ye, O come ye to Beth-le-hem; Come and be-hold Him,
sing, all ye bright hosts of heav'n a-bove; Glo-ry to God, all
Je-sus, to Thee be all glo-ry giv'n; Word of the Fa-ther,

REFRAIN

born the King of an-gels.
glo-ry in the high-est. O come, let us a-dore Him, O come, let us a-
now in flesh ap-pear-ing.

dore Him, O come, let us a-dore Him, Christ, the Lord. A-men.

317 RING OUT THE OLD, RING IN THE NEW

Alfred Tennyson

J. Baptiste Calkin

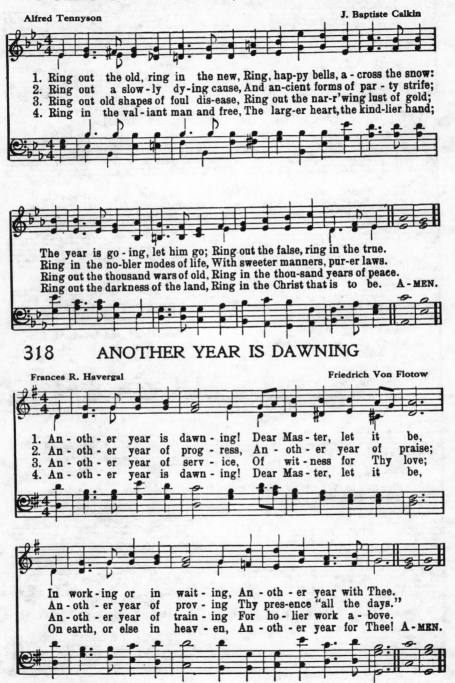

1. Ring out the old, ring in the new, Ring, hap-py bells, a-cross the snow:
2. Ring out a slow-ly dy-ing cause, And an-cient forms of par-ty strife;
3. Ring out old shapes of foul dis-ease, Ring out the nar-r'wing lust of gold;
4. Ring in the val-iant man and free, The larg-er heart, the kind-lier hand;

The year is go-ing, let him go; Ring out the false, ring in the true.
Ring in the no-bler modes of life, With sweeter manners, pur-er laws.
Ring out the thousand wars of old, Ring in the thou-sand years of peace.
Ring out the darkness of the land, Ring in the Christ that is to be. A-MEN.

318   ANOTHER YEAR IS DAWNING

Frances R. Havergal

Friedrich Von Flotow

1. An-oth-er year is dawn-ing! Dear Mas-ter, let it be,
2. An-oth-er year of prog-ress, An-oth-er year of praise;
3. An-oth-er year of serv-ice, Of wit-ness for Thy love;
4. An-oth-er year is dawn-ing! Dear Mas-ter, let it be,

In work-ing or in wait-ing, An-oth-er year with Thee.
An-oth-er year of prov-ing Thy pres-ence "all the days."
An-oth-er year of train-ing For ho-lier work a-bove.
On earth, or else in heav-en, An-oth-er year for Thee! A-MEN.

319 O SACRED HEAD, NOW WOUNDED

MUNICH 7. 6. 7. 6. D.

Tr. by J. W. Alexander

Arr. by Felix Mendelssohn-Bartholdy

1. O sa - cred Head, now wound - ed, With grief and shame weighed down,
2. What language shall I bor - row To thank Thee, dear-est Friend,
3. Be near me when I'm dy - ing, Oh! show Thy cross to me;

Now scorn-ful - ly sur - round - ed With thorns, Thine on - ly crown;
For this, Thy dy - ing sor - row, Thy pit - y with - out end?
And, for my suc - cor fly - ing, Come, Lord, and set me free:

O sa - cred Head, what glo - ry, What bliss, till now was Thine!
Oh! make me Thine, for - ev - er; And should I faint-ing be,
These eyes, new faith re - ceiv - ing, From Je - sus shall not move;

Yet, though despised and gor - y, I joy to call Thee mine.
Lord, let me nev - er, nev - er, Out - live my love to Thee.
For he who dies be - liev - ing, Dies safe - ly, thro' Thy love. A - men.

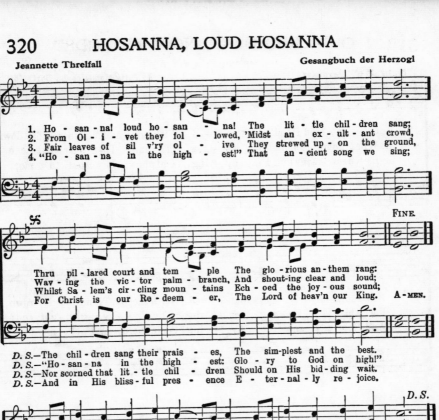

320 HOSANNA, LOUD HOSANNA

Jeannette Threlfall

Gesangbuch der Herzogl

1. Ho - san - na! loud ho - san - na! The lit - tle chil - dren sang;
2. From Ol - i - vet they fol - lowed, 'Midst an ex - ult - ant crowd,
3. Fair leaves of sil v'ry ol - ive They strewed up - on the ground,
4. "Ho - san - na in the high - est!" That an - cient song we sing;

Thru pil - lared court and tem - ple The glo - rious an - them rang;
Wav - ing the vic - tor palm - branch, And shout-ing clear and loud;
Whilst Sa - lem's cir - cling moun - tains Ech - oed the joy - ous sound;
For Christ is our Re - deem - er, The Lord of heav'n our King.   A-MEN.

FINE

D. S.—The chil - dren sang their prais - es, The sim-plest and the best.
D. S.—"Ho - san - na in the high - est: Glo - ry to God on high!"
D. S.—Nor scorned that lit - tle chil - dren Should on His bid - ding wait.
D. S.—And in His bliss - ful pres - ence E - ter - nal - ly re - joice.

To Je - sus who had blessed them, Close fold - ed to His breast,
Bright an - gels joined the cho - - rus Be - yond the cloud - less sky—
The Lord of men and an - - gels Rode on in low - ly state,
O may we ev - er praise Him With heart, and life, and voice,

D. S.

321 MUST JESUS BEAR THE CROSS ALONE?

Thomas Shepherd

George N. Allen

1. Must Je - sus bear the cross a - lone, And all the world go free?
2. How hap - py are the saints a - bove, Who once went sor-rowing here!
3. The con - se - cra - ted cross I'll bear, Till death shall set me free;
4. Up - on the crys - tal pavement, down At Je - sus' pierc - ed feet,

MUST JESUS BEAR THE CROSS ALONE?

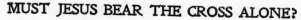

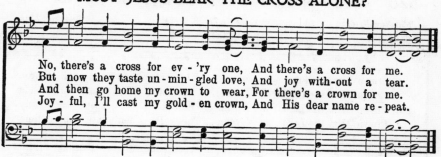

No, there's a cross for ev - 'ry one, And there's a cross for me.
But now they taste un - min - gled love, And joy with-out a tear.
And then go home my crown to wear, For there's a crown for me.
Joy - ful, I'll cast my gold - en crown, And His dear name re - peat.

322 TELL THE WORLD THAT JESUS SAVES

A. H. A.

A. H. Ackley

1. Tell the world there is a Sav - iour Who ful - fills His ev - 'ry claim;
2. Tell the souls weighed down with sor - row, Tried and tempt - ed, lone and weak,
3. Tell the na - tions in sub - jec - tion, There is hope in Christ the Lord;
4. Has - ten, Chris - tian, to pro - claim it, Hun - gry souls He waits to feed;

He is a - ble to de - liv - er All who call up - on His name.
They can know His full sal - va - tion, Find in Him the help they seek.
He will lib - er - ate from bond - age All who heed His bless - ed Word.
God in His great love has giv - en Christ to meet man's ev - 'ry need.

CHORUS

Tell the world, Tell the world, Tell the world that Je - sus saves.

323 CROWN HIM WITH MANY CROWNS

Matthew Bridges   DIADEMATA S. M. D.   George J. Elvey

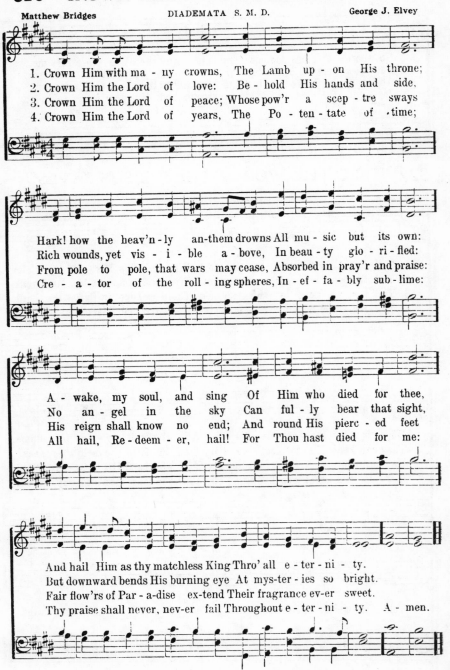

1. Crown Him with ma - ny crowns, The Lamb up - on His throne;
2. Crown Him the Lord of love: Be - hold His hands and side,
3. Crown Him the Lord of peace; Whose pow'r a scep - tre sways
4. Crown Him the Lord of years, The Po - ten - tate of time;

Hark! how the heav'n - ly an-them drowns All mu - sic but its own:
Rich wounds, yet vis - i - ble a - bove, In beau - ty glo - ri - fied:
From pole to pole, that wars may cease, Absorbed in pray'r and praise:
Cre - a - tor of the roll - ing spheres, In - ef - fa - bly sub - lime:

A - wake, my soul, and sing Of Him who died for thee,
No an - gel in the sky Can ful - ly bear that sight,
His reign shall know no end; And round His pierc - ed feet
All hail, Re - deem - er, hail! For Thou hast died for me:

And hail Him as thy matchless King Thro' all e - ter - ni - ty.
But downward bends His burning eye At mys-ter - ies so bright.
Fair flow'rs of Par - a-dise ex-tend Their fragrance ev-er sweet.
Thy praise shall never, nev-er fail Throughout e - ter - ni - ty. A - men.

324 CHRIST, THE LORD, IS RISEN TODAY

Charles Wesley   (WORGAN)   From "Lyra Davidica"

1. Christ the Lord is ris'n to-day.   Al - - - le - lu - ia!
2. Lives a-gain our glo-rious King: Al - - - le - lu - ia!
3. Love's re-deem-ing work is done,   Al - - - le - lu - ia!
4. Soar we now, where Christ has led,   Al - - - le - lu - ia!

Sons of men and an-gels say: Al - - - le - lu - ia!
Where, O death, is now thy sting?   Al - - - le - lu - ia!
Fought the fight, the bat-tle won;   Al - - - le - lu - ia!
Fol-l'wing our ex-alt-ed Head;   Al - - - le - lu - ia!

Raise your joys and tri-umphs high,   Al - - - le - lu - ia!
Dy-ing once, He all doth save: Al - - - le - lu - ia!
Death in vain for-bids Him rise;   Al - - - le - lu - ia!
Made like Him, like Him we rise;   Al - - - le - lu - ia!

Sing, ye heav'ns, and earth re-ply,   Al - - - le - lu - ia!
Where thy vic-to-ry, O grave?   Al - - - le - lu - ia!
Christ has o-pened Par-a-dise.   Al - - - le - lu - ia!
Ours the cross, the grave, the skies.   Al - - - le - lu - ia!

325 COME, YE FAITHFUL, RAISE THE STRAIN

John of Damascus
Tr. by John M. Neale

Arthur S. Sullivan

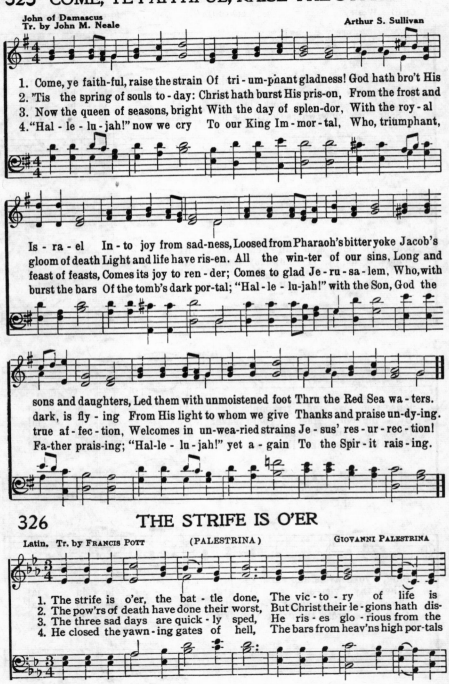

1. Come, ye faith-ful, raise the strain Of tri-um-phant gladness! God hath bro't His
2. 'Tis the spring of souls to-day: Christ hath burst His pris-on, From the frost and
3. Now the queen of seasons, bright With the day of splen-dor, With the roy-al
4. "Hal-le-lu-jah!" now we cry To our King Im-mor-tal, Who, triumphant,

Is-ra-el In-to joy from sad-ness, Loosed from Pharaoh's bitter yoke Jacob's
gloom of death Light and life have ris-en. All the win-ter of our sins, Long and
feast of feasts, Comes its joy to ren-der; Comes to glad Je-ru-sa-lem, Who, with
burst the bars Of the tomb's dark por-tal; "Hal-le-lu-jah!" with the Son, God the

sons and daughters, Led them with unmoistened foot Thru the Red Sea wa-ters.
dark, is fly-ing From His light to whom we give Thanks and praise un-dy-ing.
true af-fec-tion, Welcomes in un-wea-ried strains Je-sus' res-ur-rec-tion!
Fa-ther prais-ing; "Hal-le-lu-jah!" yet a-gain To the Spir-it rais-ing.

326 THE STRIFE IS O'ER

Latin. Tr. by FRANCIS POTT   (PALESTRINA)   GIOVANNI PALESTRINA

1. The strife is o'er, the bat-tle done, The vic-to-ry of life is
2. The pow'rs of death have done their worst, But Christ their le-gions hath dis-
3. The three sad days are quick-ly sped, He ris-es glo-rious from the
4. He closed the yawn-ing gates of hell, The bars from heav'ns high por-tals

THE STRIFE IS O'ER

won; The song of tri-umph has be-gun. Al-le-lu-ia!
persed: Let shout of ho-ly joy out-burst. Al-le-lu-ia!
dead: All glo-ry to our ris-en Head! Al-le-lu-ia!
fell, Let hymns of praise His tri-umphs tell! Al-le-lu-ia!

327 ALONE

B. H. P.

Ben H. Price

DUET

1. It was a-lone the Sav-iour prayed In dark Geth-sem-a-ne;
2. It was a-lone the Sav-iour stood In Pi-late's judgment hall;
3. A-lone up-on the cross He hung That oth-ers He might save;
4. Can you re-ject such matchless love? Can you His claim dis-own?

A-lone He drained the bit-ter cup, And suf-fered there for me.
A-lone the crown of thorns He wore, For-sak-en thus by all.
For-sak-en then by God and man, A-lone, His life He gave.
Come, give your all in grat-i-tude, Nor leave Him thus a-lone.

REFRAIN *Quartet*

A-lone, a-lone, He bore it all a-lone; He
it was a-lone, yes, all a-lone, yes, all a-lone;

ff *dim.* *pp*

gave Him-self to save His own, He suffered, bled and died a-lone, a-lone.

328 CHRIST AROSE

R. L.

Robert Lowry

1. Low in the grave He lay— Je-sus my Sav-iour! Wait-ing the com-ing day—
2. Vain-ly they watch His bed—Je-sus my Sav-iour! Vain-ly they seal the dead—
3. Death cannot keep his prey—Je-sus my Sav-iour! He tore the bars a-way—

REFRAIN *Faster*

Je-sus my Lord! Up from the grave He a-rose,
He a-rose!
With a

might-y tri-umph o'er His foes;
He a-rose!
He a-rose a Vic-tor from the

dark do-main, And He lives for-ev-er with His saints to reign, He a-

rose! He a-rose! Hal-le-lu-jah! Christ a-rose!
He a-rose! He a-rose!

329 NOW THANK WE ALL OUR GOD

Martin Rinkart
Tr. by Catherine Winkworth

Crüger's Praxis Pietatis Melica

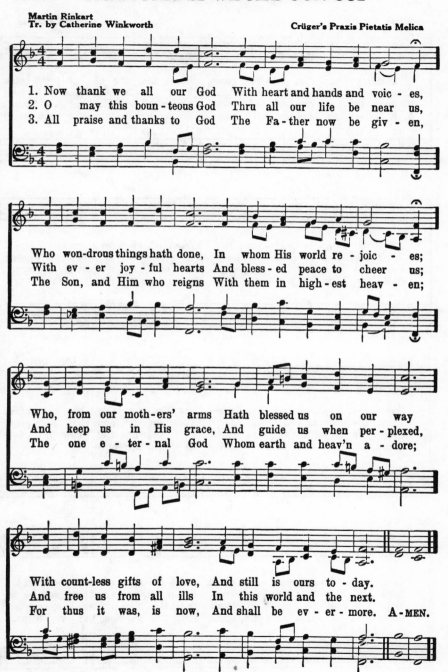

1. Now thank we all our God With heart and hands and voic - es,
2. O may this boun - teous God Thru all our life be near us,
3. All praise and thanks to God The Fa - ther now be giv - en,

Who won-drous things hath done, In whom His world re - joic - es;
With ev - er joy - ful hearts And bless - ed peace to cheer us;
The Son, and Him who reigns With them in high - est heav - en;

Who, from our moth-ers' arms Hath blessed us on our way
And keep us in His grace, And guide us when per - plexed,
The one e - ter - nal God Whom earth and heav'n a - dore;

With count-less gifts of love, And still is ours to - day.
And free us from all ills In this world and the next.
For thus it was, is now, And shall be ev - er - more. A - MEN.

COME, YE THANKFUL PEOPLE

HENRY ALFORD   George J. Elvey

1. Come, ye thank-ful peo-ple, come, Raise the song of har-vest-home:
2. All the world is God's own field, Fruit un-to His praise to yield;
3. For the Lord our God shall come, And shall take His har-vest home;
4. E-ven so, Lord, quick-ly come To Thy fi-nal har-vest-home;

All is safe-ly gath-ered in, Ere the win-ter storms be-gin;
Wheat and tares to-geth-er sown, Un-to joy or sor-row grown;
From His field shall in that day All of-fens-es purge a-way;
Gath-er Thou Thy peo-ple in, Free from sor-row, free from sin;

God, our Ma-ker, doth pro-vide For our wants to be sup-plied:
First the blade, and then the ear, Then the full corn shall ap-pear:
Give His an-gels charge at last In the fire the tares to cast;
There, for-ev-er pu-ri-fied, In Thy pres-ence to a-bide:

Come to God's own tem-ple, come, Raise the song of har-vest-home.
Lord of har-vest, grant that we Wholesome grain and pure may be.
But the fruit-ful ears to store In His gar-ner ev-er-more.
Come, with all Thine an-gels, come, Raise the glo-rious har-vest-home.

WE GATHER TOGETHER

Folksong of the Netherlands
Arr. by E. Kremser

1. We gath - er to - geth - er   to   ask the Lord's bless - ing,
2. Be - side us to guide us, our God with us join - ing,
3. We all   do ex - tol Thee, Thou Lead - er in   bat - tle,

He chas - tens and has - tens His will   to make known;
Or - dain - ing, main - tain - ing His king - dom di - vine;
And pray   that Thou still onr De - fend - er wilt be.

The wick - ed op - press - ing cease them from dis - tress - ing,
So from   the be - gin - ning the fight   we were win - ning,
Let Thy con - gre - ga - tion es - cape   trib - u - la - tion;

Sing prais - es to His name, He for - gets not His own.
Thou, Lord, wast at our side, — the glo - ry be Thine!
Thy name be ev - er praised. O   Lord make us free! A - MEN.

The first two stanzas should be sung in unison (alternately by the male and female voices if
desired), and the last stanza in full harmony.

THE LORD IS MY SHEPHERD

James S. Montgomery

Thomas Koschat

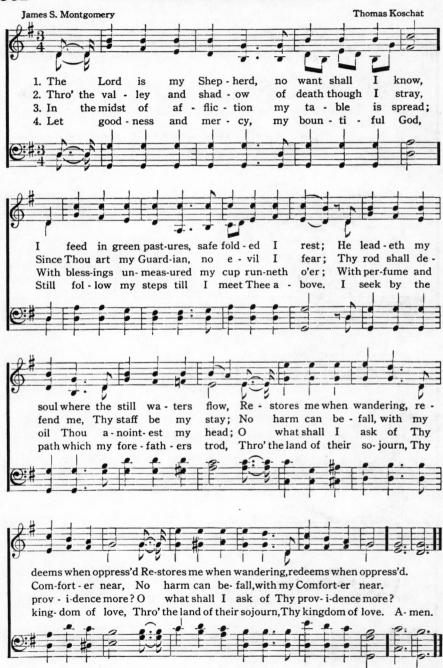

1. The Lord is my Shep - herd, no want shall I know,
2. Thro' the val - ley and shad - ow of death though I stray,
3. In the midst of af - flic - tion my ta - ble is spread;
4. Let good - ness and mer - cy, my boun - ti - ful God,

I feed in green past-ures, safe fold - ed I rest; He lead - eth my
Since Thou art my Guard-ian, no e - vil I fear; Thy rod shall de -
With bless-ings un - meas-ured my cup run-neth o'er; With per-fume and
Still fol - low my steps till I meet Thee a - bove. I seek by the

soul where the still wa - ters flow, Re - stores me when wandering, re -
fend me, Thy staff be my stay; No harm can be - fall, with my
oil Thou a - noint-est my head; O what shall I ask of Thy
path which my fore - fath - ers trod, Thro' the land of their so-journ, Thy

deems when oppress'd Re-stores me when wandering, redeems when oppress'd.
Com-fort - er near, No harm can be-fall, with my Comfort-er near.
prov - i-dence more? O what shall I ask of Thy prov-i-dence more?
king- dom of love, Thro' the land of their sojourn, Thy kingdom of love. A-men.

333 WONDERFUL JESUS

(The Gipsy Smith Campaign Song)

Annie B. Russell   Ernest O. Sellers

1. There is nev-er a day so drear-y, There is nev-er a
2. There is nev-er a cross so heav-y, There is nev-er a
3. There is nev-er a care or bur-den, There is nev-er a
4. There is nev-er a guilt-y sin-ner, There is nev-er a

night so long, (so long,) But the soul that is trust-ing Je-sus Will
weight of woe, (of woe,) But that Je-sus will help to car-ry Be-
grief or loss, (or loss,) But that Je-sus in love will light-en When
wan-d'ring one, (not one,) But that God can in mer-cy par-don Thro'

CHORUS

some-where find a song. (a song.)
cause He lov-eth so. (loves so.)
car-ried to the cross. (the cross.) Won-der-ful, won-der-ful Je-sus,
Je-sus Christ, His Son. (His Son.)

In the heart He im-plant-eth a song:........ A song of de-

He plant-eth a song:

liv-'rance, of courage, of strength, In the heart He im-plant-eth a song. (a song.)

334 JESUS IS THE SWEETEST NAME I KNOW

Lela Long

1. There have been names that I have loved to hear, But nev-er has there
2. There is no name in earth or heav'n a-bove, That we should give such
3. And some day I shall see Him face to face To thank and praise Him

been a name so dear To this heart of mine, as the name di-vine, The
hon-or and such love, As the bless-ed name, let us all ac-claim, That
for His won-drous grace, Which He gave to me, when He made me free, The

pre-cious, pre-cious name of Je-sus.
wondrous, glo-rious name of Je-sus. Je-sus is the sweet-est name I
bless-ed Son of God called Je-sus.

know, And He's just the same as His love-ly name, And that's the rea-son

why I love Him so; Oh, Je-sus is the sweet-est name I know.

335 OUR BEST

S. C. Kirk
With dignity

Grant Colfax Tullar

1. Hear ye the Mas-ter's call, "Give Me thy best!" For, be it great or small,
2. Wait not for men to laud, Heed not their slight; Win-ning the smile of God
3. Night soon comes on a-pace, Day has-tens by; Workman and work must face

That is His test. Do then the best you can, Not for re-ward, Not for the
Brings its de-light! Aid-ing the good and true Ne'er goes un-blest, All that we
Test-ing on high. Oh, may we in that day Find rest, sweet rest, Which God has

CHORUS

praise of man, But for the Lord.
think or do, Be it the best. Ev - 'ry work for Je-sus will be blest,
promised those Who do their best.

But He asks from ev - 'ry - one his best. Our tal-ents may be few,

These may be small, But un - to Him is due Our best, our all.

336 THE BEAUTIFUL GARDEN OF PRAYER

ELEANOR ALLEN SCHROLL   J. H. FILLMORE

1. There's a gar-den where Je-sus is wait-ing, There's a place that is
2. There's a gar-den where Je-sus is wait-ing, And I go with my
3. There's a gar-den where Je-sus is wait-ing, And He bids you to

won-drous-ly fair; For it glows with the light of His pres-ence, 'Tis the
bur-den and care, Just to learn from His lips words of com-fort, In the
come meet Him there; Just to bow and re-ceive a new bless-ing, In the

REFRAIN

beau-ti-ful gar-den of pray'r. O the beau-ti-ful gar-den, the

garden of pray'r, O the beau-ti-ful gar-den of pray'r; There my Savior a-

waits, and He o-pens the gates To the beau-ti-ful gar-den of pray'r.

337 THE STRANGER BY THE SEA

C. A. M.

C. Austin Miles

1. The stran-gers to God, His grace and His love, Were gathered by blue Gal-i-
2. They sat at His feet And looked in His face, Con-tent in His pres-ence to
3. Their souls were athirst; They drank at the Fount Of wa-ters, life-giv-ing and

lee, To lis-ten with joy To words from the lips Of the Stran-ger who
be; For no one be-fore Had cared for their souls, Like the Stranger who
free; Their strength was renewed, Their hope was re-vived By the Stran-ger who

CHORUS

sat by the sea. They came and they were blest; He gave the wea-ry,

rest, He made the blind-ed eyes to see (to see); He fed the hun-gry

soul And made the wounded whole, By the wa-ters of blue Gal-i-lee. . . .

338 WONDERFUL PEACE

W. D. Cornell, alt.

W. G. Cooper

1. Far a-way in the depths of my spir-it to-night Rolls a
2. What a treas-ure I have in this won-der-ful peace, Bur-ied
3. I am rest-ing to-night in this won-der-ful peace, Rest-ing
4. And me-thinks when I rise to that cit-y of peace, Where the
5. Ah, soul! are you here with-out com-fort and rest, March-ing

mel - o - dy sweet-er than psalm; In ce-les-tial-like strains it un-
deep in the heart of my soul, So se-cure that no pow-er can
sweet-ly in Je-sus' con-trol; For I'm kept from all dan-ger by
Au - thor of peace I shall see, That one strain of the song which the
down the rough path-way of time? Make Je-sus your Friend ere the

ceas-ing-ly falls O'er my soul like an in-fi-nite calm.
mine it a-way, While the years of e-ter-ni-ty roll!
night and by day, And His glo-ry is flood-ing my soul!
ran-somed will sing In that heav-en-ly king-dom will be:
shad-ows grow dark; O ac-cept of this peace so sub-lime!

CHORUS

Peace, peace, won-der-ful peace, Coming down from the Fa-ther a-bove! Sweep

o - ver my spir-it for-ev-er, I pray, In fath-om-less bil-lows of love!

339 PARDONING GRACE

A. H. Ackley

B. D. Ackley

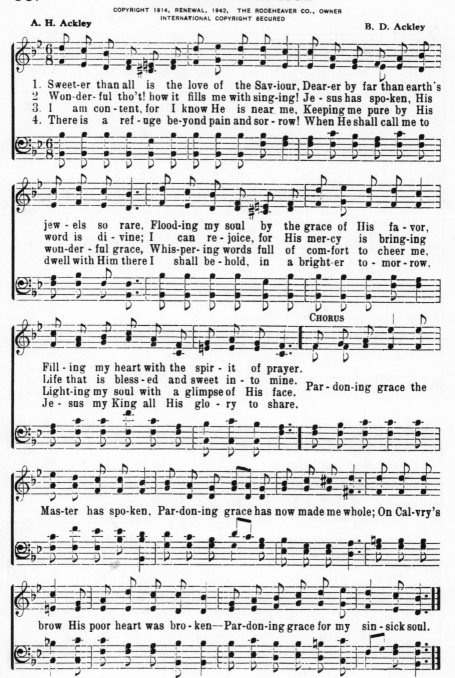

1. Sweet-er than all is the love of the Sav-iour, Dear-er by far than earth's
2. Won-der-ful tho't! how it fills me with sing-ing! Je-sus has spo-ken, His
3. I am con-tent, for I know He is near me, Keeping me pure by His
4. There is a ref-uge be-yond pain and sor-row! When He shall call me to

jew-els so rare, Flood-ing my soul by the grace of His fa-vor,
word is di-vine; I can re-joice, for His mer-cy is bring-ing
won-der-ful grace, Whis-per-ing words full of com-fort to cheer me.
dwell with Him there I shall be-hold, in a bright-er to-mor-row,

Fill-ing my heart with the spir-it of prayer.
Life that is bless-ed and sweet in-to mine.
Light-ing my soul with a glimpse of His face.
Je-sus my King all His glo-ry to share.

CHORUS

Par-don-ing grace the Mas-ter has spo-ken, Par-don-ing grace has now made me whole; On Cal-vry's

brow His poor heart was bro-ken—Par-don-ing grace for my sin-sick soul.

340 HALLELUJAH! HALLELUJAH!

Virgil P. Brock   Blanche Kerr Brock

1. Hal - le - lu - jah! Hal - le - lu - jah! God hath brought us to this day; With His
2. Hal - le - lu - jah! Hal - le - lu - jah! Son of God for sin - ners slain; Our Re -
3. Hal - le - lu - jah! Hal - le - lu - jah! To our glo-rious sov-reign King; Soon ap -

ban - ner lift - ed o'er us We will fol - low, come what may. Hith - er-
deem - er, in - ter-cess - or, Ev - er - more to live and reign. Tho' des-
pear - ing from the heav - ens, Com - ing back His hosts to bring. When the

to our God hath led us, And He still will lead us on; Our De-
pised and once re - ject - ed, At His feet we hum - bly fall; Voi - ces
trump of God is sound - ed, And our Lord re - turns a - gain, Com-ing

fend - er, Shield and Buck - ler. Our Mes - si - ah and our song. Hal - le-
raised in glad Ho - san - nas, Now we crown Him lord of all. Hal - le-
with great pow'r and glo - ry, He for - ev - er - more shall reign. Hal - le-

rit.

lu - jah, Hal - le - lu - jah! Our Mes - si - ah and our song!
lu - jah, Hal - le - lu - jah! Now we crown Him lord of all!
lu - jah, Hal - le - lu - jah! He for - ev - er - more shall reign!

FOLLOW THE GLEAM

Silver Bay Prize Song
BRYN MAWR COLLEGE

Sallie Hume Douglas

1. To the Knights in the days of old, Keep-ing watch on the moun-tain height, Came a vi-sion of Ho-ly Grail And a voice thru the wait-ing night, Fol-low, fol-low, fol-low the gleam, Ban-ners un-furled o'er all the world, Fol-low, fol-low, fol-low the gleam Of the Chal-ice that is the Grail.

2. And we who would serve the King And loy-al-ly Him o-bey, In the con-se-crate si-lence know That the challenge still holds to-day. Fol-low, fol-low, fol-low the gleam, Stand-ards of worth o'er all the earth, Fol-low, fol-low, fol-low the gleam Of the light that shall bring the dawn.

342 THE BANNER OF THE CROSS

D. W. Whittle   James McGranahan

1. There's a roy-al ban-ner giv-en for dis-play To the sol-diers
2. Though the foe may rage and gath-er as the flood, Let the stand-ard
3. O-ver land and sea, wher-ev-er man may dwell, Make the glo-rious
4. When the glo-ry dawns—'tis draw-ing ver-y near—It is hast'ning

of the King; As an en-sign fair we lift it up to-day,
be dis-played; And be-neath its folds, as sol-diers of the Lord,
ti-dings known; Of the crim-son ban-ner now the sto-ry tell,
day by day— Then be-fore our King the foe shall dis-ap-pear,

CHORUS

While as ran-somed ones we sing.
For the truth be not dis-mayed!   March-ing on, ... march-ing
While the Lord shall claim His own!   on, on,
And the cross the world shall sway!

on, ... For Christ count ev-'ry-thing but loss! ..... And to
on, on, For Christ count ev-'ry-thing, ev-'ry-thing but loss!

crown Him King, toil and sing 'Neath the ban-ner of the cross!
               we'll toil and sing Be-neath

343 HIS WAY WITH THEE

C. S. N.

Cyrus S. Nusbaum

1. Would you live for Je - sus, and be al-ways pure and good? Would you walk with
2. Would you have Him make you free, and fol-low at His call? Would you know the
3. Would you in His king-dom find a place of constant rest? Would you prove Him

Him with - in the nar-row road? Would you have Him bear your bur-den, car-ry
peace that comes by giv-ing all? Would you have Him save you, so that you need
true in prov - i - den-tial test? Would you in His serv-ice la - bor al-ways

CHORUS

all your load? Let Him have His way with thee.
nev - er fall? Let Him have His way with thee. His pow'r can make you what you
at your best? Let Him have His way with thee.

ought to be; His blood can cleanse your heart and make you free; His love can

rit.

fill your soul, and you will see 'Twas best for Him to have His way with thee. A-MEN.

344 WHEN I KNEEL DOWN TO PRAY

A. H. Ackley   B. D. Ackley

1. Some-how the Sav-iour seems a lit-tle near-er, When I kneel
2. A se-cret place of qui-et med-i-ta-tion, When I kneel
3. I tar-ry there with Christ a lit-tle long-er, When I kneel

down to pray, And fel-low-ship with Him a lit-tle dear-er,
down to pray, In-creas-es all the joy of that re-la-tion,
down to pray, And rise to face the world a lit-tle strong-er,

REFRAIN

When I kneel down to pray. I know that He will al-ways

hear me, For He is nev-er far a-way, And yet He

seems a lit-tle clos-er to me, When I kneel down to pray.

345 JESUS, ROSE OF SHARON

COPYRIGHT 1922, RENEWAL 1950
THE RODEHEAVER CO., OWNER
INTERNATIONAL COPYRIGHT SECURED

Ida A. Guirey

Charles H Gabriel

1. Je - sus, Rose of Shar - on, bloom with - in my heart; Beau - ties of Thy
2. Je - sus, Rose of Shar - on, sweet - er far to me Than the fair - est
3. Je - sus, Rose of Shar - on, balm for ev - 'ry ill, May Thy ten - der
4. Je - sus, Rose of Shar - on, bloom for - ev - er - more; Be Thy glo - ry

truth and ho - li - ness im - part, That wher-e'er I go my life may
flow'rs of earth could ev - er be, Fill my life com-plete - ly, add - ing
mer - cy's healing pow'r dis - til For af - flic - ted souls of wea - ry,
seen on earth from shore to shore, Till the na-tions own Thy Sov'-reign-

shed a-broad Fra-grance of the knowledge of the love of God.
more each day Of Thy grace di - vine and pur - i - ty, I pray.
bur-dened men, Giv - ing need - y mor·tals health and hope a - gain.
ty complete, Lay their hon - ors down and worship at Thy feet.

REFRAIN

Je - sus, ... Rose of Shar - on, ...
Bless - ed Je - sus, Rose of Shar - on,

Bloom in ra - diance and in love with - in my heart.

346 JESUS CHRIST, THE CRUCIFIED

Johann C. Schwedler

H. A. César Malan

1. Ask ye what great thing I know That delights and
2. Who defeats my fiercest foes? Who consoles my
3. Who is life in life to me? Who the death of
4. This is that great thing I know; This delights and

stirs me so? What the high reward I win? Whose the Name I
saddest woes? Who revives my fainting heart, Healing all its
death will be? Who will place me on His right, With the countless
stirs me so: Faith in Him who died to save, Him who triumphed

glory in? Jesus Christ, the Crucified.
hidden smart? Jesus Christ, the Crucified.
hosts of light? Jesus Christ, the Crucified.
o'er the grave, Jesus Christ, the Crucified. A-MEN.

347 RISE UP, O MEN OF GOD

William P. Merrill

William H. Walter

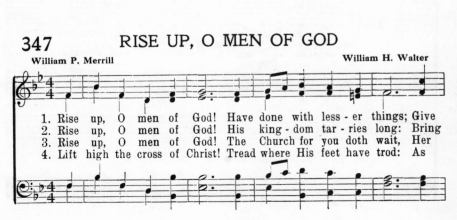

1. Rise up, O men of God! Have done with lesser things; Give
2. Rise up, O men of God! His kingdom tarries long: Bring
3. Rise up, O men of God! The Church for you doth wait, Her
4. Lift high the cross of Christ! Tread where His feet have trod: As

SOLDIERS OF CHRIST, ARISE

Charles Wesley. Arranged

George J. Elvey

1. Sol - diers of Christ, a - rise, And put your ar - mor on,
2. Stand then in His great might, With all His strength en - dued,
3. Leave no un-guard - ed place, No weak-ness of the soul,

Strong in the strength which God sup-plies Thru His e - ter - nal Son;
And take, to arm you for the fight, The pan - o - ply of God;
Take ev - 'ry vir - tue, ev - 'ry grace, And for - ti - fy the whole.

Strong in the Lord of hosts, And in His might - y pow'r,
That hav - ing all things done, And all your con - flicts past,
From strength to strength go on, Wres - tle and fight and pray,

Who in the strength of Je - sus trusts Is more than con-quer - or.
Ye may o'er-come thru Christ a - lone, And stand en-tire at last.
Tread all the pow'rs of dark-ness down, And win the well-fought day.

AMERICA THE BEAUTIFUL

Katharine Lee Bates

Samuel A. Ward

1. O beau-ti-ful for spa-cious skies, For am-ber waves of grain;
2. O beau-ti-ful for pil-grim feet, Whose stern, im-pas-sioned stress
3. O beau-ti-ful for he-roes proved In lib-er-at-ing strife,
4. O beau-ti-ful for pa-triot dream That sees be-yond the years

For pur-ple moun-tain maj-es-ties A-bove the fruit-ed plain!
A thor-ough-fare for free-dom beat A-cross the wil-der-ness!
Who more than self their coun-try loved, And mer-cy more than life!
Thine al-a-bas-ter cit-ies gleam Un-dimmed by hu-man tears!

A-mer-i-ca! A-mer-i-ca! God shed His grace on thee,
A-mer-i-ca! A-mer-i-ca! God mend thine ev-'ry flaw,
A-mer-i-ca! A-mer-i-ca! May God thy gold re-fine
A-mer-i-ca! A-mer-i-ca! God shed His grace on thee,

And crown thy good with broth-er-hood From sea to shin-ing sea!
Con-firm thy soul in self-con-trol, Thy lib-er-ty in law!
Till all suc-cess be no-ble-ness, And ev-'ry gain di-vine!
And crown thy good with broth-er-hood From sea to shin-ing sea!

351 THE STAR-SPANGLED BANNER

Service version. Prepared for the Army and Navy song and band books, and for School and Community singing, by Committee of 12.

Francis Scott Key

John Stafford Smith

With spirit f

1. O say, can you see, by the dawn's ear-ly light, What so proud-ly we
2. On the shore, dim-ly seen thro' the mists of the deep, Where the foe's haughty
3. O thus be it ev-er when free-men shall stand Be-tween their loved

hailed at the twilight's last gleaming? Whose broad stripes and bright stars, thro' the
host in dread si-lence re-pos-es, What is that which the breeze, o'er the
homes and the war's des-o-la-tion! Blest with vic-t'ry and peace, may the

per-il-ous fight, O'er the ram-parts we watched, were so gal-lant-ly streaming?
tow-er-ing steep, As it fit-ful-ly blows, half con-ceals, half dis-clos-es?
heav'n-res-cued land Praise the Pow'r that hath made and preserved us a na-tion!

mf

And the rock-et's red glare, the bombs bursting in air, Gave proof thro' the
Now it catch-es the gleam of the morn-ing's first beam, In full glo-ry re-
Then con-quer we must, when our cause it is just, And this be our

CHORUS f

night that our flag was still there. O say, does that Star-span-gled
flect-ed now shines on the stream: 'Tis the Star-span-gled Ban-ner, O
mot-to: "In God is our trust!" And the Star-span-gled Ban-ner in

fff

Ban - ner still wave O'er the land of the free, and the home of the brave?
long may it wave O'er the land of the free, and the home of the brave.
tri - umph shall wave O'er the land of the free, and the home of the brave.

352   MY COUNTRY, 'TIS OF THEE

Samuel F. Smith

Henry Carey

1. My coun - try, 'tis of thee, Sweet land of lib - er - ty,
2. My na - tive coun - try, thee, Land of the no - ble free,
3. Let mu - sic swell the breeze, And ring from all the trees
4. Our fa - thers' God! to Thee, Au - thor of lib - er - ty,

Of thee I sing; Land where my fa - thers died, Land of the
Thy name I love; I love thy rocks and rills, Thy woods and
Sweet freedom's song; Let mor - tal tongues a - wake; Let all that
To Thee we sing; Long may our land be bright With free - dom's

pil - grims' pride, From ev - 'ry moun - tain side Let free - dom ring!
tem - pled hills; My heart with rap - ture thrills Like that a - bove.
breathe par - take; Let rocks their si - lence break, The sound pro - long.
ho - ly light; Pro - tect us by Thy might, Great God, our King.

353 DO LORD

Arr. by Griffith J. Jones

DUET *Allegro*

1. I've got a home in glo-ry land That out-shines the sun
2. I took Je-sus as my Sav-iour You take Him too

hal-le-lu-yah

I've got a home in glo-ry land That out shines the sun I've got a home in
I took Je-sus as my Sav-iour You take Him too I took Je-sus

glo-ry land That out-shines the sun Way be-yond the blue.
as my Sav-iour You take Him too Way be-yond the blue. (blue, blue, blue)

CHORUS

Do Lord, O do Lord, O do re-mem-ber me, Do Lord, O do Lord, O do re-mem-ber

me, Do Lord, O, do Lord, O do re-mem-ber me, Way be-yond the blue.
(re-mem-ber,)

354 PRAY TILL THE LIGHT BREAKS THRU

Annette Dennstedt

B. D. Ackley

Pray till the light breaks thru, Pray till the light breaks thru; There is
breaks thru,

strength and pow'r For the try-ing hour, If you pray till the light breaks thru.

355 I SEE JESUS

A. H. A.

A. H. Ackley

In the morn-ing I see His face, ... In the

eve-ning His form I trace; . . . In the dark-ness His voice I

know; . . . I see Je-sus ev-'ry-where I go. . . .

FIRE SONG

356

THE RODEHEAVER CO. OWNER COPYRIGHT, 1928. RENEWAL, 1956

Hum

1. O my lov-in' sis-ter, when the world's on
2. O my lov-in' broth-er, when the world's on
3. O my poor mourn-er, when the world's on
4. O ye con-gre-ga-tion, when the world's on

Hum

fire, . . . Don't you want God's bos-om to be your pil-low? Hide me

o - ver in the Rock of A - ges, Rock of A - ges, cleft for me.

357 HIS LOVE IS WONDERFUL TO ME

To Bishop E. S. Woodring

COPYRIGHT, 1933, BY PAUL WHITE

P. W.

Paul White

His love is won-der-ful to me, ... His love is won-der-ful to me; . . . For Je-sus

loved me so, He did to Cal-v'ry go; His love is won-der-ful to me . . . .

358 GOD BLESS YOU EVERYONE

A. H. A.

A. H. ACKLEY

God bless you ev - 'ry one, God bless you is my prayer, God

bless and keep you in His lov - ing care. (A MEN.)

359 HEARTACHES

A. H. A.

A. H. Ackley

Heart-aches, take them all to Je - sus, Go to Him to - day, do it

now with-out de - lay; Heart-aches, take them all to Je - sus,

He will take your heart-aches all a - way.
He will take them all a - way.

360 YOU CAN SMILE

THE RODEHEAVER CO., OWNER

A. H. A.

A. H. Ackley

CHORUS.

You can smile when you can't say a word, You can smile when you cannot be heard,

You can smile . . .when its cloudy or fair, You can smile any time, a-ny-where.

361 SEND A GREAT REVIVAL IN MY SOUL

B. B. McK.

B. B. McKinney

Send a great re-vi-val in my soul, Send a great re-
in my soul,

vi-val in my soul, Let the Ho-ly Spir-it come and
in my soul,

take con-trol, And send a great re-vi-val in my soul.
in my soul.

362 CHRIST IS THE ANSWER

Homer Rodeheaver

B. D. Ackley

Christ is the an-swer to all of our prob-lems,

He holds the key to the whole world's peace. If we be-lieve Him,

if we re-ceive Him, Christ is the an-swer to all our needs.

363 KEEP ON PRAYING

I. P. W.

Ina Pearle Whaley

Keep on praying, God is ev-er near; Keep on praying, He will surely hear

If you will,

Keep on pray-ing, keep on trusting, too, Keep on praying, God will answer you.

364 WHAT WOULD WE DO WITHOUT THE SAVIOUR?

A. H. A.

A. H. Ackley

What would we do . . . . . with-out the sun-shine,

What would we do with - out the sun-shine,

What would we do . . . . . with-out the rain, What would we

What would we do with - out the rain,

do . . . . with-out the Sav-iour To keep us till He comes a-gain?

What would we do with-out the Sav-iour

365 SOMETHING HAPPENED

A. H. A.

A. H. Ackley

Something happened when He saved me, Happened in my

Some - thing real - ly hap-pened,

heart, hap-pened in my heart, Something happened when He

O yes it

When He

SOMETHING HAPPENED

saved me, when He saved me, Some-thing happened in my heart.

WIDE AS THE OCEAN

COPYRIGHT 1917 IN "JUBILATE"
RENEWAL, 1945, THE RODEHEAVER CO., OWNER

366

C. A. M.

C. Austin Miles

Wide, wide as the o - cean, High as the heavens a - bove;
Wide as the o - cean, deep as the sea, a - bove;

Deep, deep as the deep-est sea, Is my Sav-iour's love; .....
Deep as the deep - est, is His love,

I, tho' so un-wor - thy, Still am a child of His care,
I, tho' un-wor - thy, Still am His child, His care,

For His word teach-es me That His love reach-es me Ev - 'ry - where.

367 FOR GOD SO LOVED THE WORLD

COPYRIGHT, 1941, BY ALFRED B. SMITH, IN "SINGSPIRATION"

Frances Townsend

Alfred B. Smith

For God so loved the world, He gave His on-ly Son, To

die on Calv'ry's tree, From sin to set me free; Some day He's com-ing

back, What glo - ry that will be! Won - der-ful His love to me. . . . .

368 HE'S THE ONE I LOVE

COPYRIGHT, 1933, BY L. P. LEHMAN
ASSIGNED TO THE RODEHEAVER CO.

N. B. V.

N. B. Vandall

He's the One I love, . . . He's the One I love, ...

HE'S THE ONE I LOVE

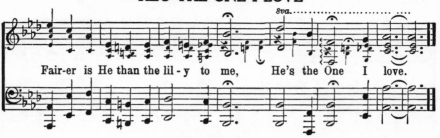

Fair-er is He than the lil-y to me, He's the One I love.

369 LOVE, WONDERFUL LOVE

(Inscribed to our friend Rev. Duncan McNeill)

COPYRIGHT, 1928, BY DUNCAN McNEILL

Seth Sykes

Love, won-der-ful love, ... The love of Christ to me. ....
Love, O the won-der-ful, won-der-ful love, The love of Christ to e - ven me.

Love, won-der-ful love, ... So rich, so full, so free; ...
Love, O the won-der-ful, won-der-ful love, so free;

Wide, wide as the o - cean, Deep, deep as the sea, ...
Deep, deep, deep as the deep-est sea,

High, high as the heav'n a - bove, His love to me.

370 CONSTANTLY ABIDING

Mrs. W. L. M.

Mrs. Will L. Murphy

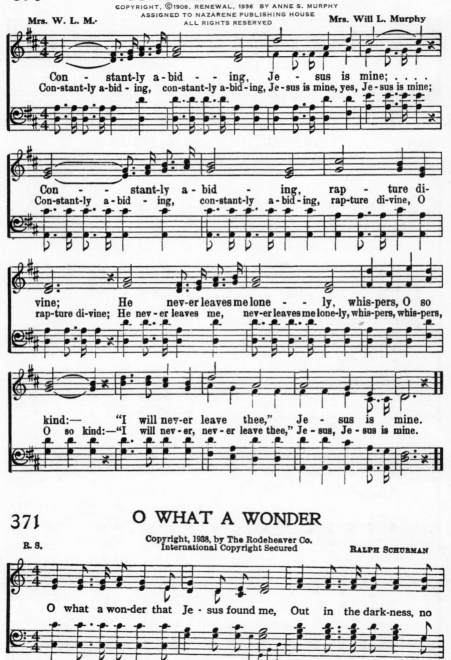

Con - stant-ly a - bid - - ing, Je - sus is mine; ....
Con-stant-ly a-bid - ing, con-stant-ly a-bid-ing, Je-sus is mine, yes, Je-sus is mine;

Con - - stant-ly a - bid - ing, rap - ture di -
Con-stant-ly a-bid - ing, con-stant-ly a-bid-ing, rap-ture di-vine, O

vine; He nev-er leaves me lone - - ly, whis-pers, O so
rap-ture di-vine; He nev-er leaves me, nev-er leaves me lone-ly, whis-pers, whis-pers,

kind:— "I will nev-er leave thee," Je - sus is mine.
O so kind:—"I will nev-er, nev-er leave thee," Je-sus, Je-sus is mine.

371 O WHAT A WONDER

R. S.

RALPH SCHURMAN

O what a won-der that Je - sus found me, Out in the dark-ness, no

O WHAT A WONDER

light could I see, O what a won-der, He put His great arm

And won-der of won-ders,

un-der, And won-der of won-ders, He saved ev-en me,

372

LOOK FOR ME!

A. A. Payn

C. Austin Miles

You may look for me, for I'll be there, I'll be

I'll be there,

there, I'll be there! You may look for

I'll be there, I'll be there!

me, for I'll be there! Glo-ry to His name!

I'll be there! Pre-cious name!

373 LORD, DISMISS US WITH THY BLESSING

John Fawcett   SICILIAN MARINERS 8. 7. 8. 7. 4. 7   Sicilian Melody

1. Lord, dis-miss us with Thy bless-ing, Fill our hearts with
2. Thanks we give and ad-o-ra-tion For Thy gos-pel's
3. So, when-e'er the sig-nal's giv-en Us from earth to

joy and peace; Let us each, Thy love pos-sess-ing,
joy-ful sound; May the fruits of Thy sal-va-tion
call a-way, Borne on an-gels' wings to heav-en,

Tri-umph in re-deem-ing grace; Oh, re-fresh us,
In our hearts and lives a-bound; May Thy pres-ence,
Glad the sum-mons to o-bey, May we ev-er,

Oh, re-fresh us, 'Trav-'ling thro' this wil-der-ness.
May Thy pres-ence With us ev-er-more be found.
May we ev-er Reign with Christ in end-less day. A-men.

374   GOD BE WITH YOU

J. E. RANKIN   W. G. TOMER

1. God be with you till we meet a-gain; By His counsels guide, uphold you,
2. God be with you till we meet a-gain; 'Neath His wings protecting hide you,
3. God be with you till we meet a-gain; When life's perils thick confound you,
4. God be with you till we meet a-gain; Keep love's banner floating o'er you;

With   His sheep se-cure-ly fold you; God be with you till we meet a-gain.
Dai-ly man-na still pro-vide you; God be with you till we meet a-gain.
Put   His arms un-fail-ing round you; God be with you till we meet a-gain.
Smite death's threat'ning wave before you; God be with you till we meet a-gain.

REFRAIN

Till we meet, ... till we meet,   Till we meet at Je-sus' feet;
Till we meet,   till we meet,   till we meet;

Till we meet, ... till we meet,   God be with you till we meet a-gain.
Till we meet,   till we meet,

AMENS

375

376 God

O come, let us sing unto the Lord; let us make a joyful noise to the rock of our salvation.

Let us come before his presence with thanksgiving, and make a joyful noise unto him with psalms.

For the Lord is a great God, and a great King above all gods.

In his hand are the deep places of the earth: the strength of the hills is his also.

The sea is his, and he made it: and his hands formed the dry land.

O come, let us worship and bow down: let us kneel before the Lord our maker.

For he is our God; and we are the people of his pasture, and the sheep of his hand.　　　　—Psalm 95:1-7.

Lord, thou hast been our dwelling place in all generations.

Before the mountains were brought forth, or ever thou hadst formed the earth and the world, even from everlasting to everlasting, thou art God.

For a thousand years in thy sight are but as yesterday when it is past, and as a watch in the night.　　　　　　—Psalm 90:1, 2, 4.

The Lord reigneth, he is clothed with majesty; the Lord is clothed with strength, wherewith he hath girded himself: the world also is stablished, that it cannot be moved.

Thy throne is established of old: thou art from everlasting.

The floods have lifted up, O Lord, the floods have lifted up their voice; the floods lift up their waves.

The Lord on high is mightier than the noise of many waters, yea, than the mighty waves of the sea.

Thy testimonies are very sure: holiness becometh thine house, O Lord, for ever.　　　　—Psalm 93.

God is a Spirit:

And they that worship him must worship him in spirit and in truth.

But the hour cometh, and now is, when the true worshippers shall worship the Father in spirit and in truth: for the Father seeketh such to worship him. —John 4:24, 23.

377 God the Comforter

Comfort ye, comfort ye my people, saith your God.

Speak ye comfortably to Jerusalem, and cry unto her, that her warfare is accomplished, that her iniquity is pardoned. —Isaiah 40:1-2.

The Lord is my light and my salvation; whom shall I fear? the Lord is the strength of my life; of whom shall I be afraid?

Though an host should encamp against me, my heart shall not fear: though war should rise against me, in this will I be confident.

For in the time of trouble he shall hide me in his pavillion: in the secret of his tabernacle shall he hide me; he shall set me up upon a rock.

And now shall mine head be lifted up above mine enemies round about me: therefore will I offer in his tabernacle sacrifices of joy; I will sing, yea, I will sing praises unto the Lord.

When my father and my mother forsake me, then the Lord will take me up.

Teach me thy way, O Lord, and lead me in a plain path, because of mine enemies.

Wait on the Lord: be of good courage, and he shall strengthen thine heart: wait, I say, on the Lord.
　　　　—Psalm 27:1, 3, 5, 6, 10, 11, 14.

He shall feed his flock like a shepherd: he shall gather the lambs with his arm, and carry them in his bosom, and shall gently lead those that are with young.

Hast thou not known? hast thou not heard, that the everlasting God, the Lord, the Creator of the ends of the earth, fainteth not, neither is weary?

There is no searching of his understanding.

He giveth power to the faint; and to them that have no might he increaseth strength.

Even the youths shall faint and be weary, and the young men shall utterly fall:

But they that wait upon the Lord shall renew their strength;

They shall mount up with wings as eagles; they shall run, and not be weary; and they shall walk, and not faint.   —Isaiah 40:11, 28-31.

378   Revelation of God as Saviour

Who hath believed our report? and to whom is the arm of the Lord revealed?

For he shall grow up before him as a' tender plant, and as a root out of a dry ground.

He is despised and rejected of men; a man of sorrows, and acquainted with grief.

And we hid as it were our faces from him; he was despised, and we esteemed him not.

Surely he hath borne our griefs, and carried our sorrows: yet we did esteem him stricken, smitten of God, and afflicted.

But he was wounded for our transgressions, he was bruised for our iniquities: the chastisement of our peace was upon him; and with his stripes we are healed.

All we like sheep have gone astray; we have turned every one to his own way.

And the Lord hath laid on him the iniquity of us all.

Yet it pleased the Lord to bruise him; he hath put him to grief.

When thou shalt make his soul an offering for sin, he shall see his seed, he shall prolong his days, and the pleasure of the Lord shall prosper in his hand.

He shall see of the travail of his soul, and shall be satisfied.

By his knowledge shall my righteous servant justify many; for he shall bear their iniquities.

Therefore shall I divide him a portion with the great, and he shall divide the spoil with the strong.

Because he hath poured out his soul unto death.

And he was numbered with the transgressors.

And he bare the sin of many, and made intercession for the transgressors.   —Isaiah 53:1-6, 10-12.

379   Revelation of God in Jesus Christ

God, who at sundry times and in divers manners spake in time past unto the fathers by the prophets.

Hath in these last days spoken unto us by his Son, whom he hath appointed heir of all things, by whom also he made the worlds.

Who being the brightness of his glory, and the express image of his person.

And upholding all things by the word of his power, when he had by himself purged our sins, sat down on the right hand of the Majesty on high.   —Hebrews 1:1-3.

Who hath delivered us from the power of darkness,

And hath translated us into the kingdom of his dear Son:

In whom we have redemption through his blood, even the forgiveness of sins:

Who is the image of the invisible God, the firstborn of every creature:

For by him were all things created, that are in heaven, and that are in earth, visible and invisible,

All things were created by him, and for him:

And he is before all things, and by him all things consist.

And he is the head of the body, the church: for it pleased the Father that in him should all fullness dwell;

And, having made peace through the blood of his cross, by him to reconcile all things unto himself.

In the body of his flesh through death, to present you holy and unblameable and unreproveable in his sight.

To whom God would make known what is the riches of the glory of this mystery among the Gentiles; which is Christ in you, the hope of glory:

Whom we preach, that we may present every man perfect in Christ Jesus.   —Colossians 1:13-20, 22, 27, 28.

380 God's Divine Purpose

Grace be unto you, and peace from God our Father, and from the Lord Jesus Christ.

Blessed be the God and Father of our Lord Jesus Christ, who hath blessed us with all spiritual blessings in heavenly places in Christ:

According as he hath chosen us in him before the foundation of the world, that we should be holy and without blame before him in love:

Having predestinated us into the adoption of children by Jesus Christ to himself, according to the good pleasure of his will,

To the praise of the glory of his grace, wherein he hath made us accepted in the beloved.

In whom we have redemption through his blood, the forgiveness of sins, according to the riches of his grace;

Wherein he hath abounded toward us in all wisdom and prudence;

Having made known unto us the mystery of his will, according to his good pleasure which he hath purposed in himself:

That in the dispensation of the fulness of times he might gather together in one all things in Christ,

Both which are in heaven, and which are on earth; even in him:

In whom also we have obtained an inheritance, being predestinated according to the purpose of him who worketh all things after the counsel of his own will.

Wherefore I also, after I heard of your faith in the Lord Jesus, and love unto all the saints,

Cease not to give thanks for you, making mention of you in my prayers;

That the God of our Lord Jesus Christ, the Father of glory, may give unto you the spirit of wisdom and revelation in the knowledge of him.   —Ephesians 1:2-11, 15-17.

381 God's Plan of Salvation

The Lord is not slack concerning his promise, as some men count slackness.

But is longsuffering to us-ward, not willing that any should perish, but that all should come to repentance. —II Peter 3:9.

And he that searcheth the hearts knoweth what is the mind of the Spirit,

Because he maketh intercession for the saints according to the will of God.

And we know that all things work together for good to them that love God,

To them who are called according to his purpose.

For whom he did foreknow, he also did predestinate to be conformed to the image of his Son.

He might be the firstborn among many brethren.

Moreover whom he did predestinate, them he also called:

And whom he called, them he also justified: and whom he justified, them he also glorified.

What shall we then say to these things? If God be for us, who can be against us?

He that spared not his own Son, but delivered him up for us all, how shall he not with him also freely give us all things?

Who shall separate us from the love of Christ? shall tribulation, or distress, or persecution, or famine, or nakedness, or sword?

Nay, in all these things we are more than conquerors, through him that loved us.

For I am persuaded, that neither death, nor life, nor angels, nor principalities, nor powers, nor things present, nor things to come,

Nor height, nor depth, nor any other creature, shall be able to separate us from the love of God, which is in Christ Jesus our Lord.
—Romans 8:27-32, 35, 37-39.

382 The Life of God's Children

God is a Spirit: and they that worship him must worship him in spirit and in truth.

It is the spirit that quickeneth; the flesh profiteth nothing: the words that I speak unto you, they are spirit, and they are life.

The wind bloweth where it listeth, and thou hearest the sound thereof.

But canst not tell whence it cometh, and whither it goeth: so is every one that is born of the Spirit.

That which is born of the flesh is flesh:

And that which is born of the spirit is spirit.

Marvel not that I said unto thee, Ye must be born again.
—John 4:24; 6:63; 3:8, 6, 7.

Behold, what manner of love the Father hath bestowed upon us, that we should be called the sons of God:

Therefore the world knoweth us not, because it knew him not.

Beloved, now are we the sons of God, and it doth not yet appear what we shall be:

But we know that, when he shall appear we shall be like him; for we shall see him as he is.

And every man that hath this hope in him purifieth himself, even as he is pure.

We know that we have passed from death unto life, because we love the brethren.

Beloved, let us love one another: for love is of God; and every one that loveth is born of God, and knoweth God. —I John 3:1-3, 14; 4:7.

383 God's Creation

In the beginning was the Word, and the Word was with God, and the Word was God.

The same was in the beginning with God.

All things were made by him; and without him was not any thing made that was made.

In him was life; and the life was the light of men.

And the light shineth in darkness; and the darkness comprehended it not.

There was a man sent from God, whose name was John.

The same came for a witness, to bear witness of the Light, that all men through him might believe.

He was not that Light, but was sent to bear witness of that Light.

That was the true Light, which lighteth every man that cometh into the world.

He was in the world, and the world was made by him, and the world knew him not.

He came unto his own, and his own received him not.

But as many as received him, to them gave he power to become the sons of God.

Even to them that believe on his name: which were born, not of blood, nor of the will of the flesh, nor of the will of man, but of God.

And the Word was made flesh, and dwelt among us, (and we beheld his glory, the glory as of the only begotten of the Father,) full of grace and truth. —John 1:1-14.

384 Confession of Sin

Have mercy upon me, O God, according to thy loving kindness: according unto the multitude of thy tender mercies blot out my transgressions.

Wash me thoroughly from mine iniquity, and cleanse me from my sin.

For I acknowledge my transgressions: and my sin is ever before me.

Against thee, thee only, have I sinned, and done this evil in thy sight:

That thou mightest be justified when thou speakest, and be clear when thou judgest.

Behold, thou desirest truth in the inward parts: and in the hidden part thou shalt make me to know wisdom.

Purge me with hyssop, and I shall be clean: wash me, and I shall be whiter than snow.

Make me to hear joy and gladness; that the bones which thou hast broken may rejoice.

Hide thy face from my sins, and blot out all mine iniquities.

Create in me a clean heart, O God; and renew a right spirit within me.

Cast me not away from thy presence; and take not thy holy spirit from me.

Restore unto me the joy of thy salvation;

And uphold me with thy free spirit.

Then will I teach transgressors thy ways; and sinners shall be converted unto thee.

O Lord, open thou my lips; and my mouth shall shew forth thy praise.

For thou desireth not sacrifice; else would I give it: thou delightest not in burnt offering.

The sacrifices of God are a broken spirit:

A broken and a contrite heart,
O God, thou wilt not despise.

—Psalm 51:1-4, 6-13, 15-17.

385   Forgiveness of Sin

Blessed is he whose transgression is forgiven, whose sin is covered.

Blessed is the man unto whom the Lord imputeth not iniquity, and in whose spirit there is no guile.

—Psalm 32:1-2.

Wash you, make you clean; put away the evil of your doings from before mine eyes; cease to do evil;

Learn to do well; seek judgment, relieve the oppressed, judge the fatherless, plead for the widow.

Come now, and let us reason together saith the Lord:

Though your sins be as scarlet, they shall be as white as snow; though they be red like crimson, they shall be as wool.

—Isaiah 1:16-18.

There is therefore now no condemnation to them which are in Christ Jesus,

Who walk not after the flesh, but after the Spirit.

For the law of the Spirit of life in Christ Jesus hath made me free from the law of sin and death.

For what the law could not do, in that it was weak through the flesh, God sending his own Son in the likeness of sinful flesh, and for sin, condemned sin in the flesh:

That the righteousness of the law might be fulfilled in us,

Who walk not after the flesh, but after the Spirit.

But if the Spirit of him that raised up Jesus from the dead dwell in you,

He that raised up Christ from the dead shall also quicken your mortal bodies by his Spirit that dwelleth in you.

Therefore, brethren, we are debtors, not to the flesh, to live after the flesh.

For if ye live after the flesh, ye shall die:

But if ye through the Spirit do mortify the deeds of the body, ye shall live.

For as many as are led by the Spirit of God, they are the sons of God.

—Romans 8:1-4, 11-14.

386   God's Mercy

Bless the Lord, O my soul, and forget not all his benefits:

Who forgiveth all thine iniquities; who healeth all thy diseases;

Who redeemeth thy life from destruction; who crowneth thee with loving kindness and tender mercies;

Who satisfieth thy mouth with good things; so that thy youth is renewed like the eagle's.

The Lord is merciful and gracious, slow to anger, and plenteous in mercy.

He will not always chide; neither will he keep his anger for ever.

He hath not dealt with us after our sins; nor rewarded us according to our iniquities.

For as the heaven is high above the earth, so great is his mercy toward them that fear him.

As far as the east is from the west, so far hath he removed our transgressions from us.

Like as a father pitieth his children, so the Lord pitieth them that fear him.

For he knoweth our frame; he remembereth that we are dust.

But the mercy of the Lord is from everlasting to everlasting upon them that fear him, and his righteousness unto children's children.

To such as keep his covenant,

And to those that remember his commandments to do them.

The Lord hath prepared his throne in the heavens; and his kingdom ruleth over all.

Bless ye the Lord, ye his angels, that excel in strength, that do his commandments, hearkening unto the voice of his word.

Bless ye the Lord, all ye his hosts, ye ministers of his, that do his pleasure.

Bless the Lord, all his works in all places of his dominion: bless the Lord, O my soul.
—Psalm 103:2-5, 8-14, 17-22.

387   God's Grace

The law was given by Moses, but grace and truth came by Jesus Christ.

And the Word was made flesh, and dwelt among us, (and we beheld his glory, the glory as of the only begotten of the Father,) full of grace and truth.   —John 1:17, 14.

By whom we have received grace and apostleship, for obedience to the faith among all nations, for his name.

Beloved of God, called to be saints: Grace to you and peace from God our Father, and the Lord Jesus Christ.

For all have sinned and come short of the glory of God;

Being justified freely by his grace through the redemption that is in Christ Jesus:

Therefore being justified by faith, we have peace with God through our Lord Jesus Christ:

By whom also we have access by faith into this grace wherein we stand, and rejoice in hope of the glory of God.

For as by one man's disobedience many were made sinners, so by the obedience of one shall many be made righteous.

Moreover the law entered, that the offence might abound. But where sin abounded, grace did much more abound:

That as sin hath reigned unto death,

Even so might grace reign through righteousness unto eternal life by Jesus Christ our Lord.
—Romans 1:5, 7; 3:23-24. 5:1-2, 19-21.

My grace is sufficient for thee.
—II Corinthians 12:9.

The grace of our Lord Jesus Christ be with you all. Amen.
—Philippians 4:23.

388 Spiritual Discernment

And I, brethren, when I came to you, came not with excellency of speech or of wisdom, declaring unto you the testimony of God.

For I determined not to know any thing among you, save Jesus Christ, and him crucified. And my speech and my preaching was not with enticing words of man's wisdom, but in demonstration of the Spirit and of power:

That your faith should not stand in the wisdom of men, but in the power of God.

But we speak the wisdom of God in a mystery, even the hidden wisdom, which God ordained before the world unto our glory:

Which none of the princes of this world knew: for had they known it, they would not have crucified the Lord of glory.

But as it is written, Eye hath not seen, nor ear heard, neither have entered into the heart of man, the things which God hath prepared for them that love him.

But God hath revealed them unto us by his Spirit:

For the Spirit searcheth all things, yea, the deep things of God.

For what man knoweth the things of a man, save the spirit of man which is in him?

Even so the things of God knoweth no man, but the Spirit of God.

Now we have received, not the spirit of the world, but the spirit which is of God.

That we might know the things that are freely given to us of God.

Which things also we speak, not in the words which man's wisdom teacheth, but which the Holy Ghost teacheth:

Comparing spiritual things with spiritual.

But the natural man receiveth not the things of the Spirit of God: for they are foolishness unto him:

Neither can he know them, because they are spiritually discerned.

But he that is spiritual judgeth all things, yet he himself is judged of no man.

For who hath known the mind of the Lord, that he may instruct him? But we have the mind of Christ.   —I Corinthians 2:1-2, 4-5, 7-16.

389   Abiding in Christ

Ye have not chosen me, but I have chosen you, and ordained you, that ye should go and bring forth fruit, and that your fruit remain:

That whatsoever ye shall ask of the Father in my name, he may give it to you.

Abide in me, and I in you. As the branch cannot bear fruit of itself, except it abide in the vine:

No more can ye, except ye abide in me.

I am the vine, ye are the branches: He that abideth in me, and I in him, the same bringeth forth much fruit.

For without me ye can do nothing.

If a man abide not in me, he is cast forth as a branch, and is withered.

And men gather them, and cast them into the fire, and they are burned.

If ye abide in me, and my words abide in you, ye shall ask what ye will, and it shall be done unto you.

As the Father hath loved me, so have I loved you: continue ye in my love.

If ye keep my commandments, ye shall abide in my love.

Even as I have kept my Father's commandments, and abide in his love.

These things have I spoken unto you, that my joy might remain in you, and that your joy might be full.

This is my commandment, That ye love one another, as I have loved you.

Greater love hath no man than this, that a man lay down his life for his friends.

Ye are my friends, if ye do whatsoever I command you.

Henceforth I call you not servants; for the servant knoweth not what his lord doeth:

But I have called you friends; for all things that I have heard of my Father I have made known unto you.   —John 15:16-17, 4-7, 9-15.

390   Christ Our Saviour

For unto us a child is born, unto us a son is given: and the government shall be upon his shoulder.

And his name shall be called Wonderful, Counsellor, The mighty God, The everlasting Father, The Prince of Peace.

Of the increase of his government and peace there shall be no end, upon the throne of David, and to establish it with judgment and with justice from henceforth even for ever.

The zeal of the Lord of hosts will perform this.

Behold my servant, whom I uphold; mine elect, in whom my soul delighteth;

I have put my spirit upon him: He shall bring forth judgment to the Gentiles.

He shall not cry, nor lift up, nor cause his voice to be heard in the street.

A bruised reed shall he not break, and the smoking flax shall he not quench:

He shall bring forth judgment unto truth.

He shall not fail nor be discouraged, till he have set judgment in the earth: and the isles shall wait for his law. —Isaiah 9:6-7; 42:1-4.

For verily he took not on him the nature of angels; but he took on him the seed of Abraham.

Wherefore in all things it behoved him to be made like unto his brethren, that he might be a merciful and faithful high priest in things pertaining to God, to make reconciliation for the sins of the people.

For in that he himself hath suffered being tempted, he is able to succour them that are tempted.

Wherefore he is able also to save them to the uttermost that come unto God by him, seeing he ever liveth to make intercession for them. Hebrews 2:16-18; 7:25.

391 Jesus Christ the Good Shepherd

The Lord is my shepherd; I shall not want.

He maketh me to lie down in green pastures: He leadeth me beside the still waters.

He restoreth my soul: He leadeth me in the paths of righteousness for his name's sake.

Yea, though I walk through the valley of the shadow of death, I will fear no evil: For thou art with me; thy rod and thy staff they comfort me.

Thou preparest a table before me in the presence of mine enemies: Thou anointest my head with oil; my cup runneth over.

Surely goodness and mercy shall follow me all the days of my life: And I will dwell in the house of the Lord for ever. —Psalm 23.

Then said Jesus unto them again, Verily, verily, I say unto you, I am the door of the sheep.

All that ever came before me are thieves and robbers: but the sheep did not hear them.

I am the door: by me if any man enter in, he shall be saved, and shall go in and out, and find pasture.

The thief cometh not, but for to steal, and to kill, and to destroy. I am come that they might have life, and that they might have it more abundantly.

I am the good shepherd: the good shepherd giveth his life for the sheep.

As the Father knoweth me, even so know I the Father: and I lay down my life for the sheep.

And I give unto them eternal

life; and they shall never perish neither shall any man pluck them out of my hand. —John 10:7-11, 15, 28.

392 Faith That Saves

They brought to him a man sick of the palsy, lying on a bed:

And Jesus seeing their faith said unto the sick of the palsy; Son, be of good cheer; thy sins be forgiven thee.

A woman, which was diseased with an issue of blood twelve years, came behind him, and touched the hem of his garment.

For she said within herself, If I may but touch his garment, I shall be whole.

But Jesus turned him about, and when he saw her, he said, Daughter, be of good comfort;

Thy faith hath made thee whole. And the woman was made whole from that hour.

When Jesus departed thence, two blind men followed him, crying, and saying,

Thou son of David, have mercy on us.

And when he was come into the house, the blind men came to him;

And Jesus saith unto them, Believe ye that I am able to do this? They said unto him, Yea, Lord.

Then touched he their eyes, saying, According to your faith be it unto you. —Matthew 9:2, 20-22, 27-29.

Without faith it is impossible to please him: for he that cometh to God must believe that he is, and that he is a rewarder of them that diligently seek him. —Hebrews 11:6.

Knowing that a man is not justified by the works of the law,

But by the faith of Jesus Christ, even we have believed in Jesus Christ, that we might be justified by the faith of Christ, and not by the works of the law. Galatians 2:16.

393 Repentance

The time is fulfilled, and the kingdom of God is at hand:

Repent ye, and believe the gospel. —Mark 1:15.

If I indeed baptize you with water unto repentance: but he that cometh after me is mightier than I.

He shall baptize you with the Holy Ghost, and with fire.
—Matthew 3:11.

Now when they heard this, they were pricked in their heart, and said unto Peter and to the rest of the apostles, Men and brethren, what shall we do?

Then Peter said unto them, Repent, and be baptized every one of you in the name of Jesus Christ for the remission of sins, and ye shall receive the gift of the Holy Ghost.

For the promise is unto you, and to your children, and to all that are afar off, even as many as the Lord our God shall call. —Acts 2:37-39.

And he said unto them, these are the words which I spake unto you, while I was yet with you, that all things must be fulfilled, which were written in the law of Moses, and in the prophets, and in the psalms, concerning me.

Then opened he their understanding, that they might understand the scriptures,

And said unto them, Thus it is written, and thus it behoved Christ to suffer, and to rise from the dead the third day:

And that repentance and remission of sins should be preached in his name.

Among all nations, beginning at Jerusalem.

And ye are witnesses of these things. —Luke 24:44-48.

Repent ye therefore, and be converted, that your sins may be blotted out, when the times of refreshing shall come from the presence of the Lord. —Acts 3:19.

394 The Holy Spirit

There is therefore now no condemnation to them which are in Christ Jesus.

Who walk not after the flesh, but after the Spirit.

For the law of the Spirit of life in Christ Jesus hath made us free from the law of sin and death.

For what the law could not do, in the flesh, God sending his own Son in the likeness of sinful flesh, and for sin, condemned sin in the flesh.

That the righteousness of the law might be fulfilled in us, who walk not after the flesh, but after the Spirit.

For they that are after the flesh do mind the things of the flesh.

But they that are after the Spirit the things of the Spirit.

For to be carnally minded is death; but to be spiritually minded is life and peace.

Because the carnal mind is enmity against God:

For it is not subject to the law of God, neither indeed can be.

So then they that are in the flesh cannot please God.

But ye are not in the flesh, but in the Spirit, if so be that the Spirit of God dwell in you.

If any man have not the Spirit of Christ, he is none of his.

And if Christ be in you, the body is dead because of righteousness. —Romans 8:1-10.

395 The Spirit's Gifts

As we have many members in one body, and all members have not the same office:

So we, being many are one body in Christ,

And every one members one of another. —Romans 12:4-5.

Now there are diversities of gifts, but the same Spirit.

And there are differences of administrations, but the same Lord.

And there are diversities of operations, but it is the same God which worketh all in all.

But the manifestation of the Spirit is given to every man to profit withal.

For to one is given by the Spirit the word of wisdom; to another the word of knowledge by the same Spirit.

To another faith by the same Spirit; to another the gifts of healing by the same Spirit.

But all these worketh that one and the self same Spirit.

For as the body is one, and hath many members, and all the members of that one body, being many, are one body: so also is Christ.

For by one Spirit are we all baptized into one body, and have been all made to drink into one Spirit.

But now hath God set the members every one of them in the body, as it hath pleased him.

Now ye are the body of Christ, and members in particular.
—I Corinthians 12:4-9, 11-13.

396 The New Birth

I say unto thee, Except a man be born again, he cannot see the kingdom of God.

Verily, verily, I say unto thee, Except a man be born of water and of the Spirit, he cannot enter into the kingdom of God.

That which is born of the flesh is flesh; and that which is born of the Spirit is spirit.

Marvel not that I said unto thee, Ye must be born again.
—John 3:3, 5-7.

He came unto his own, and his own received him not.

But as many as received him, to them gave he power to become the sons of God, even to them that believe on his name.

Which were born, not of blood, nor of the will of the flesh, nor of the will of man, but of God.
—John 1:11-13.

Therefore if any man be in Christ, he is a new creature: old things are passed away; behold, all things are become new.

And all things are of God, who hath reconciled us to himself by Jesus Christ, and hath given to us the ministry of reconciliation.

We pray you in Christ's stead, be ye reconciled to God.

For he hath made him to be sin for us, who knew no sin; that we might be made the righteousness of God in him.
—II Corinthians 5:17-18, 20-21.

That ye put off concerning the former conversation the old man,

And be renewed in the spirit of your mind.

And that ye put on the new man, which after God is created in righteousness and true holiness.
—Ephesians 4:22-24.

397   The New Life

Blessed are the poor in spirit; for their's is the kingdom of heaven.

Blessed are they that mourn: for they shall be comforted.

Blessed are the meek; for they shall inherit the earth.

Blessed are they which do hunger and thirst after righteousness: for they shall be filled.

Blessed are the merciful: for they shall obtain mercy.

Blessed are the pure in heart: for they shall see God.

Blessed are the peacemakers: for they shall be called the children of God.

Blessed are they which are persecuted for righteousness' sake; for their's is the kingdom of heaven.

Blessed are ye, when men shall revile you, and say all manner of evil against you falsely, for my sake.

Rejoice, and be exceeding glad: for great is your reward in heaven: for so persecuted they the prophets which were before you.

Ye are the salt of the earth: but if the salt have lost his savour, wherewith shall it be salted?

Ye are the light of the world. A city that is set on an hill cannot be hid.

Neither do men light a candle, and put it under a bushel, but on a candlestick; and it giveth light unto all that are in the house.

Let your light so shine before men, that they may see your good works, and glorify your Father which is in heaven. —Matthew 5:3-16.

398   The Resurrection

But now is Christ risen from the dead, and become the first fruits of them that slept.

For since by man came death, by man came also the resurrection of the dead.

For as in Adam all die, even so in Christ shall all be made alive.

But some man will say, How are

the dead raised up? and with what body do they come?

Thou fool, that which thou sowest is not quickened, except it die: and that which thou sowest, thou sowest not that body that shall be, but bare grain, it may chance of wheat, or of some other grain:

But God giveth it a body as it hath pleased him, and to every seed his own body.

So also is the resurrection of the dead. It is sown in corruption; it is raised in incorruption:

It is sown in dishonor; it is raised in glory: it is sown in weakness, it is raised in power:

It is sown a natural body; it is raised a spiritual body. There is a natural body, and there is a spiritual body.

And so it is written, The first man Adam was made a living soul; the last Adam was made a quickening spirit.

Behold, I shew you a mystery; We shall not all sleep, but we shall all be changed,

For this corruptible must put on incorruption, and this mortal must put on immortality.

But thanks be to God, which giveth us the victory through our Lord Jesus Christ.

Therefore, my beloved brethren, be ye steadfast, unmoveable, always abounding in the work of the Lord, forasmuch as ye know that your labour is not in vain in the Lord.

—I Corinthians 15:20-22, 35-38, 42-45, 51, 53, 57-58.

399 Christ's Prayer for His Own

Jesus lifted up his eyes to heaven, and said, Father, the hour is come·

glorify thy Son, that thy Son also may glorify thee:

As thou hast given him power over all flesh, that he should give eternal life to as many as thou hast given him.

And this is life eternal, that they might know thee the only true God, and Jesus Christ whom thou hast sent.

I have manifested thy name unto the men which thou gavest me out of the world: thine they were, and thou gavest them me; and they have kept thy word.

Now they have known that all things whatsoever thou hast given me are of thee.

For I have given unto them the words which thou gavest me; and they have received them, and have known surely that I came out from thee, and they have believed that thou didst send me.

I pray for them: I pray not for the world, but for them which thou hast given me; for they are thine.

And all mine are thine, and thine are mine; and I am glorified in them.

And now I am no more in the world, but these are in the world, and I come to thee.

Holy Father, keep through thine own name those whom thou hast given me, that they may be one, as we are.

I in them, and thou in me, that they may be made perfect in one; and that the world may know that thou hast sent me, and hast loved them, as thou hast loved me.

Father, I will that they also, whom thou hast given me, be with me where I am; that they may behold my glory, which thou hast given me: for thou lovedst me before the foundation of the world.

—John 17:1-3, 6-11, 23-24.

400   The Law of God

I am the Lord thy God, which have brought thee out of the land of Egypt, out of the house of bondage.

Thou shalt have no other gods before me.

Thou shalt not make unto thee any graven image, or any likeness of any thing that is in heaven above, or that is in the earth beneath, or that is in the water under the earth:

Thou shalt not bow down thyself to them, nor serve them: for I the Lord thy God am a jealous God, visiting the iniquity of the fathers upon the third and fourth generation of them that hate me;

And shewing mercy unto thousands of them that love me, and keep my commandments.

Thou shalt not take the name of the Lord thy God in vain; for the Lord will not hold him guiltless that taketh his name in vain.

Remember the sabbath day, to keep it holy.

Six days shalt thou labour, and do all thy work.

Honour thy father and thy mother: that thy days may be long upon the land which the Lord thy God giveth thee.

Thou shalt not kill.

Thou shalt not commit adultery.

Thou shalt not steal.

Thou shalt not bear false witness against thy neighbor.

Thou shalt not covet thy neighbour's house, thou shalt not covet thy neighbour's wife, nor his manservant, nor his maidservant, nor his ox, nor his ass, nor any thing that is thy neighbour's.

—Exodus 20:2-9, 12-17.

Thou shalt love the Lord thy God with all thy heart, and with all thy soul, and with all thy mind.

—Matthew 22:37.

401   Statutes of God

The law of the Lord is perfect, converting the soul: the testimony of the Lord is sure, making wise the simple.

The statutes of the Lord are right, the commandment of the Lord is pure, enlightening the eyes.

The fear of the Lord is clean, enduring for ever: the judgments of the Lord are true and righteous altogether.

More to be desired are they than gold, yea, than much fine gold: sweeter also than honey and the honeycomb.

Moreover by them is thy servant warned: and in keeping of them there is great reward.

Wherewithal shall a young man cleanse his way? by taking heed thereto according to thy word.

With my whole heart have I sought thee: O let me not wander from thy commandments.

Thy word have I hid in mine heart, that I might not sin against thee.

Blessed art thou, O Lord; teach me thy statutes.

With my lips have I declared all the judgments of thy mouth.

I have rejoiced in the way of thy testimonies, as much as in all riches.

I will meditate in thy precepts, and have respect unto thy ways.

I will delight myself in thy statutes: I will not forget thy word.

Let the words of my mouth, and the meditation of my heart, be acceptable in thy sight, O Lord, my strength, and my redeemer.

—Psalm 19:7-11; 119:9-16; 19:14.

402 The Church

He saith unto them, but whom say ye that I am?

And Simon Peter answered and said, Thou art the Christ, the Son of the living God.

And Jesus answered and said unto him, Blessed art thou, Simon Barjona: for flesh and blood hath not revealed it unto thee, but my father which is in heaven.

And I say also unto thee, that thou art Peter, and upon this rock I will build my church; and the gates of hell shall not prevail against it.
—Matthew 16:15-18.

I therefore, beseech you that ye walk worthy of the vocation wherewith ye are called.

With all lowliness and meekness, with longsuffering, forbearing one another in love;

Endeavouring to keep the unity of the Spirit in the bond of peace.

There is one body, and one Spirit, even as ye are called in one hope of your calling;

One Lord, one faith, one baptism.

One God and Father of all, who is above all, and through all, and in you all.

But unto every one of us is given grace according to the measure of the gift of Christ.

And he gave some, apostles; and some, prophets; and some, pastors and teachers;

For the perfecting of the saints, for the work of the ministry, for the edifying of the body of Christ:

Till we all come in the unity of the faith: and of the knowledge of the Son of God, unto a perfect man, unto the measure of the stature of the fulness of Christ.
—Ephesians 4:1-7, 11-13.

403 The Lord's Supper
Communion

Verily, verily, I say unto you, He that believeth on me hath everlasting life.

I am that bread of life.

Your fathers did eat manna in the wilderness, and are dead.

This is the bread which cometh down from heaven, that a man may eat thereof, and not die.

I am the living bread which came down from heaven: if any man eat of this bread, he shall live for ever:

And the bread that I will give is my flesh, which I will give for the life of the world.

He that eateth my flesh, and drinketh my blood, dwelleth in me, and I in him.

As the living Father hath sent me, and I live by the Father: so he that eateth me, even he shall live by me.

This is that bread which came down from heaven: not as your fathers did eat manna, and are dead; He that eateth of the bread shall live forever.

Then said they unto him, Lord, evermore give us this bread.

And Jesus said unto them, I am the bread of life; he that cometh to me shall never hunger; and he that believeth on me shall never thirst.

Then Jesus said unto them,

Verily, verily, I say unto you, Except ye eat the flesh of the Son of man, and drink his blood, ye have no life in you.

Whoso eateth my flesh, and drinketh my blood, hath eternal life.

And I will raise him up at the last day.

For my flesh is meat indeed, and my blood is drink indeed.

—John 6:47-51, 56-58, 34-35, 53-55.

404 The Coming Judgment

When the Son of man shall come in his glory, and all the holy angels with him, then shall he sit upon the throne of his glory.

And before him shall be gathered all nations: and he shall separate them one from another, as a shepherd divideth his sheep from the goats.

And he shall set the sheep on his right hand, but the goats on the left.

And the King shall say unto them, Verily I say unto you, Inasmuch as ye have done it unto one of the least of these my brethren, ye have done it unto me.

Then shall he say also unto them on the left hand, Depart from me, ye cursed, into everlasting fire, prepared for the devil and his angels.

For I was an hungred, and ye gave me no meat: I was thirsty, and ye gave me no drink:

I was a stranger, and ye took me not in: naked, and ye clothed me not: sick, and in prison, and ye visited me not.

Then shall they also answer him, saying, Lord, when saw we thee an hungred, or athirst, or a stranger, or naked, or sick, or in prison, and did not minister unto thee?

Then shall he answer them, saying, Verily I say unto you, Inasmuch as ye did it not to one of the least of these, ye did it not to me.

And these shall go away into everlasting punishment: but the righteous into life eternal.

Matthew 25:31-33, 40-46.

Be not deceived; God is not mocked: for whatsoever a man soweth, that shall he also reap.

For he that soweth to his flesh shall of the flesh reap corruption; but he that soweth to the Spirit shall of the Spirit reap life everlasting.

—Galatians 6:7-8.

405   Wisdom

My son, if thou wilt receive my words, and hide my commandments with thee:

So that thou incline thine ear unto wisdom, and apply thine heart to understanding.

Yea, if thou criest after knowledge, and liftest up thy voice for understanding;

If thou seekest her as silver, and searchest for her as for hid treasures:

Then shalt thou understand the fear of the Lord, and find the knowledge of God.

For the Lord giveth wisdom: out of his mouth cometh knowledge and understanding.

He layeth up sound wisdom for the righteous: he is a buckler to them that walk uprightly.

He keepeth the paths of judgment, and preserveth the way of his saints.

Then shalt thou understand righteousness, and judgment, and equity; yea, every good path.

When wisdom entereth into thine heart, and knowledge is pleasant unto thy soul;

Discretion shall preserve thee, understanding shall keep thee:

To deliver thee from the way of the evil man, from the man that speaketh froward things;

—Proverbs 2:1-12.

Mark the perfect man, and behold the upright: for the end of that man is peace.

But the transgressors shall be destroyed together: the end of the wicked shall be cut off.

But the salvation of the righteous is of the Lord: he is their strength in the time of trouble.

And the Lord shall help them, and deliver them: he shall deliver them from the wicked, and save them, because they trust in him.

—Psalm 37:37-40.

406   Christian Service

I beseech you therefore, brethren by the mercies of God, that ye present your bodies a living sacrifice, holy, acceptable, unto God, which is your reasonable service.

And be not conformed to this world: but be ye transformed by the renewing of your mind, that ye may prove what is that good, and acceptable, and perfect, will of God.

For I say, through the grace given unto me, to every man that is among you, not to think of himself more highly than he ought to think.

But to think soberly, according as God hath dealt to every man the measure of faith.

For as we have many members in one body, and all members have not the same office:

So we, being many, are one body in Christ, and every one members one of another.

Having then gifts differing according to the grace that is given to us, whether prophecy, let us prophesy according to the proportion of faith.

Or ministry, let us wait on our ministering: or he that teacheth, on teaching.

Or he that exhorteth, on exhortation: he that giveth, let us do it with simplicity; he that ruleth, with diligence; he that sheweth mercy, with cheerfulness.

Let love be without dissimulation. Abhor that which is evil; cleave to that which is good.

Be kindly affectioned one to another with brotherly love; in honour preferring one another;

Not slothful in business; fervent in spirit; serving the Lord;

Rejoicing in hope; patient in tribulation; continuing instant in prayer.

Be not overcome of evil, but overcome evil with good.

—Romans 12:1-12, 21.

407   Heaven

And I saw a new heaven and a new earth: for the first heaven and the first earth were passed away; and there was no more sea.

And I John saw the holy city, new Jerusalem, coming down from God out of heaven, prepared as a bride adorned for her husband.

And I heard a great voice out of heaven saying, Behold, the tabernacle of God is with men, and they shall be his people, and God himself shall be with them, and be their God.

And God shall wipe away all tears from their eyes; and there shall be no more death, neither sorrow, nor crying, neither shall there be any more pain: for the former things are passed away.

And he that sat upon the throne said, Behold, I make all things new.

And he said unto me, Write: for these words are true and faithful. I will give unto him that is athirst of the fountain of the water of life freely.

He that overcometh shall inherit

337

all things; and I will be his God, and he shall be my son.

And he shewed me a pure river of water of life, clear as crystal, proceeding out of the throne of God and of the Lamb.

And there shall be not more curse:

But the throne of God and of the Lamb shall be in it; and his servants shall serve him;

And they shall see his face; and his name shall be in their foreheads.

And there shall be no night there; and they need no candle, neither light of the sun; for the Lord giveth them light: and they shall reign for ever and ever.
—Revelation 21:1-7; 22:1, 3-5.

408   Mother's Day

Who can find a virtuous woman? for her price is far above rubies.

The heart of her husband doth safely trust in her, so that he shall have no need of spoil.

She will do him good and not evil all the days of her life.

She seeketh wool, and flax and worketh willingly with her hands.

She is like the merchant's ships; she bringeth her food from afar.

She riseth also while it is yet night, and giveth meat to her household, and a portion to her maidens.

She considereth a field, and buyeth it; with the fruit of her hands she planteth a vineyard.

She girdeth her loins with strength, and strengtheneth her arms.

She perceiveth that her merchandise is good: her candle goeth not out by night.

She layeth her hands to the spindle, and her hands hold the distaff.

She stretcheth out her hand to the poor; yea, she reacheth forth her hands to the needy.

She is not afraid of the snow for her household: for all her household are clothed with scarlet.

She maketh herself coverings of tapestry; her clothing is silk and purple.

Her husband is known in the gates, when he sitteth among the elders of the land.

She maketh fine linen, and selleth it; and delivereth girdles unto the merchant.

Strength and honour are her clothing; and she shall rejoice in time to come.   —Proverbs 31:10-25.

409   Easter

In the end of the sabbath, as it began to dawn toward the first day of the week, came Mary Magdalene and the other Mary to see the sepulchre.

And, behold, there was a great earthquake: for the angel of the Lord descended from heaven, and came and rolled back the stone from the door, and sat upon it.

His countenance was like lightning, and his raiment white as snow:

And the angel answered and said unto the women, Fear not ye: for I know that ye seek Jesus, which was crucified.

He is not here: for he is risen, as he said. Come, see the place where the Lord lay.

And go quickly, and tell his disciples that he is risen from the dead; and, behold, he goeth before you into Galilee; there shall ye see him: lo, I have told you.

And they departed quickly from the sepulchre with fear and great joy; and did run to bring his disciples word.

And as they went to tell his disciples, behold, Jesus met them, saying, All hail, And they came and held him by the feet, and worshipped him.

Then said Jesus unto them, Be not afraid; go tell my brethren that they go into Galilee, and there shall they see me.

Now when they were going, behold, some of the watch came into the city, and shewed unto the chief priests all the things that were done.

And when they were assembled with the elders, and had taken counsel, they gave large money unto the soldiers,

Saying, Say ye, His disciples came by night, and stole him away while we slept.

And if this come to the governor's ears, we will persuade him, and secure you.

So they took the money, and did as they were taught: and this saying is commonly reported among the Jews until this day.

—Matthew 28:1-15.

410 Children's Day

And the child grew, and waxed strong in spirit, filled with wisdom: and the grace of God was upon him.

Now his parents went to Jerusalem every year at the feast of the passover.

And when he was twelve years old, they went up to Jerusalem after the custom of the feast.

And when they had fulfilled the days, as they returned, the child Jesus tarried behind in Jerusalem; and Joseph and his mother knew not of it.

But they, supposing him to have been in the company, went a day's journey; and they sought him among their kinfolk and acquaintance.

And when they found him not, they turned back again to Jerusalem, seeking him.

And it came to pass, that after three days they found him in the temple, sitting in the midst of the doctors, both hearing them, and asking them questions.

And all that heard him were astonished at his understanding and answers.

And when they saw him, they were amazed: and his mother said unto him, Son, why hast thou thus dealt with us? behold, thy father and I have sought thee sorrowing.

And he said unto them, how is it that ye sought me? wist ye not that I must be about my Father's business?

And they understood not the saying which he spake unto them.

And he went down with them, and came to Nazareth, and was subject unto them:
But his mother kept all these sayings in her heart.

And Jesus increased in wisdom and stature, and in favour with God and man. —Luke 2:40-52.

411 Thanksgiving

All the commandments which I command thee this day shall ye observe to do, that ye may live, and multiply, and go in and possess the land which the Lord sware unto your fathers.

And thou shalt remember all the way which the Lord thy God led thee these forty years in the wilderness to humble thee, and to prove thee, to know what was in thine heart, whether thou wouldest keep his commandments, or no.

Thou shalt also consider in thine heart, that, as a man chasteneth his son, so the Lord thy God chasteneth thee.

Therefore thou shalt keep the commandments of the Lord thy God, to walk in his ways, and to fear him.

For the Lord thy God bringeth thee into a good land, a land of brooks of water, of fountains and depths that spring out of valleys and hills;

A land wherein thou shalt eat bread without scarceness, thou shalt not lack any thing in it; a land whose stones are iron, and out of whose hills thou mayest dig brass.

When thou hast eaten and art full, then thou shalt bless the Lord thy God for the good land which he hath given thee.

Beware that thou forget not the Lord thy God, in not keeping his commandments, and his judgments, and his statutes, which I command thee this day:

Lest when thou hast eaten and art full, and hast built goodly houses, and dwelt therein;

And when thy herds and thy flocks multiply, and thy silver and thy gold is multiplied, and all that thou hast is multiplied;

Thou shalt remember the Lord thy God: for it is he that giveth thee power to get wealth that he may establish his covenant which he sware unto thy fathers, as it is this day. —Deuteronomy 8:1-2, 5-7, 9-13, 18.

412   Christmas

And it came to pass in those days, that there went out a decree from Caesar Augustus, that all the world should be taxed.

(And this taxing was first made when Cyrenius was governor of Syria.)

And all went to be taxed, every one into his own city.

And Joseph also went up from Galilee, out of the city of Nazareth, into Judaea, unto the city of David, which is called Bethlehem; (because he was of the house and lineage of David:)

To be taxed with Mary his espoused wife, being great with child.

And so it was, that, while they were there, the days were accomplished that she should be delivered.

And she brought forth her first-born son, and wrapped him in swaddling clothes, and laid him in a manger; because there was no room for them in the inn.

And there were in the same country shepherds abiding in the field, keeping watch over their flock by night.

And, lo, the angel of the Lord came upon them, and the glory of the Lord shone round about them: and they were sore afraid.

And the angel said unto them, Fear not: for, behold, I bring you good tidings of great joy, which shall be to all people.

For unto you is born this day in the city of David a Saviour, which is Christ the Lord.

And this *shall be* a sign unto you; Ye shall find the babe wrapped in swaddling clothes, lying in a manger.

And suddenly there was with the angel a multitude of the heavenly host praising God, and saying,

Glory to God in the highest, and on earth peace, good will toward men.   —Luke 2:1-14.

RESPONSIVE READINGS
INDEX

TOPICAL INDEX

TOPICAL INDEX

TOPICAL INDEX

GENERAL INDEX

Titles in CAPITALS — First lines in lower case — Chorus in *Italics*

348

GENERAL INDEX

GENERAL INDEX

RAINBOW LITHOGRAPHING CO.
MUSIC PRINTERS·CHICAGO, ILL.

How Great Thou Art

O STORE GUD Irregular with Refrain

CARL BOBERG, 1859-1940
Trans. by STUART K. HINE, 1899-

Swedish Folk Melody
Arr. by MANNA MUSIC, INC.

1. O Lord my God! When I in awe-some won - der Con - sid - er all the worlds thy hands have made, I see the stars, I hear the roll - ing thun - der, thy pow'r through-out the un - i - verse dis - played,
2. When through the woods and for - est glades I wan - der And hear the birds sing sweet-ly in the trees; When I look down from loft - y moun - tain gran - deur And hear the brook and feel the gen - tle breeze;
3. And when I think that God, his Son not spar - ing, Sent him to die, I scarce can take it in; That on the cross, my bur - den glad - ly bear - ing, He bled and died to take a - way my sin;
4. When Christ shall come with shout of ac - cla - ma - tion And take me home, what joy shall fill my heart! Then I shall bow in hum - ble ad - o - ra - tion And there pro - claim, my God, how great thou art!

Refrain

Then sings my soul, my Sav-ior God to thee; How great thou art, how great thou art! Then sings my soul, my Sav-ior God to thee; How great thou art, how great thou art!

*Translator's original words are "works" and "mighty".

BLESS THOU THE GIFTS

Samuel Longfellow   Arr. from Robert A. Schumann

Bless Thou the gifts our hands have bro't: Bless Thou the work our hearts have planned;

Ours is the faith, the will, the tho't; The rest, O God, is in Thy hand.

ALL THINGS COME OF THEE

Arranged from Beethoven

All things come of Thee, O Lord; and of Thine own have we giv-en Thee. A-MEN.

HEAR OUR PRAYER, O LORD

George Whelpton

Hear our prayer, O Lord, Hear our prayer, O Lord; Incline Thine ear to us, And grant us Thy peace. A-MEN.

MIZPAH

C. H. G.

Slowly

The Lord watch between me and thee When we are ab-sent one from the other. A-MEN.